400 Home Plans

PLAN #	PLAN NAME	SQ. FT.	PAGE
1129	Calumet	1125	22
5479	Oakfield	1191	22
8532	Kendrick	1195	23
2376	Dover	1205	23
8093	Kirby Farm	1212	24
43010	Bridgewater	1268	24
1551	Logan	1271	25
43011	Taunton	1275	25
3907	Reynolds	1316	26
6787	Richland	1333	26
6731	Tollefson	1335	27
3102	Aspen	1339	27
2761	Mayberry	1341	28
1963	Kaplin	1347	28
24048	Cartwright	1359	29
8091	Winter Woods	1360	29
5464	Janssen	1379	30
8013	Gabriel Bay	1392	30
3010	Quimby	1422	31
1379	Pendleton	1429	31
8089	Chandler Hills	1433	32
5476	Culverton	1437	32
8160	Bradford Pointe	1449	33
2173	Fraser	1451	33
8090	Spring Valley	1453	34
5034	Payson	1472	34
3260	Kirby	1478	35
3019	Kelsey	1479	35
43046	Celina	1482	36
43047	Gastonia	1482	36
2300	Adair	1496	37
3555	Laramy	1518	37
5035	Canton	1552	38
3127	Haley	1554	38
24214	Lawndale	1560	39
2196	Granite	1561	39
8087	Collins Falls	1579	40
2324	Oakridge	1583	40
43034	Altamont	1592	41
43035	Redmond	1592	41
3578	Stonybrook	1595	42
24141	Seabeck	1604	42
1767	Rosebury	1604	43
2923	Sutton	1622	43
8080	Maple Grove	1628	44
2377	Leighton	1636	44
5466	Somerdale	1636	45
2818	Orchard	1651	45
2907	Ashley	1658	46
2290	Monterey	1666	46
8016	Jennys Brook	1691	47

PLAN #	PLAN NAME	SQ. FT.	PAGE
1032	Monte Vista	1697	47
8078	North Cliffs	1707	48
2355	Waverly	1710	48
43007	Carthage	1719	49
43008	Laundale	1719	49
2212	Seville	1735	50
43016	Bay Hill	1755	50
43017	Saugatuck	1755	51
4948	Bradbury	1758	51
24003	Tuxford	1762	52
24185	James	1768	52
3577	Bennett	1782	53
5465	Christine	1790	53
3587	Charleston	1796	54
3006	Grayson	1806	54
24206	Westlake	1807	55
1559	Bancroft	1808	55
24212	Madeline	1812	56
43058	Corridon	1820	56
42001	Farrington	1820	57
43059	Goodman	1820	57
24140	Everton	1842	58
8059	Indian Springs	1842	58
2461	Shawnee	1850	59
2799	Hawthorne	1887	59
30016	Carrigan	1899	60
8516	Rayford	1902	60
1748	Sinclair	1911	61
8019	Hunters Crossing	1919	61
3031	Jonesville	1978	62
24203	Hardwick	1985	62
1539	Mansfield	1996	63
29501	Dekyan	2038	63
9171	Westcott Manor	2040	64
8122	Alberta Falls	2042	64
4208	Creighton	2057	65
29095	Gammon	2065	65
2222	Plainview	2068	66
43031	Rigby	2069	66
43032	West Forks	2081	67
24038	Clarkson	2126	67
3597	Concorde	2132	68
1689	Newman	2133	68
24210	Inglenook	2140	69
2213	Essex	2149	69
8045	Coopers Farm	2151	70
5036	Cameron	2167	70
2326	Greensboro	2172	71
29157	Mallory	2173	71
3005	Wrenwood	2186	72
24215	Longvale	2194	72

educational & informative articles

Plan to Entertain	p6
The Entertaining Kitchen	p8
De-Stressing	p10
Homes for Today's Blended Families	p12
Storage	p14
Garage Storage	p16
Flexibility	p18
Flexible Design	p20
The Moment of Discovery	p73
Getting Away	p104
Planning Your New Home	p154
Decorating With Light	p201
Life at Home: The Paybacks of Energy Efficiency	p244
10 Things to Consider	p292
Will Your Home Welcome Everyone?	p309
Can Luxury Showering Be Green?	p310
Color Intelligence	p318

EDITOR	Kevin Blair
PLANS MANAGER	Tina Blair
GRAPHIC DESIGNERS	Jeff Dedlow
	Beverly Nelligan
	Heather Guthrie
	Annette Guy
CO-PUBLISHERS	Dennis Brozak
	Linda Reimer
C.E.O	Dennis Brozak
PRESIDENT	Linda Reimer
DIRECTOR OF MARKETING	Kevin Blair
BUSINESS DEVELOPMENT	Paul Foresman
CONTROLLER	Janie Murnane

The Canterbury, Plan #2411-9JJ, as seen on the cover is also available on page 195. Photos may differ from plans as originally designed.

HOME PLAN DESIGN SERVICE

DESIGN BASICS PUBLICATIONS
11112 JOHN GALT BLVD., OMAHA, NE 68137
www.designbasics.com
800-947-7526

Library of Congress Control Number:
2005923033
ISBN: 1-892150-39-5

PLAN #	PLAN NAME	SQ. FT.	PAGE
24159	Britebay	2218	74
6672	Baywood	2223	75
5141	Enfield	2242	76
29510	Tiffany Brooke	2242	77
29097	Stokley	2255	78
42025	Kathryn	2274	79
2321	Aberdeen	2276	80
3058	Montgomery	2311	81
2651	Fairway	2317	82
9207	Briar Manor	2331	83
24205	Montana	2340	84
24207	Richgrove	2354	85
42026	Hennessey	2390	86
9264	W. Univ. Manor	2430	87
2778	Comstock	2456	88
24109	Maribel	2462	89
2206	Hawkesbury	2498	90
3535	Hallmark	2504	91
42002	Heatherstone	2506	92
2652	Lawrence	2512	93
9199	Kingwood Showcase	2517	94
3057	Ascott	2538	95
42027	McAllister	2598	96
9262	Georgetown Showcase	2640	97
42006	Haskell	2641	98
5003	Saybrooke	2750	99
24208	Palomar	2766	100
29509	Behrens Court	2956	101
29096	Proel	2962	102
9120	Whitmore	3312	103

1½-Story Home Plans

PLAN #	PLAN NAME	SQ. FT.	PAGE
3123	Bethany	1596	107
8027	Ellies Knoll	1615	107
5475	Catalina	1617	108
24083	Millhome	1628	108
43037	Limington	1638	109
43038	Tillamook	1638	109
3121	Bellamy	1660	110
24096	Maplehurst	1671	110
24132	Moore	1688	111
8095	Sun Valley	1694	111
3089	Parnell	1712	112
8094	Angel Cove	1715	112
5151	Sedona	1755	113
4133	Marcell	1772	113
2281	Ingram	1778	114
3385	Brittany	1788	114
5463	Kelvington	1798	115
3076	Sayler	1798	115
5462	Finley	1799	116
8037	Carriage Hills	1802	116
8509	Weaver	1818	117

PLAN #	PLAN NAME	SQ. FT.	PAGE
8096	Pine Ridge	1837	117
4646	Kirkwood	1853	118
2236	Bermier	1855	118
8077	Meadow Creek	1858	119
8084	Brook Valley	1865	119
24146	Largo	1867	120
1330	Trenton	1869	120
24016	Barons	1897	121
2551	Girard	1927	121
2554	Lansing	1948	122
3063	Taylor	1957	122
8076	Holly Mills	1973	123
2719	Eldorado	1976	123
24154	Stendal	1980	124
9170	Buckland Showase	1984	124
42004	Middlebury	1991	125
8075	Timber Point	1994	125
8053	Stevens Woods	1996	126
1863	Andover	1999	126
1380	Paterson	1999	127
24136	Weldon	2005	127
8035	Jordan Oaks	2016	128
42000	Kiran	2019	128
24112	Bakerville	2023	129
8065	Hannifan Lane	2029	129
3381	Amanda	2037	130
3064	Eldridge	2055	130
9266	Buckhead Showcase	2067	131
2745	Sierra	2089	131
2951	Newlin	2109	132
2312	Meredith	2113	132
8054	Kerry Crossing	2115	133
2285	Prairie	2115	133
2220	Gentry	2139	134
8124	Silver Springs	2150	134
8549	Roscoe	2164	135
24213	Pepperwood	2171	135
24129	Redbay	2176	136
9180	Oak Crest Manor	2237	136
24118	Fillmore	2241	137
24004	Bardel	2248	137
8012	Pawnee Point	2266	138
1554	Chandler	2276	138
2811	Ashville	2277	139
3249	Tanner	2282	139
3020	Douglas	2285	140
2836	Aurora	2308	140
8055	Autumn Hills	2322	141
24204	Julian	2334	141
5148	Bowden	2339	142
2701	Ambrose	2340	142
1862	Manchester	2353	143
9166	Troon Manor	2361	143
24028	Butler	2384	144

PLAN #	PLAN NAME	SQ. FT.	PAGE
2203	Ashton	2391	144
2261	Arant	2405	145
5150	Magrath	2421	145
2311	Pinehurst	2486	146
24182	Delaney	2487	146
3284	Pinnacle	2496	147
9173	Chasleton Manor	2537	147
24085	Farmington	2546	148
2956	Briarwood	2562	148
24202	Riverbank	2562	149
4081	Hanna	2576	149
2309	Edmonton	2579	150
24063	Bayard	2587	150
3510	Addams	2597	151
2894	Rollins	2603	151
4134	Schuyler	2613	152
2649	Hillcrest	2639	152
9165	Wilks Manor	2639	153
7231	Nelson	2642	153
2723	Armburst	2645	157
43020	Clarinda	2651	158
43019	Plainfield	2651	159
9160	Woodlands Showcase	2655	160
24011	Oliver	2688	161
30001	Deville	2690	162
2460	Bridgeport	2695	163
42003	Westfield	2704	164
2174	Cordeaux	2708	165
3484	MacCready	2764	166
43040	Brookings	2765	167
43041	Vermillion	2772	168
24211	Irwindale	2809	169
29132	Chadsworth	2843	170
3494	Thornhill	2850	171
1486	Remington	2865	172
2476	Dundee	2884	173
2458	Hartford	2932	174
24007	Pembrook	2978	175
2800	Appleton	2979	176
29500	Korbyn	2999	177
3326	Oakdale	3017	178
2671	Durand	3029	179
4144	Marlow	3040	180
2322	Northland	3067	181
9162	Tealwood Estate	3072	182
42005	Channing	3080	183
9169	Kempton Court	3094	184
29098	Dyson	3124	185
2249	Normandy	3172	186
30000	Olsen	3250	187
24084	Valleyford	3270	188
24209	Pomona	3381	189
9138	Drakewood Manor	3397	190
24187	Humphrey	3451	191

PLAN #	PLAN NAME	SQ. FT.	PAGE
1588	Carlton	3473	192
29141	Stallworth	3545	193
2475	Winchester	3556	194
2411	Canterbury	3623	195
2218	Le Grand	3689	196
9143	Oak Grove Estate	3750	197
2733	Fairchild	3904	198
9114	Meadowview Manor	4139	199
9254	Ashwood Manor	4629	200

2-Story Home Plans

PLAN #	PLAN NAME	SQ. FT.	PAGE
5470	Alenhurst	1564	206
2579	Bartels	1594	206
2526	Arbor	1605	207
43028	Wendell	1649	207
2248	Laverton	1650	208
8139	Harbor Lane	1654	208
43029	Menlo	1660	209
8105	Adams Creek	1685	209
3103	Ashworth	1700	210
5469	Englewood	1706	210
2545	Deming	1728	211
2890	Jefferson	1732	211
8029	Linden Acres	1753	212
3096	Torrey	1768	212
3581	Paige	1771	213
2308	Juniper	1775	213
2952	Francis	1799	214
5478	Evandale	1807	214
5458	Creswell	1814	215
1752	Lancaster	1846	215
8098	Sherman Oaks	1881	216
5085	Branford	1928	216
2963	Columbus	1933	217
2648	Cyprus	1951	217
8082	Bentley Woods	1952	218
2315	Harrisburg	1993	219
2619	Oakbrook	1998	220
3552	Ballobin	2028	221
8031	Robins Lane	2029	222
2401	Curtiss	2058	223
1870	Bristol	2078	224
2217	Yorke	2085	225
2638	Linden	2103	226
2618	Paisley	2131	227
4952	Caldera	2144	228
43023	Burlington	2155	229
43022	Monona	2168	230
2216	Collier	2174	231
8500	Castalia	2200	232

PLAN #	PLAN NAME	SQ. FT.	PAGE
1019	Hazelton	2219	233
2408	Crawford	2270	234
4105	Eldon	2282	235
8024	Millard Oaks	2298	236
3333	Hartman	2308	237
8524	Elgin	2331	238
2414	Stanton	2343	239
2316	Franklin	2345	240
4135	Gerard	2349	241
8515	Glendon	2354	242
1553	Kendall	2387	243
2949	Hartley	2404	248
2919	Fulton	2412	249
5086	Patagonia	2417	250
43014	Drifton	2429	251
43013	Moss Bluff	2429	252
9172	Bibury Manor	2438	253
2346	Fayette	2480	254
2898	Lawler	2497	255
29507	Kinnersley	2499	256
43049	Whiteville	2501	257
43050	Keene	2505	258
2229	Morrison	2545	259
43025	Waterloo	2549	260
4156	Karlynda	2558	261
43026	Algona	2574	262
2656	Castelar	2585	263
1455	Newberry	2594	264
43055	Kirksville	2609	265
43056	Westboro	2609	266
4106	Calabretta	2613	267
3246	Jennings	2644	268
2779	Leawood	2689	269
8512	Oakboro	2705	270
9161	Woodvine Manor	2715	271
43001	Chestnut Knoll	2736	272
43002	Dublin Hill	2736	273
5083	Attleboro	2752	274
9265	Broadmead Court	2766	275
43004	Alloway	2797	276
43005	Hitchins	2850	277
2293	Newport	2890	278
43052	Somersworth	2892	279
2207	Manning	2914	280
43053	Karli Rose	2917	281
24052	Goldendale	3002	282
987	Santa Ana	3025	283
2839	Edgewood	3057	284
3156	Jacksonville	3273	285
1510	Abbey	3306	286
3174	Harrison	3404	287

PLAN #	PLAN NAME	SQ. FT.	PAGE
9263	Briarglan Estate	3454	288
3388	Glencross	3611	289
2332	Corinth	3775	290

Narrow Home Plans

PLAN #	PLAN NAME	SQ. FT.	PAGE
6789N	Clearfield	1395	294
6783N	Bonneville	1400	294
6780N	Woodington	1423	295
6781N	Wayside	1490	295
6713N	Overbrook	1580	296
6710N	Kincaid	1297	296
29079	Winstrom	1440	297
6791N	Kelford	1453	297
6706N	Copeland	1471	298
8534N	Erwin	1473	298
8537N	Keiser	1473	299
6792N	Martelle	1475	299
6715N	Sycamore	1495	300
8614	Annapolis	1540	300
8615	Fairborn	1540	301
8616	Grosse Point	1540	301
8613	Potomac	1540	302
43044	Chenoweth	1550	302
43043	Colbourne	1550	303
8554N	Joliet	1560	303
8535N	Ravena	1561	304
8555N	Ansley	1568	304
8553N	Hollister	1575	305
6705N	Hopewell	1641	305
8558N	Gardena	1649	306
8556N	Wellman	1649	306
8557N	Edinburg	1703	307
8631	Bloomington	2325	307
8632	Tiburon	2344	308
8633	Urbandale	2346	308

Multi-Family Home Plans

PLAN #	PLAN NAME	SQ. FT.	PAGE
4614	Deerfield	2436	311
8174	Crimson Creek	2445	312
7603	Allston	2622	313
4625	Landsford	2688	314
4618	Fairhope	2784	315
4632	Ellington	2956	316
4011	Clarendon	3882	317

Livability at a Glance™

Livability
at a Glance™

Storing
Entertaining
Flexible Living
De-Stressing

How does the home Live?

photo courtesy of medallion cabinetry

Turning the dream of building a home into reality can be a daunting challenge, with thousands of decisions along the way. Choosing a plan can be the most intimidating because it's often difficult to visualize the finished home and how it will live. To make it easier, Design Basics has created a new way to present floor plans to help you narrow the search for a design that fits your personal lifestyle and needs.

Each floor plan in this plan book is shown in a conventional layout and a color-coded version that highlights four different categories especially important to women: Entertaining (yellow), De-Stressing (blue), Storing (orange) and Flexible Living (green).

For more information on Plan 29510-9JJ see pg. 77

www.designbasics.com/9JJ

entertaining

Yellow areas encompass:

- formal rooms for entertaining
- informal, open living spaces
- outdoor "rooms"
- kitchens that encourage guests to gather around a snack bar
- rooms for media-related get-togethers (watching movies or sports events)
- areas ideal for groups playing cards or board games

de-stressing

If you're looking for ways to de-stress your life, you'll appreciate homes with a lot of blue spaces. Some blue areas offer relaxation, such as:

- personal getaways
- a privately located master suite
- a walk-in shower or whirlpool
- a quiet porch or a craft area

Others provide unusual organizational features such as:

- split vanities
- mudrooms
- drop zones that keep keys, brief-cases, umbrellas, cell phones and laptops in one convenient spot

storing

If you never have enough storage, you'll be drawn to homes with more orange areas, that highlight:

- extra storage capacity in the garage or laundry room
- rear foyer storage
- generous kitchen pantries and linen closets
- over-sized bedroom closets
- additional unfinished areas in the basement or on the upper level

flexible living

Green areas designate rooms that offer flexible living spaces that can adapt to unique situations:

- rooms that can be combined to create in-law-suites
- home offices (occasionally even his and her offices)
- bedroom/bath arrangements that work well for blended families
- music rooms
- homeschool rooms
- craft or gardening centers
- offices that can become dining rooms
- dens that become guest rooms

photo courtesy of medallion cabinetry

For more information on Plan 42025-9JJ see pg. 79

Plans Highlight Four Important Categories That Show the Way You Live

plan to
Entertain

Livability
at a Glance™

Storing
Entertaining
Flexible Living
De-Stressing

Formal Eating Area

Candlelight, soft music, ample room for guests and great conversation make dinner parties a delight. Whether it's a formal dinner party or a family holiday dinner, memories are intertwined with meals together. The main things to look for are space, proximity to the kitchen and flexibility. Is the dining area a comfortable size for the table, chairs and hutch, if you have one? Is it close to the kitchen, reducing steps when carrying hot dishes, or clearing the table? Should you desire privacy, can the space be closed off? If you have larger gatherings, are there two dining areas, perhaps the kids are at one table with the adults at another. Or, does your dining space flow openly into an adjacent space for additional seating?

In addition, flooring choices, color, wall textures, ceiling treatments and window coverings are primary considerations. In addition to the aesthetics, look at maintenance issues – a high chandelier with lots of light bulbs can become a real pain when it's time to change those bulbs. Having control over lighting is critical to enhance your get-together. This includes accessible, easily adjustable window shades/coverings as well as separately switched, direct and indirect artificial lighting on dimmers.

Informal Eating Area

A table for breakfast and a snack bar for quick dinners provides several informal eating areas. The snack bar also makes a great spot to set-up a buffet.

Everyday meals mean everyday use for dinettes and snack bars. Because of its frequent use, maintenance and easy cleaning are central issues. Expect spills when you are considering flooring choices. Will you have to move chairs out of the way to sweep or vacuum? Especially at snack bars, seating suspended from the island or peninsula is a wonderful solution to ensure accessible seating that's easy to clean under. It also helps prevent damage to the flooring from chairs!

Open Living Spaces

With the eating area, kitchen and great room all open to each other, everyone is part of the fun. An open floor plan really pulls entertaining or family life together.

More than just eliminating walls, today's kitchens are being designed with attention to views of fireplaces and entertainment centers. Open designs have also focused new attention on views into the kitchen. This has been one reason for the rising popularity of stainless steel appliances and glass front cabinets.

Outdoor Living Spaces

We are naturally drawn to the outdoors. After a hectic day at work, relaxing in the outdoors helps release tension. Research even shows that exposure to sunlight and trees has numerous health benefits.

Whether it's a barbeque or outside games, outdoor entertaining should be a natural extension of your home's flow. Covered porches are especially appreciated if inclement weather threatens your outdoor plans. For some, adding screens around the porch to control bugs means being able to truly enjoy being outside. Still others will opt for windows all around, turning their outdoor living space into a true four seasons room.

Low maintenance, durability, price and aesthetics all come into play when choosing the material your porch or deck will be crafted from. Wood fiber/composite decking as well as vinyl have gained in popularity as prices have come down and finish selections have increased. Wood offers unmatched beauty, but requires periodic maintenance.

Media-Related Entertaining

With today's media choices running the gamut from gaming to movies or sports to the internet, until the issue of where the big screen TV goes is settled, we can't seriously consider building or remodeling.

Lighting and sound are the major issues to be addressed. Glare from windows or other lighting can ruin the multi-media experience, so this must be under control. While one group wants to crank up the volume, others may want to carry on normal conversation or even get some shut-eye. Sound isolation clips for drywall walls and ceilings, insulating those cavities, or using acoustic sound mats are all reasonable approaches to controlling sound levels. Also, be sure to use a solid core, weather-stripped door to finish sealing off a media room.

Split Bedrooms to Control Noise

Its inevitable when friends get together that someone else in the home needs privacy – whether studying, catching up on work brought home, or needing to get some sleep. Splitting secondary bedrooms from the master suite, and distancing bedrooms from entertaining areas, provides much needed quiet.

Few things in life are more important than getting a good nights sleep. Inside the home, look for quiet products such as kitchen or bath fans and appliances. Who wants to move to another room, just because the dishwasher is running? You can also limit noise coming from outdoors through advanced insulating, caulking and air sealing measures when your home is being built, plus quality windows and doors.

Finished Basements

A finished lower level not only adds needed square footage but allows for more informal entertaining. If you are fortunate enough to be building on a basement, today's engineered floor systems make wide-open basement spaces feasible and affordable, as they can span greater distances than conventional lumber.

In many areas, builders are responding to tougher energy codes by insulating basements – a great start towards a comfortable living space. Make sure you know where you will want electrical and other wiring to be run, and meet with your electrician to go over the plans.

Moisture and humidity are key issues in tandem with temperature. A little extra spent on basement waterproofing measures could save you from expensive repairs later. And even though your air conditioner is designed to remove excess humidity from your home in the summer, you may well find you need to run a freestanding de-humidifier in the basement as well to control humidity, mold, mildew and possible moisture damage.

Kids Play Area

If there are children in your home, you will value a place where they can go and play. A place where toys and games are stored and Lego creations can be left for a another day. In other words, a place where kids can be kids. Separate from their bedrooms, this flexible space may or may not have been finished space when the home was initially built.

Consider the types of activities your children will enjoy. If it is painting, for example, you will want a flooring surface that cleans up easily with a sink nearby. Also, consider how the space may be used differently as the kids age. Keep fanciful themes to more easily changed aspects which will also keep costs down when it's time to replace Winnie The Pooh with your boy's favorite sports theme.

the Entertaining Kitchen

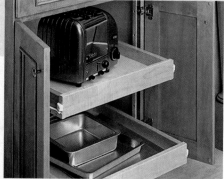

photo courtesy of Medallion cabinetry

photo courtesy of Medallion cabinetry

photo courtesy of Schrock cabinetry

Many of the best times of our lives revolve around being with family and friends. Whether it's hosting formal get-together, holiday dinners or your children's birthday parties, the kitchen is the hub of activity. A little extra attention spent planning flow, layout and product selections will reward you with a kitchen that is more functional and efficient.

Due to the popularity of today's open floor plans with kitchens in full view, designing kitchens is all about zones related to the flow of activity. Kitchen design is being further refined by an emerging knowledge of how layout and product choices can actually help reduce stress, particularly while entertaining.

Storage is the initial zone, because you want items to be stored in places convenient to where they will be used. For example, you're going to want storage for your good dishes, glassware and silverware near the serving or dining area, such as a butler pantry.

It's also essential to reduce clutter, ease accessibility and arrange items in an organized way. Include some roll-out drawers or trays. Drawer inserts keep small items, spices, silverware and utensils organized. But what about small, frequently used appliances? Countertop appliance garages for blenders, toasters, and coffee makers may be just what you,re looking for. On the other hand, if you want to keep your counter space free, consider going underneath the counter. You can include a pull-out mixer shelf, which comes out of the cabinet and swings up – bringing your heavy mixer even with the countertop.

The **food preparation zone** depends on lots of counter space, plus close proximity to the refrigerator, range/oven and pantry. Ideally, this is a separate space from the serving area, allowing both areas to function simultaneously.

Above Left: With kitchen space at a premium, cabinet manufacturers have introduced innovative designs with increased storage and organization. **Above Right:** Your back will appreciate roll-out trays, perfect for heavier small appliances and other items. **Above Lower-Right:** Keep the kitchen clean and Mom happy by including cabinets with pull-out wastebaskets and recycling trays.

If you have a smaller island in your kitchen which will be used for food preparation, keeping the countertop a uniform height will provide the maximum work space. If your island is large enough to accommodate different levels, a 36-inch work level will be appreciated by bakers, while a taller side (usually 42 inches) shields work clutter from view and accommodates bar stools.

Your **cooking zone**, convenient to the food prep area, is centered around your cooktop and ovens. Two cooks in the home will require more utensils, pots and pans, so plan storage accordingly. In addition, you may opt for separate counter spaces, cooking areas and sinks. Common ovens and waste containment may need wider corridors around a central working area.

If you are looking at an island with cooktop, make sure there is sufficient room next to the cooktop to place large items such as a big pot of boiling pasta. Also, warming drawers are great features for entertaining. They allow you to warm multiple dishes

simultaneously and keep hot cooked foods at serving temperature.

Some **serving zones** are more formal, such as a built-in buffet in the dining area, or a butler's pantry along the path from the kitchen. For casual entertaining, islands or peninsulas may be just the ticket. If your guests are usually adults, consider a 42-inch height for the serving bar area.

Your **eating zone** may consist of a formal dining area, an informal breakfast nook, a snack bar, or some combination of all three. Many folks find themselves most often dining at a snack bar and rarely using their dinette. If that's you, carefully consider what height best suits your family. If you have small children, they won't be able to get up on higher stools (or worse yet, they may fall off of them!)

Clean-up is the final, but very important, zone when planning for entertaining. As two sinks have gained popularity, so have second dishwashers. In front of sinks, consider a small tilt-out tray to keep sponges and pot scrubbers out of view. Another item that can reduce clutter in your entertaining kitchen is a liquid soap dispenser which comes up through the countertop next to the sink.

What about trash? Typical solutions have been the unsightly tall kitchen wastebasket openly on display (or a smaller wastebasket under the kitchen sink.) Besides having to bend over to use the latter, ever notice how much stuff misses the wastebasket? Opt for a pull-out wastebasket tray in your base cabinetry.

Beyond how our kitchens flow, there are several other major considerations, such as ease of cleaning and durability. Think sinks, countertops, flooring and appliances. Laminate countertops offer the greatest variety in colors, patterns and edge finishes. They don't require special cleansers nor do they need to be re-sealed every year or two.

While aesthetics and price may be the top influences for kitchen flooring choices, scratches, everyday wear and low maintenance are major de-stressing aspects. Will spilled spaghetti sauce or grape juice stain the flooring? (Darker colors of grout for tile floors are increasingly popular for this very reason.) Will heavy or sharp items accidentally dropped damage the floor?

Flooring choices in adjacent areas also play a large role in kitchen flooring, as many of us prefer a continuity of floor covering (which makes the entire area feel more spacious.)

Appliances are one of the first items you and your guests see in the kitchen. Are the surfaces easy to clean, especially the oven/range tops and inside the microwave? How about the exterior finish? The stainless steel look has been quite popular, but it attracts fingerprints like a giant magnet. Look for new finishes which don't show fingerprints and are easy to clean.

Quiet is an often overlooked aspect of a dream kitchen. Few things are more annoying than having to vacate the kitchen just to hear each other talk. Pay special attention when selecting your dishwasher and kitchen vent/hood. Some models are actually so quiet you're not even aware they are running!

Almost universally, people describe the amount of light in their kitchens as inadequate. A light, bright and airy kitchen is de-stressing for you, your family and your guests.

As kitchens have become more open to adjacent areas of the home, they are benefiting from increased levels of natural light coming from these areas. More recently, glass block or small traditional

windows are appearing between kitchen counter backsplashes and upper cabinets.

Today, recessed ceiling lighting has replaced the standard light fixture approach common years ago. As well, task lighting concealed under the upper kitchen cabinets offers a pleasant light level and helps reduce eyestrain.

Whatever lighting approach you choose, make sure you're in control. From window coverings to dimmers, lighting helps establish the mood for your next get-together.

While you might want all available light when preparing dinner, controlled light levels are much more comfortable for everyone later in the evening.

Pay extra attention to where electrical outlets are located. Only you know how you intend to use the kitchen, so don't leave it up to the electrician's imagination where to locate outlets and switches. Then there's cable TV and the internet. Plan now where wiring needs to go.

Finally, consider decorating and how you reveal who you are through what you display and how you decorate your kitchen. Most women use words such as "comfortable"

or "homey" to describe their dream kitchen. Color choices throughout can have an exciting or a calming effect. Do you decorate according to the season? Is there space above the upper cabinets for display niches or plant shelves?

We cherish relationships. We take pride in a functional and orderly kitchen. With a little extra forethought and planning, our kitchens will beckon to entertain a simple family dinner or an extravagant gala!

De-Stressing

Personal Space

After a long and hectic day, find personal space to decompress is as important as breathing. Everyone has their own way to de-stress. Find a place in your home that works for you. What you like to do while you unwind will help shape this space.

If reading or watching a little TV is how you like to unwind, a sitting area in the master bedroom or a cozy hearthroom may be the perfect answer. Enjoy nature? Then covered outdoor living spaces will be high on your list. If you like to work off stress by working out, an exercise room works for you!

Large Pantry

As a nation, we're cooking less, but not eating less. Some grew up in homes where a hot cooked breakfast was the daily norm. Today, a bowl of cereal, Pop-Tarts or a granola bar might be more common. That means an increasing need for storage for prepared foods.

Do you need space for your bread maker, indoor grill, food processor or mixer? Don't let clutter on your countertop stress you put them in the pantry.

In addition to making pantries bigger, there's an evolving industry helping to make pantries more organized, through innovative storage solutions. With items organized and on display, we can quickly scan the pantry before a restocking trip to the grocery store~saving both time and the aggravation of returning home only to find you forgot something.

Rear Foyer

A funny thing happened over the past couple decades. The door in from the garage became our principal entry to the home. Sure, a formal front entry to greet guests is important and is often a focal point of the home's design, but we're becoming increasingly comfortable with family and friends coming through the garage.

An emerging trend is to think of the entry from the garage as a rear foyer. And, just as you probably wouldn't make your laundry room a part of your front entryway, you probably don't want folks traipsing past piles of laundry on their way in from the garage. Note – you may want to modify your homeplan if originally designed with the laundry/mudroom, entry from the garage.

Our research revealed nothing is more stressful for Moms than getting the family out the door on-time in the morning, with everything they need. Rear foyers may offer solutions such as lockers for each of the kids, and even walk-in closets. A bench for removing shoes, is also popular.

Drop Zone

Mail, keys, cell phones, cameras – wouldn't it be great to have a convenient place to drop our stuff so it doesn't end up as kitchen clutter, or worse? Today's hot new concept "the drop zone" is the answer. Typically made to match kitchen cabinetry and 3 to 4 feet in width, drop zones often incorporate a recharging center, mail sorting, drop-off counter, plus cabinets and drawers for everything from flashlights to sunglasses.

Some drop zones are designed with doors behind which everything is concealed. They may include one or more locking cabinet doors or drawers for expensive items such as a camcorder or notebook PC. They may also double as a family message center when outfitted with cork board or a white write-on board.

Stress-free living includes knowing you,ll never lose your keys again and where your fully charged cell phone is when you leave the house.

Split Bedrooms

After a stressful day at work retreat to the master suite which is separated from secondary bedrooms for privacy. Designers typically try to buffer the master bedroom from other bedrooms by careful placement of closets, hallways and baths.

As opposed to designing a bedroom wing for the home, one-story designs in which the secondary bedrooms are situated far from the master bedroom are becoming more popular.

Walk-In Shower

Because they are used everyday in our time-starved society, showers are becoming the focal point of many bathrooms. As showers are getting bigger in today's homes, they are also getting more luxurious. Multiple shower heads are commonplace, as are seats in the shower.

How long does it take for clear shower doors to show white streaks? Low-maintenance showers are in demand, as well as walk-in showers which have no shower door to make cleaning easier. If your shower does require a door, look at the frameless versions which are elegant and easier to clean.

Split Vanities

Women take more time in the morning in the bathroom getting ready than men do. And, a fair amount of that time is spent leaning over the countertop. Split vanities provide handy storage solutions for items each spouse uses daily, keeping your vanity neat and organized. And, if one partner likes things clean and orderly while the other doesn't even notice this type of thing, neither will be annoyed at the condition of their vanity area.

Recognizing that men are on average several inches taller than women, building the vanities to be different heights is another aspect of a comfortable, distressing bath.

Garden/Whirlpool Tubs

When asked about what they would like to do to de-stress after a long day, many women envision taking a relaxing bath. The experience is both soothing and rejuvenating – especially when surrounded by aromatic candles and pretty soaps.

Standard tubs have given way to soaking tubs and jetted (whirlpool) tubs. Look at the height of the tub in terms of getting in and out. A step up, or sinking the tub 7 or 8 inches lower than the surrounding floor, both make it easier to get in and out of the tub.

Another aspect to consider is if there is a window over the tub. Privacy is as important as natural light. How easy will it be to reach over the tub and close the shades? You may want to opt for glass block or for the new privacy glass windows which go from clear to opaque at the flip of a switch.

Craft/Gardening Area

How many times do you have a project spread out on the kitchen or dining room table? An area out of public view would take the stress out of constant picking up. Having room in the home to pursue these and other hobbies can contribute to distressing, especially if works-in-progress can be left undisturbed.

The primary considerations for such spaces are related to the type of activity. Gardening is ideally suited for an area with a sink in it and being close to an outside door. Sewing and needlework projects are enhanced by high light levels. Woodworking fits well with concrete floors for easy clean-up, plus plenty of electrical outlets for various power tools.

Outdoor Living

Most people long to spend time outdoors. This is good, as research shows being outside is beneficial for both our physical and mental health.

Like many other product decisions, balancing cost, aesthetics, low maintenance and durability are principal considerations for porches, decks and patios. But these same aspects also apply to landscaping and irrigation, exterior lighting, play structures and other backyard decisions.

homes for Today's Blended Families

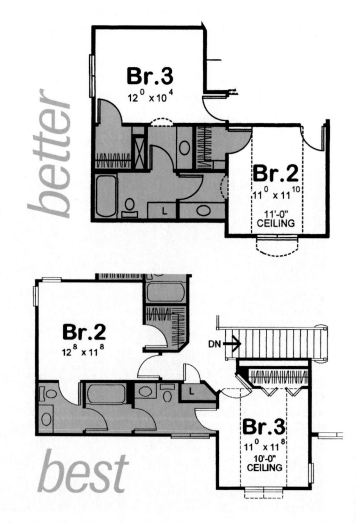

good

Each of these three floor plans illustrate bathroom options for the blended family.

GOOD - (Plan 43056) a typical compartmented bath.
BETTER - (Plan 42000) a bath with vanities in each bedroom.
BEST - (Plan 42003) half-baths in each bedroom with a shared bathing area.

better

best

The Brady Bunch gave us a few laughs as well as insights into issues families face as they try to unite two families as one through re-marriage. Certainly, the Brady's housekeeper, Alice, helped smooth over some of the inevitable conflict. While most of us do not enjoy the luxury of a live-in housekeeper, there are steps which can be taken when building or remodeling a home which can reduce parents, angst of bringing two families together.

Moms know their girls spend a lot of time in the bathroom – which usually doubles as their dressing, hair care and make-up center. Girls need space to keep these items, as well as other feminine products. Boys generally don't give bathrooms much consideration (as evidenced by the toilet seat being left up as well as dirty clothes and wet towels strewn about.)

Of course, separate baths for each of the kids, bedrooms would be ideal, but the expense and space required can make it impractical. Still, parents of blended families have legitimate concerns, especially if boys and girls from different backgrounds will be sharing the same bath area.

Compartmented baths are a welcome solution! A traditional compartmented bath places a door between the sink/vanity and the toilet/tub area, allowing two family members to use the bath area at the same time. As secondary baths in some designs have grown larger, two sinks reduces stress when several people are getting ready at the same time.

Even better is the emerging solution of having vanity/sink areas private to each secondary bedroom, with private access to a shared toilet/tub area. This is especially welcome if one of the kids is a "cleanie" and the other a "messy", as they can have their sink/vanity area to their liking!

The occasional child presents different challenges. Imagine having your 6-year old daughter, Mandy, who lives with you only on weekends and for a month during the summer. First and foremost is her emotional well-being. In this regard, stability and familiarity are paramount.

Mandy needs a place in the home that is hers, even if the room is used for other purposes while she is away. Ideally, Mandy's room should be on par with other childrens, bedrooms in your home, so she doesn't feel like a second-class family member. She also needs a place for her things and ideally a place where she can keep projects in progress, such as half-finished puzzles or Lego® creations.

A room that functions as a home office or hobby area during the week is an excellent solution, particularly when outfitted with a daybed or Murphy bed, one which folds up into the wall when not in use. A walk-in closet for Mandy's room provides numerous creative opportunities. While she's younger, this area can double as Mandy's private play space. Consider a drywall opening into the closet area from the bedroom – a window, into that space. As she grows, this space will naturally fill with Mandy's things.

Parents, particularly parents in blended families, want to interact with all of the children and allow the kids to spend time together. Open floorplans, especially designs where the kitchen is open to the family room, enhance opportunities for communication – even if the parent is just working in the kitchen while keeping an eye on what the kids are doing.

Of course, children need privacy as well. All parents share the experience of arguments with kids over music volume coming from bedrooms. Insulating interior bedroom walls and usuing solid core doors are a sure way to set your homes apart in the minds of these buyers.

Even laundry rooms are a design consideration for blended families. No one wants to see another family member's undergarments. While laundry rooms which double as the entry to the home from the garage are common, many buyers prefer designs where the laundry area can be closed off. (If necessary, this can be accomplished by modifying an existing plan.)

Storage

Plan for Storing "Stuff"

Have you ever met someone who had too much storage space in their home? It's probably never happened. For many of us, the lack of space, disorganization and clutter become significant sources of stress. In fact, according to published studies, Americans on average lose up to 150 hours every year looking for lost or misplaced items. Take control over your life and give yourself a little more time by addressing the storage opportunities of your home.

1. Linens

One of the hallmarks of a well-thought-out homeplan is linen storage. Typically located in or near bath areas, will the linen closets/cabinets be adequate for extra pillows, comforters and sheet sets, as well as towels and washcloths? So many linens are oversized: towels, bedding, blankets. You don't want to have to default to using other bathroom storage, taking away from places for blow dryers and personal care items.

2. Bikes, lawnmowers, sporting goods, etc.

Its no secret that garages are getting bigger, and today's larger vehicles are only part of the reason why. Four bicycles, golf clubs, every kind of ball imaginable, skates, scooters—all in a pile—yuck!

Adequate storage makes the mess go away. Today's garage systems help organize your garage and your life by having a place for tools, gardening supplies, sporting goods, etc.

3. Sizable bedroom closets.

"More closet space" is one of the most often mentioned reasons for buying a new home. Stuff multiplies–we're not sure how! But in addition to bigger closets, closet systems can actually help you organize and store twice as many items as the standard rod and shelf approach! Ventilated (wire) closet hanging systems have become very popular due to its flexibility and the ability for air to move between clothes and through shelving—keeping clothes fresher longer.

4. Games, holiday decorations.

The day after Thanksgiving and it's time for holiday decorations to come out. But where are they? Mixed up with St. Patrick's Day, Valentine's Day and Halloween!

From Christmas trees and lights to Monopoly®, we want convenient places to keep our stuff. Storage solutions may include closets, or unfinished areas of the home.

5. Kitchen storage.

Table settings for twelve, pots and pans, the 36-cup coffee maker, a dozen cans of tuna and gourmet cookbooks! Large families and packrats need lots of storage in the kitchen!

With the kitchen as the activity hub in most homes, more thought should go into storage and serving issues. Will items be stored convenient to where they will be used? What about big pots and pans? Or, pretty dishware and other items you would like to display? Pantry storage for prepared foods? Only you know how you want your kitchen to function, so talk with a kitchen cabinet specialist regarding products and solutions available to create your dream kitchen!

6. Cell phones, keys, umbrellas, mail

A drop zone. Everybody needs one and everybody has one. It's just that too many of us use a kitchen island, breakfast table or other area that just happens to be convenient to drop off keys, pocket change, the mail, cell phones, etc. Eliminate

unsightly clutter by putting in a cabinet near the entry from the garage to organize these things. Be sure to incorporate a recharging center for cell phones and the video camera. You may also want to add a tal space for hanging umbrellas, and a cork board or write-on board to turn this into a message center as well.

Stress-free living includes knowing you'll never lose your keys again and where your fully charged cell phone is when you leave the house!

7. Long-term storage

Johnny's history is often in a box—baby clothes, baptism, first day of school, birthday cards, a brilliant essay, all kinds of awards. Until Johnny is old enough to take them off your hands, you have a storage challenge!

Items with tremendous personal value but infrequently accessed need dry, long-term storage. Garage storage or unfinished areas of the home can be ideal long term storage spots. Be sure to use the right kind of containers—as cardboard boxes can deteriorate and contribute to a musty basement smell.

8. Bulk items/Cleaning supplies.

We all love a good bargain, but where do you keep the jumbo 12-roll pack of paper towels? Or cleaning supplies, some of which need to be stored out of the reach of children?

Ideally you would like to keep these items close to where they will be used. Convenient to the kitchen, a walk-in coat closet off the garage entry offers shelving for such items while in the laundry room, a broom closet and generous cabinetry offer plenty of additional storage.

9. Everyday coats, shoes, boots, etc.

If you live in a cold winter climate, have a larger family or entertain frequently, you'll appreciate adequate coat storage easily accessed from the front door, garage entry, or both.

Nothing is more stressful than getting the family out the door with everything they need, on time in the morning. If you have lockers near the garage entry, that's where the kids will find their lunches (or lunch money), backpacks, gym clothes, etc.

Garage Storage

Today's garages are so much more than simply a place where cars are kept. As with homes overall, garages have become larger and are serving more purposes. In addition to auto supplies, garages are 'home' to lawn and garden products, tools, sports equipment, wintertime products, paint, and much more.

If, when parked in the garage, your daily commute to your car weaves around bikes, steps over garden tools and dodges dodge balls, you're not alone. In fact, the stress associated with this reality has given rise to garage storage and organization systems becoming one of the hottest markets in both new construction and remodeling. The promise of a neat, tidy, organized garage is compelling both rationally and emotionally.

Whether you are building a new home, or looking to reorganize the garage of your existing home, the first step is to identify any activity zones, such as a workbench or a gardening center, as these may dictate specialized storage needs. Second, determine what you really want to keep in the garage. With an existing home, that means throwing some stuff away! Be prepared– you just may need to rent a dumpster for all that stuff that's been collecting in your garage.

Knowing the activity zones and items which will be stored in the garage is the first step in designing your storage solu- tion. With blueprints (or garage measure- ments) in hand, identify spaces along the walls which don't interfere with opening the doors on your cars or walkways into the house. Sometimes there are also storage opportunities between parked vehicles or even overhead if your garage has a high ceiling.

Since keeping the garage reasonably clean is important from many perspectives (including safety, pest control and overall appearance,) you'll want to get most items up and off the floor. Various garage wall storage systems are available, offering hanging for tools, shelving, cabinetry, and sporting goods storage options. Mobile storage—wheeled storage cabinets for example—address the same need as these units are easily moved to clean around.

PHOTOS COURTESY OF RUBBERMAID

The choice of open shelving vs. cabinet storage is often comes down to aesthetics, personal preference and price. But another consideration should be child safety. Sharp or dangerous items (pesticides, for example) are best kept in cabinets concealed from curious eyes. Optimally, these cabinets would be lockable.

Sporting goods, particularly bicycles, present their own challenges. With an active family, these frequently used items need to be readily available. But what do you do with four bikes? Garage organization suppliers offer numerous solutions which help store bikes out of the way, many times off the floor, yet are easily accessible.

The far end of the garage (when parked, the wall closest to your car's front bumper) offers a special storage opportunity, particularly for less frequently needed and larger items. Deep cabinets can be mounted high enough on the wall so that when you pull your car in, the hood clears underneath these cabinets.

Also, many innovative overhead storage products are becoming available. These solutions are ideal for seasonal storage (where do you store the Christmas lights and decorations for the other eleven months?) At the same time, you must consider safe accessibility. Climbing ladders to retrieve heavy or bulky items is obviously unwise.

Though not strictly storage, one final issue merits its own consideration—guys who spend a lot of time in the garage pursuing hobbies or even watching TV while playing cards. If that's you, don't overlook heating (keeping your favorite space usable year-round); refrigeration (cold beverages, not frozen beverages); and even where to put the cable TV jack.

One final tip if you are going to install a garage storage system in your present home. After the dumpster is hauled away, you just might want to rent a U-Haul truck to store everything else from your garage during the installation of your new storage system!

Garage storage and organization systems are an excellent investment for your own sanity and peace of mind. They may also be an amenity that helps you someday resell your home for a higher price and in a quicker timeframe. You'll never regret spending a little extra time carefully planning this aspect of your home!

Flexibility

Combine Rooms for In-Laws/Guest Suite

With the aging of America and boom-a-rang children, a house plan that can combine bedroom and a private bath makes a great suite. If the situation changes, the rooms can be used for other needs.

Even more accommodating, some homeowners are utilizing a pair of adjacent secondary bedrooms as an in-law suite. Such arrangements offer considerable privacy, with the in-law suite offering both a sleeping area and its own living space as well.

4-Seasons Room

Bringing the outside in and views to the outside are important to many people. Many of us work in an office all day, so we like to incorporate outside living into our lives at home. Whether the area is screened in, enclosed with windows or just an open patio, it is an important element to daily living.

When asked "what is your favorite place in your home?" a surprising number of people answer their porch or deck. If you can identify with this group, consider adding (operable) windows all around your outdoor living space along with supplemental baseboard heating, enabling you to enjoy this space anytime!

Kid's Playroom

Whether it is your own family, company with children, or neighborhood kids, it is always important that you find a place for a playroom. It helps with everyone's sanity to keep the noise and toys away from adults.

Ironically, a kids, playroom just might be one of your most prized luxuries in your new home. By having most of their toys, games, puzzles, etc. in this one room, keeping the rest of the house presentable an achievable reality!

Home Schooling Room

Increasingly popular, home schooling parents have a particular challenge with today's more open home designs–the need for privacy so their kids can concentrate on their studies or tests. When planning this space, consider storqage, workspaces, lighting (especially natural light) and computer hook-ups.

Ideally, a room in the home can be dedicated to schooling. More often, it will double as a school room and serve another purpose at other times, so make sure the space is flexible. Pay particular attention to floor coverings if school or other activities are likely to include messy projects, crafts, etc.

Craft/Gardening Areas

When it comes to unwinding from our hurried lives or pursuing something we really enjoy, many people like to relax with a special hobby or craft. How many times do you have a project spread out on the kitchen or dining room table? An area out of public view would take the stress out of constant picking up. Therefore, having room in the home to pursue these and other hobbies in and of itself can contribute to distressing, especially if 'works-in-progress' can be left undisturbed.

The primary considerations for such spaces are related to the type of activity. Gardening, for example, is ideally suited for an area with a sink in it and being close to an outside door. Sewing and needlework projects are enhanced by high light levels. Woodworking fits well with concrete floors for easy clean-up plus plenty of electrical outlets for various power tools.

Whatever your favorite pursuit, what things could you do with your home which would enhance the experience? How about special task lighting? This is sometimes a hard area to identify, simply because we learn to cope with the shortcomings inherent to our present situation. The answers lie in things which frustrate you when engaged in these activities.

Bedroom/Bath Arrangements for Blended Families

Blending families can be a difficult task but picking a home plan that has been designed to address bedroom/bath needs makes the task so much easier.

Especially when combining boys and girls from two families into one new family, thought needs to be given regarding bedroom and bathroom accommodations. Everyone needs a sense of privacy and a sense of space which they can call their own. And when it comes to sharing a bathroom, dual lavatories are a big plus, as is a toilet/shower area separate from the lavs.

Home Offices (His and Her)

Kevin and Tina both work at home. Sharing an office is not working so they found a plan that gives them his and her offices. They can work in their own spaces but more than that; it makes for a pleasant marriage.

People who succeed in working from home attest to the importance of having a dedicated home office space where they can focus on their work. Today's economy coupled with downsizing and early retirement is giving birth to numerous cottage industries.

The type of work you do out of your home will dictate your space needs. Pay careful attention to storage and any special wiring, as well as privacy.

Formal Dining

Candlelight, soft music, ample room for guests and great conversation make dinner parties a delight. The formal dining room also makes an excellent backdrop for a great dining room suite. Since entertaining inevitably involves food. Look at how you home enhances the dining experience. Be mindful of seating, which always becomes an issue. Homes designed with an open floorplan, especially ones in which the dining room flows uninterrupted into a great room, offer numerous entertaining options.

Room to Grow

An item no one wants to think about is outgrowing their home. But the reality is that family situations change and our needs and wants for space in the home change too. The solution? Unfinished areas of the home, especially on a second level or over a garage or in a basement.

You may not need this space when you first move into your home, but it will give you room to add a bedroom, media room, playroom, etc. Families can grow into these spaces and configure them as the need arises, without having the initial cost of finishing the space affecting their mortgage qualifications or mortgage payment.

'Flexible Design'

'Change' is all around us, having become the norm in American society. And as our lives change, we begin to appreciate homes whichwere designed to adapt to our changing situations. It's called flexible design.

To some extent, we've all grown up with the 'flexible' concept, such as when we turned a spare bedroom into a 'TV room' by replacing the bed with a sofa and chair. But flexible design goes further than that–having a lot to do with how rooms are accessed and what other rooms they are adjacent to. While flexible living doesn't change the footprint of a home, it does encourage looking for ways to change spaces to meet a particular need. It typically also involves minor changes to the design, such as adding, removing or repositioning doors, closets, shelving, etc.

The 'Redmond' homeplan (#43035 featured on page 41) illustrates the flex room concept well. This efficient design works nicely for many buyer profiles, from singles to couples to smaller families. It will also accommodate larger families when built on a basement foundation and part of the basement space is finished.

A flex room is so labeled to suggest buyers themselves determine how the space will be used. Many people would envision the flex room in this home used as a third bedroom (see illustration above right) When doing so, the passage to the kitchen is eliminated and the entrance into this space

is via an alcove and door conveniently placed near the bathroom. Statistics also show that after being launched out on their own, "half of our adult children return home within 30 months, sometimes bringing a spouse or child back with them." Middle adulthood may also mean moving in aging parents no longer able to live independently. With the adjacent bath, this flex room converts nicely as a modest suite.

Another likely utilization of the flex space in this design would be as a formal dining room. At 14' x 10" the room is nicely proportioned for an oval table. The entry pillars, 10' high boxed ceiling and double window enhances the dining experience, as does the easy kitchen connection.

A quick review of this homeplan elicited uses ranging from "media room," "library," and "music room" to "a home-schooling room". If a media room, extra soundproofing measures will mean some of the guys can be in there watching the big game, while others enjoy conversation in the family room and kitchen. Home schoolers, on the other hand, would appreciate plenty of shelving. For even more flexibility, a Murphy bed (one which folds up into the wall) or a day bed means the same space can serve multiple purposes as needed.

But more common was to hear people express their intention that the flex space would become a den or home office. Abundant natural light has been shown to enhance concentration and reduce stress, so in addition to the double window, consider adding a skylight. In addition to eliminating the passageway to the kitchen, a pair of full-lite French doors could be added to close off the space when privacy is desired.

You may also want to consider turning bedroom #2, the flex room and bath into a full guest suite. Well-separated from the master suite, either bedroom #2 or the flex room can function as the actual bedroom, with the other room being a private living space for your guest, boomerang child or elderly parent. This arrangement also services another emerging trend–an elderly or widowed sibling coming to live with you.

Designs which embody such flexibility are in demand by homebuyers. How you intend to use the space is entirely up to you. But thinking about how a home's design can adapt to your future needs should be a prime consideration before you build.

the
Calumet
1129-9JJ
pricecode 11

Total Square Ft. **1125**

Standard Foundation: Basement

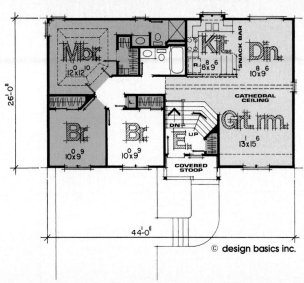

Mbr.
12x12

Kit.
8x9

Dn
10x9

SNACK BAR

R.

CATHEDRAL CEILING

Br.
10x9

Br.
10x9

DN

UP

Grt. rm.
13x15

COVERED STOOP

26'-0"

44'-0"

© design basics inc.

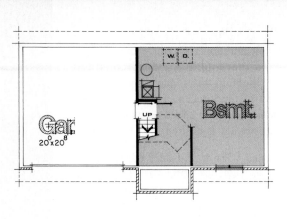

Gar.
20x20

W. D.

UP

Bsmt.

the
Oakfield
5479-9JJ
pricecode 11

Total Square Ft. **1191**

Standard Foundation: Basement

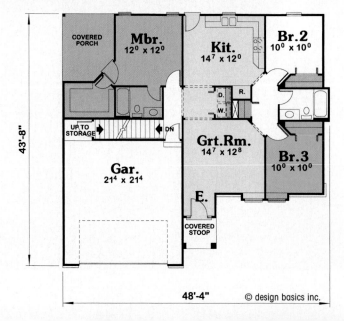

COVERED PORCH

Mbr.
12⁰ x 12⁰

Kit.
14⁷ x 12⁰

Br.2
10⁰ x 10⁰

UP TO STORAGE

DN

Gar.
21⁴ x 21⁴

D. R.

W.

Grt.Rm.
14⁷ x 12⁸

Br.3
10⁰ x 10⁰

E.

COVERED STOOP

43'-8"

48'-4"

© design basics inc.

Livability
at a Glance™

Storing
Entertaining
Flexible Living
De-Stressing

www.designbasics.com/9JJ

the
Kendrick
8532-9JJ
pricecode 11

Total Square Ft.   **1195**

Standard Foundation: Basement

COVERED PORCH

Mbr.
12⁰ x 13⁰

Br.2
10⁰ x 10⁶

Kit.
11⁰ x 9³

DINING AREA

Br.3
10⁰ x 10⁶

Fam. Room
13⁸ x 20⁰

DN

W D

Gar.
19⁴ x 21⁴

COVERED PORCH

© dbi

48'-8"

40'-0"

the
Dover
2376-9JJ
pricecode 12

Total Square Ft.   **1205**

Standard Foundation: Basement

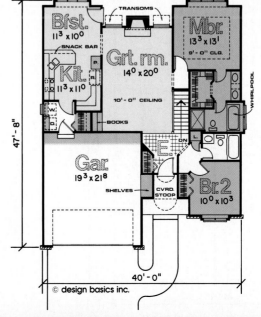

Bfst.
11³ x 10⁰

TRANSOMS

Mbr.
13³ x 13¹
9'-0" CLG.

SNACK BAR

Grt. rm.
14⁰ x 20⁰
10'-0" CEILING

Kit.
11³ x 11⁰

WHIRLPOOL

W D

BOOKS

Gar.
19³ x 21⁸

DN

SHELVES

CVRD. STOOP

Br.2
10⁰ x 10³

47'-8"

40'-0"

© design basics inc.

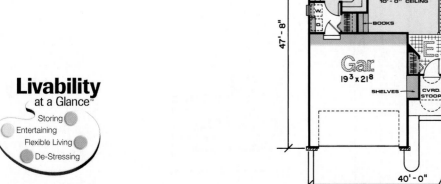

Livability
at a Glance™

Storing
Entertaining
Flexible Living
De-Stressing

800.947.7526

23

the Kirby Farm
8093-9JJ
price code 12

Total Square Ft. **1212**

Standard Foundation: Basement

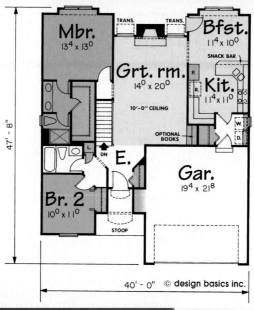

Mbr.
13⁴ x 13⁰

TRANS.   TRANS.

Bfst.
11⁴ x 10⁰

SNACK BAR

Grt. rm.
14⁰ x 20⁰

10'-0" CEILING

P.
R.

Kit.
11⁴ x 11⁰

W.
D.

OPTIONAL BOOKS

E.

DN

Gar.
19⁴ x 21⁸

Br. 2
10⁰ x 11⁰

STOOP

47' - 8"

40' - 0"   © design basics inc.

---

the Bridgewater
43010-9JJ
price code 12

Total Square Ft. **1268**

Standard Foundation: Slab

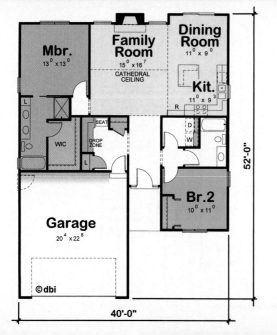

Mbr.
13⁰ x 13⁰

Family Room
15⁰ x 16⁷
CATHEDRAL CEILING

Dining Room
11⁰ x 9⁰

Kit.
11⁰ x 9³

WIC

SEAT

DROP ZONE

D
W

Br. 2
10⁰ x 11⁰

Garage
20⁴ x 22⁸

©dbi

52'-0"

40'-0"

Dining Room
11⁰ x 9⁰

Kit.
11⁰ x 9³

P   R

Optional Kitchen

WIC

SEAT

DROP ZONE

DN

Optional Basement Stair Location

Livability
at a Glance™

Storing
Entertaining
Flexible Living
De-Stressing

24

www.designbasics.com/9JJ

the
Logan
1551-9JJ
price code 12

Total Square Ft. **1271**

Standard Foundation: Basement

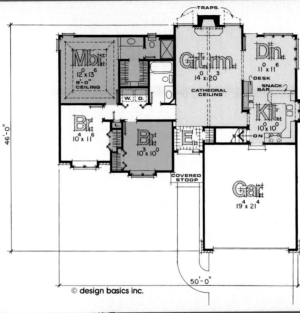

Mbr.
12⁰ x 13⁶
9'-0" CEILING

Br.
10⁴ x 11⁶

Br.
10³ x 10⁰

W. D.

Gr. rm.
14⁰ x 20³
CATHEDRAL CEILING

TRAPS.

Dn.
11⁰ x 11

DESK

SNACK BAR

Kit.
10⁰ x 10⁰

DN

COVERED STOOP

Gar.
19⁴ x 21⁴

46'-0"

50'-0"

© design basics inc.

the
Taunton
43011-9JJ
price code 12

Total Square Ft. **1275**

Standard Foundation: Slab

Dining Room
11⁰ x 9⁰

Kit.
11⁰ x 9³

P   R

Optional Kitchen

L

WIC

SEAT

DROP ZONE

DN

Optional Basement Stair Location

Mbr.
13⁰ x 13⁰

Family Room
15⁰ x 16⁷
CATHEDRAL CEILING

Dining Room
11⁰ x 9⁰

Kit.
11⁰ x 9³

L

WIC

SEAT

DROP ZONE

L

D   W

Garage
20⁴ x 22⁸

Br.2
10⁰ x 11⁰

52'-0"

40'-0"

© dbi

Livability
at a Glance™

Storing
Entertaining
Flexible Living
De-Stressing

800.947.7526

25

the
Reynolds
3907-9JJ
pricecode 13

Total Square Ft. **1316**

Standard Foundation: Basement

Br. 2
11⁰ x 12⁰

Mbr.
14⁰ x 12⁰

10'-0"
CLG.

TRANS.

Grt. rm.
17⁷ x 19³
10'-0" CEILING

Bfst.
10⁰ x 11⁰

SNACK BAR

DN

P.
R.

Kit.
13⁴ x 11⁴

COVERED STOOP

Gar.
19⁴ x 23⁰

69' - 4"

32' - 0"

© design basics inc.

the
Richland
6787-9JJ
pricecode 13

Total Square Ft. **1333**

Standard Foundation: Basement

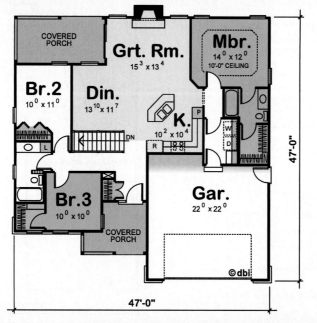

COVERED PORCH

Grt. Rm.
15³ x 13⁴

Mbr.
14⁰ x 12⁰
10'-0" CEILING

Br. 2
10⁰ x 11⁰

Din.
13¹⁰ x 11⁷

K.
10² x 10⁴

P

DN

W
D

R

Br. 3
10⁰ x 10⁰

COVERED PORCH

Gar.
22⁰ x 22⁰

47'-0"

47'-0"

©dbi

Livability
at a Glance™

Storing
Entertaining
Flexible Living
De-Stressing

26

the Tollefson
6731-9JJ
price code 13

Total Square Ft. **1335**

Standard Foundation: Basement

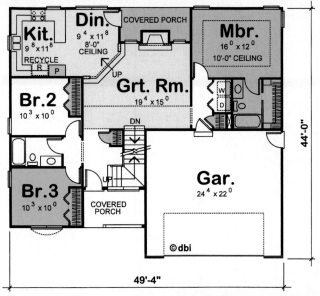

Kit.
9^8 x 11^8
RECYCLE
R   P

Din.
9^4 x 11^8
8'-0" CEILING

COVERED PORCH

Mbr.
16^0 x 12^0
10'-0" CEILING

UP

Grt. Rm.
19^4 x 15^0

Br.2
10^3 x 10^0

W
D

DN

Br.3
10^3 x 10^0

UP

COVERED PORCH

Gar.
24^4 x 22^0

© dbi

44'-0"

49'-4"

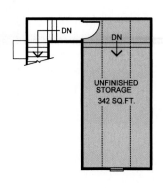

DN

DN

UNFINISHED STORAGE
342 SQ.FT.

the Aspen
3102-9JJ
price code 13

Total Square Ft. **1339**

Standard Foundation: Basement

Bfst.
10^0 x 9^0

DN

Grt. rm.
14^0 x 17^4
10'-0" CEILING

Mbr.
12^0 x 14^0
9'-0" CLG.

WHIRLPOOL

SNACK BAR

P.

COVERED

Kit.
10^0 x 10^4

W.
D.

STORAGE

COVERED STOOP

Gar.
19^4 x 25^8

Br.2
10^0 x 10^0

Br.3
10^0 x 10^0

46'-0"

50'-0"

© design basics inc.

Livability
at a Glance™

Storing
Entertaining
Flexible Living
De-Stressing

the
Mayberry
2761-9JJ
price code 13

Total Square Ft. **1341**

Standard Foundation: Basement

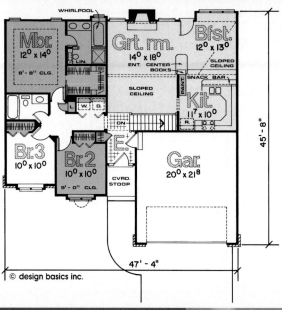

WHIRLPOOL

Mbr.
12⁰ x 14⁰

8'- 8" CLG.

LIN.

Grt. rm.
14⁰ x 18⁰
ENT. CENTER
BOOKS

Bfst.
12⁰ x 13⁰

SLOPED CEILING

SNACK BAR

PANT.

SLOPED CEILING

W. D.

Kit.
11⁷ x 10⁰

R.

DN.

Br. 3
10⁰ x 10⁰

Br. 2
10⁰ x 10⁰

9'- 0" CLG.

CVRD. STOOP

Gar.
20⁰ x 21⁸

45'- 8"

47'- 4"

© design basics inc.

the
Kaplin
1963-9JJ
price code 13

Total Square Ft. **1347**

Standard Foundation: Basement

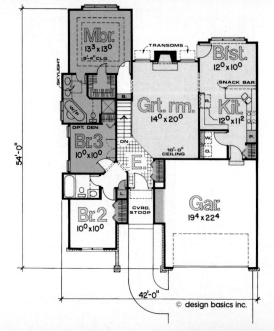

SKYLIGHT

Mbr.
13³ x 13⁰

9'-4" CLG.

TRANSOMS

Bfst.
12⁰ x 10⁰

SNACK BAR

WIP

OPT. DEN

Grt. rm.
14⁰ x 20⁰

Kit.
12⁰ x 11²

P.

Br. 3
10⁰ x 10⁰

DN.

10'- 0" CEILING

W. D.

54'- 0"

Br. 2
10⁰ x 10⁰

CVRD. STOOP

Gar.
19⁴ x 22⁴

42'-0"

© design basics inc.

Livability
at a Glance™

Storing
Entertaining
Flexible Living
De-Stressing

the Cartwright
24048-9JJ
pricecode 13

Total Square Ft. **1359**

Standard Foundation: Slab

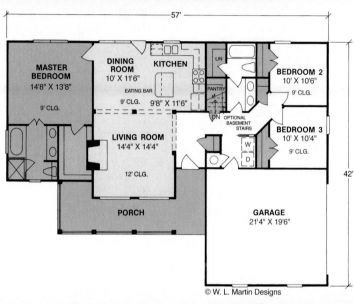

- 57'
- 42'

MASTER BEDROOM 14'8" X 13'8"
9' CLG.

DINING ROOM 10' X 11'6"
EATING BAR
9' CLG.

KITCHEN
9'8" X 11'6"

LIN

PANTRY

DN OPTIONAL BASEMENT STAIRS

BEDROOM 2 10' X 10'6"
9' CLG.

BEDROOM 3 10' X 10'4"
9' CLG.

LIVING ROOM 14'4" X 14'4"
12' CLG.

W D

PORCH

GARAGE 21'4" X 19'6"

© W. L. Martin Designs

the Winter Woods
8091-9JJ
pricecode 13

Total Square Ft. **1360**

Standard Foundation: Basement

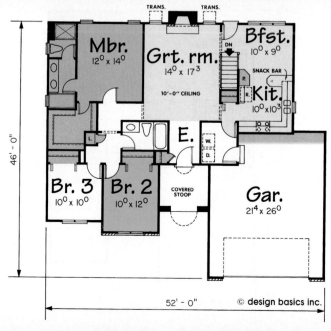

TRANS.   TRANS.

Mbr. 12⁰ x 14⁰

Grt. rm. 14⁰ x 17³
10'-0" CEILING

DN

Bfst. 10⁰ x 9⁰

SNACK BAR

Kit. 10⁰ x 10³

E.

W. D.

Br. 3 10⁰ x 10⁰

Br. 2 10⁰ x 12⁰

COVERED STOOP

Gar. 21⁴ x 26⁰

46' - 0"

52' - 0"

© design basics inc.

Livability at a Glance™
- Storing
- Entertaining
- Flexible Living
- De-Stressing

the Janssen
5464-9JJ
pricecode 13

Total Square Ft. **1379**

Standard Foundation: Basement

COVERED PORCH

Mbr.
13⁴ x 14⁴
10'-0" CEIL.

Grt.Rm.
14⁸ x 15⁵
10'-0" CEIL.

Kit.
12⁸ x 12⁰

DN

Bfst.
10⁰ x 11⁰

R.

48'-8"

Gar.
21⁴ x 21⁰

W. D.

E.

Study
12⁸ x 12⁰
11'-0" CEIL.

COVERED PORCH

55'-4"

© design basics inc.

---

the Gabriel Bay
8013-9JJ
pricecode 13

Total Square Ft. **1392**

Standard Foundation: Basement

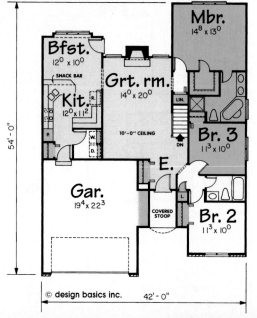

Bfst.
12⁰ x 10⁰

SNACK BAR

Kit.
12⁰ x 11²

R.

Grt. rm.
14⁰ x 20⁰

10'-0" CEILING

DN

Mbr.
14⁸ x 13⁰

LIN.

Br. 3
11³ x 10⁰

W. D.

E.

L

Br. 2
11³ x 10⁰

Gar.
19⁴ x 22³

COVERED STOOP

54' - 0"

42' - 0"

© design basics inc.

Livability
at a Glance™

Storing
Entertaining
Flexible Living
De-Stressing

www.designbasics.com/9JJ

the
Quimby
3010-9JJ
pricecode 14

Total Square Ft. **1422**

Standard Foundation: Basement

© design basics inc.

50'-0"

58'-0"

Mbr.
14⁰ x 12²
9'-0" CEILING

Grt. rm.
14⁰ x 20⁰
12'-0" CEILING

Din.
12³ x 10⁰

COVERED PORCH

Kit.
12⁰ x 10⁰

Sto.
8⁴ x 10⁴

Br. 2
10⁰ x 11⁰

Br. 3
10⁰ x 11²
10'-0" CLG.
OPT. DEN

WORK BENCH

Gar.
20⁴ x 21⁸

CVRD. STOOP

LIN.

WHIRLPOOL

BOOKS

the
Pendleton
1379-9JJ
pricecode 14

Total Square Ft. **1429**

Standard Foundation: Basement

Bfst.
11 x 9

Kit.
11 x 10

Dn.
12 x 11

Grt. rm.
14 x 17

Mbr.
11 x 16
9'-0" CLG.

Br.
11 x 11

Br.
10 x 10

COVERED PORCH

OCT.

UP
DN

© design basics inc.

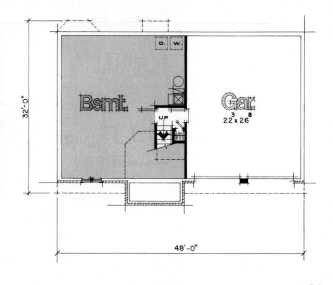

Bsmt.

Gar.
22 x 26

UP

D. W.

32'-0"

48'-0"

Livability
at a Glance

Storing

Entertaining

Flexible Living

De-Stressing

the Chandler Hills
8089-9JJ
price code 14

Total Square Ft. **1433**

Standard Foundation: Basement

58' - 0"

Bfst. 12⁰ x 10⁰

Grt. rm. 14⁰ x 20⁰

Mbr. 14⁰ x 12¹

SNACK BAR

Kit. 12⁰ x 10⁰

12'-0" CEILING

E.

Br. 3 10⁰ x 11²

Br. 2 10⁰ x 11⁰

Gar. 22⁸ x 21⁸

COVERED PORCH

© design basics inc.   50' - 0"

the Culverton
5476-9JJ
price code 14

Total Square Ft. **1437**

Standard Foundation: Basement

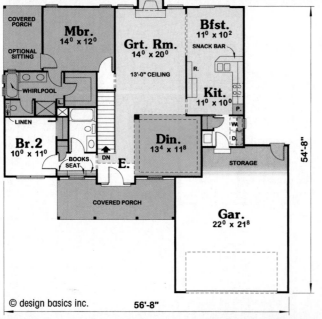

COVERED PORCH

Mbr. 14⁰ x 12⁰

OPTIONAL SITTING

WHIRLPOOL

LINEN

Br. 2 10⁰ x 11⁰

BOOKS SEAT

DN

E.

Grt. Rm. 14⁰ x 20⁰

13'-0" CEILING

Din. 13⁴ x 11⁸

COVERED PORCH

Bfst. 11⁰ x 10²

SNACK BAR

R.

Kit. 11⁰ x 10⁰

P.

W.
D.

STORAGE

Gar. 22⁰ x 21⁸

54'-8"

© design basics inc.   56'-8"

Livability at a Glance™

Storing
Entertaining
Flexible Living
De-Stressing

www.designbasics.com/9JJ

the Bradford Pointe

8160-9JJ
pricecode 14

Total Square Ft. **1449**

Standard Foundation: Basement

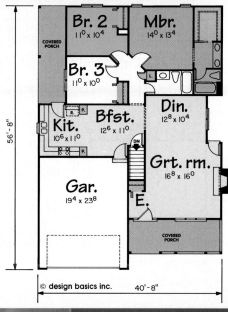

Br. 2
11⁰ x 10⁴

Mbr.
14⁰ x 13⁴

Br. 3
11⁰ x 10⁰

COVERED PORCH

Kit.
10⁶ x 11⁰

Bfst.
12⁶ x 11⁰

Din.
12⁸ x 10⁴

Grt. rm.
16⁸ x 16⁰

Gar.
19⁴ x 23⁸

E.

COVERED PORCH

56'-8"

40'-8"

© design basics inc.

the Fraser

2173-9JJ
pricecode 14

Total Square Ft. **1451**

Standard Foundation: Basement

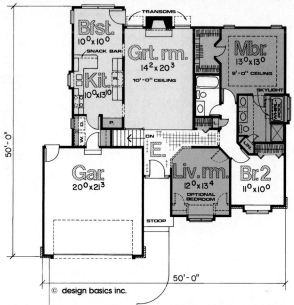

TRANSOMS

Bfst.
10⁰ x 10⁰

SNACK BAR

Grt. rm.
14² x 20³
10'-0" CEILING

Mbr.
13⁰ x 13⁰
9'-0" CEILING

SKYLIGHT

Kit.
10⁰ x 13¹⁰

WHIRL POOL

Gar.
20⁰ x 21³

E.

Liv. rm.
12⁰ x 13⁴
OPTIONAL BEDROOM

Br. 2
11⁰ x 10⁰

STOOP

50'-0"

50'-0"

© design basics inc.

Livability
at a Glance™

Storing
Entertaining
Flexible Living
De-Stressing

800.947.7526

33

the
Spring Valley
8090-9JJ
pricecode 14

Total Square Ft. **1453**

Standard Foundation: Basement

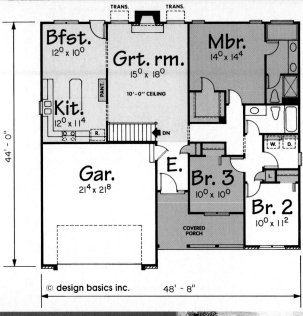

TRANS. TRANS.

Bfst.
12⁰ x 10⁰

Grt. rm.
15⁰ x 18⁰

10'-0" CEILING

Mbr.
14⁰ x 14⁴

Kit.
12⁰ x 11⁴

PANT.

R.

DN

Gar.
21⁴ x 21⁸

E.

Br. 3
10⁰ x 10⁰

W. D.

L.

Br. 2
10⁰ x 11²

COVERED PORCH

44'-0"

48'-8"

© design basics inc.

---

the
Payson
5034-9JJ
pricecode 14

Total Square Ft. **1472**

Standard Foundation: Basement

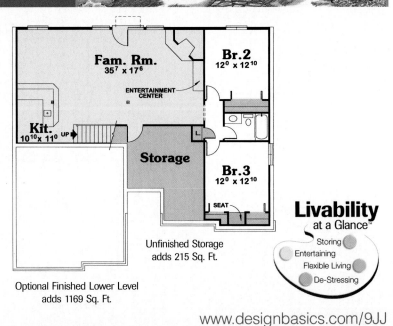

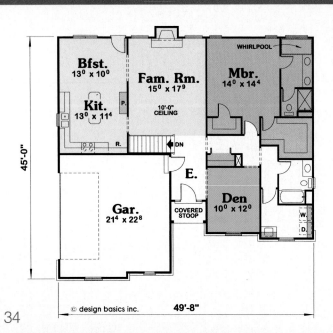

Bfst.
13⁰ x 10⁰

Fam. Rm.
15⁰ x 17⁹

WHIRLPOOL

Mbr.
14⁰ x 14⁴

Kit.
13⁰ x 11⁴

P.

10'-0" CEILING

R.

DN

E.

Gar.
21⁴ x 22⁸

COVERED STOOP

Den
10⁰ x 12⁰

W. D.

45'-0"

49'-8"

© design basics inc.

Fam. Rm.
35⁷ x 17⁶

ENTERTAINMENT CENTER

Br. 2
12⁰ x 12¹⁰

Kit.
10¹⁰ x 11⁰

UP

L.

Storage

Br. 3
12⁰ x 12¹⁰

SEAT

Unfinished Storage
adds 215 Sq. Ft.

Optional Finished Lower Level
adds 1169 Sq. Ft.

Livability
at a Glance™

Storing
Entertaining
Flexible Living
De-Stressing

www.designbasics.com/9JJ

the Kirby
3260-9JJ
price code 14

Total Square Ft. **1478**

Standard Foundation: Basement

Optional Third Bedroom

Br. 3
11³ x 10⁰

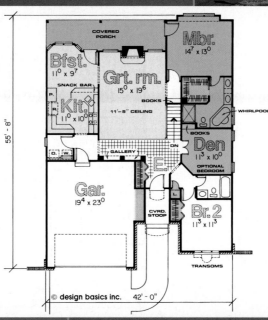

COVERED PORCH

Bfst.
11⁰ x 9⁷

SNACK BAR

Grt. rm.
15⁰ x 19⁶

11'-5" CEILING

Mbr.
14⁷ x 13⁰

BOOKS

WHIRLPOOL

BOOKS

Kit.
11⁰ x 10⁰

Den
11³ x 10⁰

OPTIONAL BEDROOM

GALLERY

DN

D. W.

Gar.
19⁴ x 23⁰

CVRD. STOOP

Br. 2
11³ x 11³

55' - 8"

42' - 0"

TRANSOMS

© design basics inc.

the Kelsey
3019-9JJ
price code 14

Total Square Ft. **1479**

Standard Foundation: Basement

Optional Third Bedroom

OPTIONAL
Br. 3
10⁰ x 10⁰
10'-0" CLG.

Livability
at a Glance™

Storing
Entertaining
Flexible Living
De-Stressing

WHIRLPOOL

Kit.
13⁰ x 11⁰

R.   P.

TRANSOMS

GLASS SHELVES

SNACK BAR

Grt. rm.
14⁰ x 18⁰

Mbr.
13⁰ x 13⁰

9'-0" CLG.

Bfst.
11⁰ x 10⁰

11'-0" CEILING

DN

D. W.

Gar.
19⁸ x 22⁰

E.

Den
10⁰ x 10⁰

OPTIONAL BEDROOM
10'-0" CLG.

Br. 2
10⁸ x 10⁰

TRANS.

COVERED PORCH

50' - 0"

48' - 0"

© design basics inc.

the Celina
43046-9JJ
price code 14

Total Square Ft. **1482**

Standard Foundation: Slab

Den
13⁰ x 10⁰

Optional Den

Optional Basement Stair Location

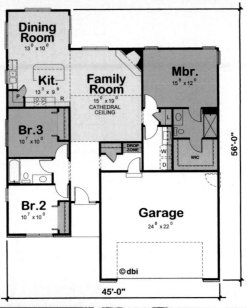

Dining Room
13⁰ x 10⁰

Kit.
13³ x 9⁹

Family Room
15⁰ x 19⁰
CATHEDRAL CEILING

Mbr.
15⁸ x 12⁰

Br.3
10⁷ x 10⁰

DROP ZONE

WIC

Br.2
10⁷ x 10⁰

Garage
24⁸ x 22⁰

©dbi

56'-0"

45'-0"

the Gastonia
43047-9JJ
price code 14

Total Square Ft. **1482**

Standard Foundation: Slab

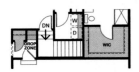

Den
13⁰ x 10⁰

Optional Den

Optional Basement Stair Location

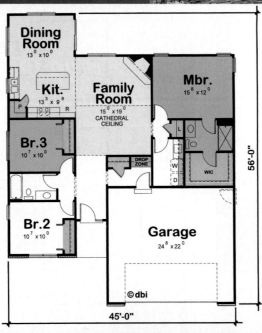

Dining Room
13⁰ x 10⁰

Kit.
13³ x 9⁹

Family Room
15⁰ x 19⁰
CATHEDRAL CEILING

Mbr.
15⁸ x 12⁰

Br.3
10⁷ x 10⁰

DROP ZONE

WIC

Br.2
10⁷ x 10⁰

Garage
24⁸ x 22⁰

©dbi

56'-0"

45'-0"

Livability at a Glance™

Storing
Entertaining
Flexible Living
De-Stressing

www.designbasics.com/9JJ

the Adair
2300-9JJ
price code 14

Total Square Ft. **1496**

Standard Foundation: Basement

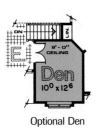

Optional Den

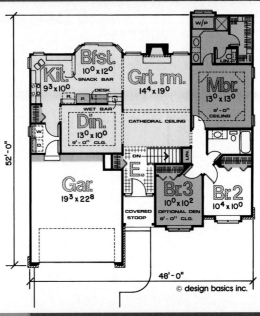

© design basics inc.

the Laramy
3555-9JJ
price code 15

Total Square Ft. **1518**

Standard Foundation: Basement

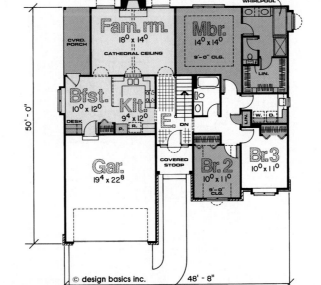

© design basics inc.

Livability
at a Glance

- Storing
- Entertaining
- Flexible Living
- De-Stressing

the Canton
5035-9JJ
pricecode 15

Total Square Ft. **1552**

Standard Foundation: Basement

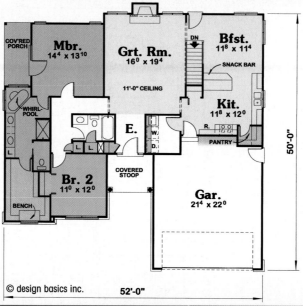

COV'RED PORCH

Mbr. 14⁴ x 13¹⁰

Grt. Rm. 16⁰ x 19⁴
11'-0" CEILING

DN

Bfst. 11⁸ x 11⁴

SNACK BAR

WHIRL POOL

E.

W. D.

Kit. 11⁸ x 12⁰

R.

PANTRY

Br. 2 11⁰ x 12⁰

COVERED STOOP

Gar. 21⁴ x 22⁰

BENCH

50'-0"

52'-0"

© design basics inc.

the Haley
3127-9JJ
pricecode 15

Total Square Ft. **1554**

Standard Foundation: Basement

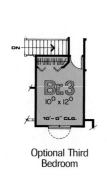

Br. 3 10⁰ x 12⁰
10'-0" CLG.

DN

Optional Third Bedroom

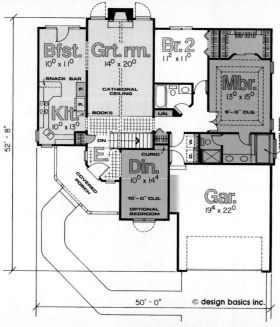

Bfst. 10⁰ x 11⁰

Grt. rm. 14⁰ x 20⁰
CATHEDRAL CEILING

Br. 2 11² x 11⁰

Mbr. 13⁰ x 15⁰
9'-0" CLG.

SNACK BAR

P.

BOOKS

LIN.

Kit. 10⁰ x 13⁰

R.

WHIRLPOOL

DN

E.

CURIO

Din. 10⁰ x 14⁴
10'-0" CLG.
OPTIONAL BEDROOM

COVERED PORCH

Gar. 19⁴ x 22⁰

52' - 8"

50' - 0"

© design basics inc.

Livability at a Glance™

Storing
Entertaining
Flexible Living
De-Stressing

38

www.designbasics.com/9JJ

the Lawndale
24214-9JJ
pricecode 15

Total Square Ft. **1560**

Standard Foundation: Slab

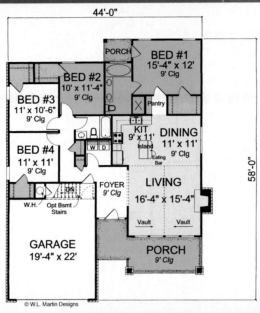

44'-0"

58'-0"

PORCH

BED #1
15'-4" x 12'
9' Clg

BED #2
10' x 11'-4"
9' Clg

BED #3
11' x 10'-6"
9' Clg

Pantry

BED #4
11' x 11'
9' Clg

KIT
9' x 11'
Island
Eating Bar

DINING
11' x 11'
9' Clg

W D

FOYER
9' Clg

LIVING
16'-4" x 15'-4"

Vault   Vault

DN
W.H.   Opt Bsmt Stairs

GARAGE
19'-4" x 22'

PORCH
9' Clg

© W.L. Martin Designs

the Granite
2196-9JJ
pricecode 15

Total Square Ft. **1561**

Standard Foundation: Basement

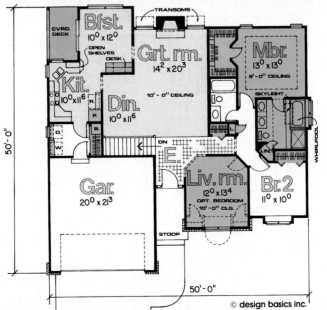

Bfst.
10⁰ x 12⁰

CVRD. DECK

TRANSOMS

OPEN SHELVES   DESK

Grt. rm.
14² x 20³

10'-0" CEILING

Mbr.
13⁰ x 13⁰
9'-0" CEILING

SKYLIGHT

Kit.
10⁰ x 11⁶

Din.
10⁰ x 11⁶

P.

WHIRLPOOL

D W

DN

Gar.
20⁰ x 21³

Liv. rm.
12⁰ x 13⁴
OPT. BEDROOM
10'-0" CLG.

Br. 2
11⁰ x 10⁰

STOOP

50'-0"

50'-0"

© design basics inc.

Livability at a Glance™

Storing
Entertaining
Flexible Living
De-Stressing

800.947.7526

39

the
Collins Falls
8087-9JJ
pricecode 15

Total Square Ft. **1579**

Standard Foundation: Basement

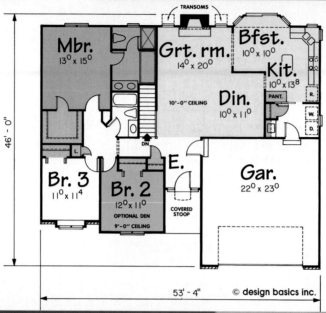

TRANSOMS

Mbr.
13⁰ x 15⁰

Grt. rm.
14⁰ x 20⁰

Bfst.
10⁰ x 10⁰

Kit.
10⁰ x 13⁸

10'-0" CEILING

Din.
10⁰ x 11⁰

PANT.

R.

W.

D.

DN

Br. 3
11⁰ x 11⁴

Br. 2
12⁰ x 11⁰
OPTIONAL DEN
9'-0" CEILING

E.

COVERED STOOP

Gar.
22⁰ x 23⁰

46' - 0"

53' - 4"

© design basics inc.

the
Oakridge
2324-9JJ
pricecode 15

Total Square Ft. **1583**

Standard Foundation: Basement

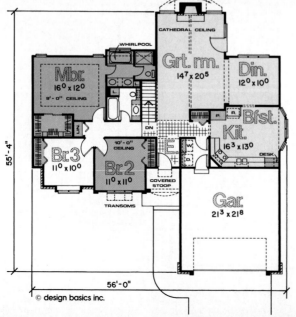

TRAPS

CATHEDRAL CEILING

WHIRLPOOL

Mbr.
16⁰ x 12⁰
9'-0" CEILING

Grt. rm.
14⁷ x 20⁵

Din.
12⁰ x 10⁰

L.

P.

R.

Bfst.

Kit.
16³ x 13⁰

DESK

DN

10'-0" CEILING

Br. 3
11⁰ x 10⁰

Br. 2
11⁰ x 11⁰

E.

W.

D.

COVERED STOOP

Gar.
21³ x 21⁸

TRANSOMS

55' - 4"

56' - 0"

© design basics inc.

Livability
at a Glance™

Storing

Entertaining

Flexible Living

De-Stressing

40

www.designbasics.com/9JJ

the Altamont

43034-9JJ

pricecode 15

Total Square Ft. **1592**

Standard Foundation: Slab

Optional Master Bath

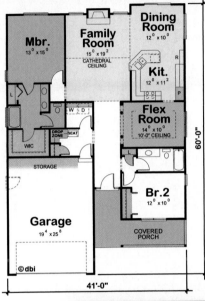

Mbr.
13⁰ x 15⁰

Family Room
15⁰ x 19²
CATHEDRAL CEILING

Dining Room
12⁰ x 10⁰

Kit.
12⁰ x 11²

Flex Room
14⁰ x 10⁰
10'-0" CEILING

Br.2
12⁰ x 10⁰

Garage
19⁴ x 25⁸

STORAGE

WIC

DROP ZONE

SEAT

W D

COVERED PORCH

© dbi

60'-0"

41'-0"

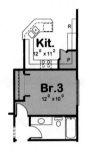

Kit.
12⁰ x 11²

Br.3
12⁰ x 10⁰

Optional Third Bedroom

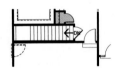

Optional Basement Stair Location
adds 76 Sq. Ft.

---

the Redmond

43035-9JJ

pricecode 15

Total Square Ft. **1592**

Standard Foundation: Slab

Kit.
12⁰ x 11²

Br.3
12⁰ x 10⁰

Optional Third Bedroom

Optional Basement Stair Location
adds 76 Sq. Ft.

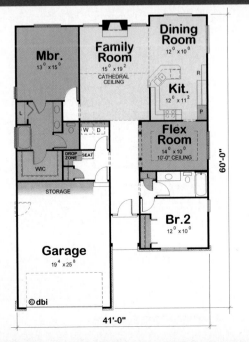

Mbr.
13⁰ x 15⁰

Family Room
15⁰ x 19²
CATHEDRAL CEILING

Dining Room
12⁰ x 10⁰

Kit.
12⁰ x 11²

Flex Room
14⁰ x 10⁰
10'-0" CEILING

Br.2
12⁰ x 10⁰

Garage
19⁴ x 25⁸

STORAGE

WIC

DROP ZONE

SEAT

W D

© dbi

60'-0"

41'-0"

Optional Master Bath

Livability
at a Glance™

Storing
Entertaining
Flexible Living
De-Stressing

the Stonybrook
3578-9JJ
pricecode 15

Total Square Ft. **1595**

Standard Foundation: Basement

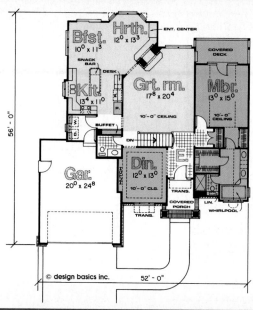

Bfst. 10⁰ x 11³

Hrth. 12⁰ x 13³

ENT. CENTER

COVERED DECK

SNACK BAR

DESK

Kit. 13⁴ x 11⁰

Grt. rm. 17⁸ x 20⁴

Mbr. 13⁰ x 15⁰

10'-0" CEILING

10'-0" CEILING

P.

BUFFET

DN

Gar. 20⁰ x 24⁸

Din. 12⁰ x 13⁰

10'-0" CLG.

TRANS.

TRANS.

COVERED PORCH

LIN.

WHIRLPOOL

56' - 0"

52' - 0"

© design basics inc.

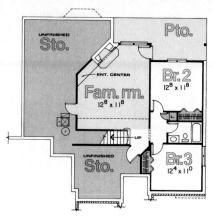

UNFINISHED Sto.

Pto.

ENT. CENTER

Fam. rm. 12⁸ x 11⁸

Br. 2 12⁸ x 11⁸

UP

UNFINISHED Sto.

Br. 3 12⁴ x 11⁰

Optional Finished Lower Level adds 790 Sq. Ft.

---

the Seabeck
24141-9JJ
pricecode 16

Total Square Ft. **1604**

Standard Foundation: Slab

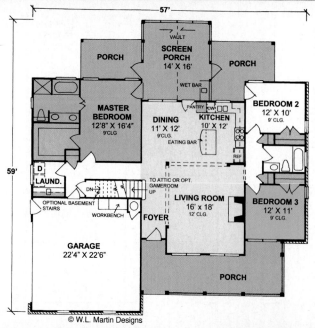

57'

VAULT

PORCH

SCREEN PORCH 14' X 16'

PORCH

WET BAR

PANTRY

MASTER BEDROOM 12'8" X 16'4" 9'CLG

DINING 11' X 12' 9'CLG.

KITCHEN 10' X 12'

BEDROOM 2 12' X 10' 9' CLG.

EATING BAR

REF

D

LAUND.

DN

TO ATTIC OR OPT. GAMEROOM UP

59'

OPTIONAL BASEMENT STAIRS

WORKBENCH

FOYER

LIVING ROOM 16' x 18' 12' CLG.

BEDROOM 3 12' X 11' 9' CLG.

GARAGE 22'4" X 22'6"

PORCH

© W.L. Martin Designs

Livability at a Glance™

Storing
Entertaining
Flexible Living
De-Stressing

www.designbasics.com/9JJ

the
Roosebury
1767-9JJ
pricecode 16

Total Square Ft.   **1604**

Standard Foundation: Basement

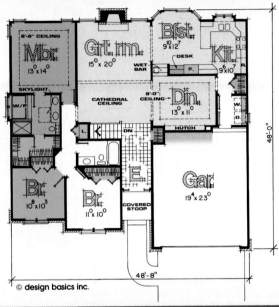

© design basics inc.

48'-0"

48'-8"

8'-8" CEILING

Mbr.
13⁰ x 14⁰

SKYLIGHT

W/P

Br.
10⁸ x 10³

Br.
11⁰ x 10⁰

Grt. rm.
15⁰ x 20⁰

CATHEDRAL CEILING

WET BAR

DN

COVERED STOOP

E

Bfst.
9⁰ x 12⁷

DESK

Kit.
9⁶ x 10⁰

9'-0" CEILING

Dn.
13⁰ x 11⁰

HUTCH

Gar.
19⁴ x 23⁰

the
Sutton
2923-9JJ
pricecode 16

Total Square Ft.   **1622**

Standard Foundation: Basement

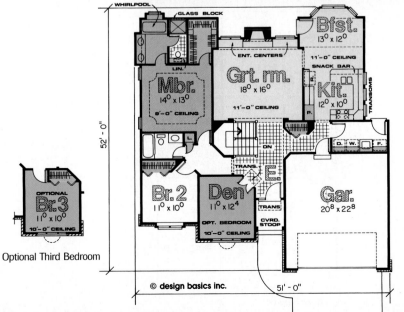

© design basics inc.

52'-0"

51'-0"

WHIRLPOOL

GLASS BLOCK

LIN.

Mbr.
14⁰ x 13⁰

8'-0" CEILING

L

Grt. rm.
18⁰ x 16⁰

11'-0" CEILING

ENT. CENTERS

11'-0" CEILING

Bfst.
13⁰ x 12⁰

11'-0" CEILING

SNACK BAR

Kit.
12⁰ x 10⁰

TRANSOMS

DN

TRANS.

E

D. W. F.

Br. 2
11⁰ x 10⁰

Den
11⁰ x 12⁴

10'-0" CEILING

OPT. BEDROOM

CVRD. STOOP

TRANS.

Gar.
20⁸ x 22⁸

Br. 3
OPTIONAL
11⁰ x 10⁰
10'-0" CEILING

Optional Third Bedroom

Livability
at a Glance™

- Storing
- Entertaining
- Flexible Living
- De-Stressing

the
Maple Grove
8080-9JJ
pricecode 16

Total Square Ft. **1628**

Standard Foundation: Basement

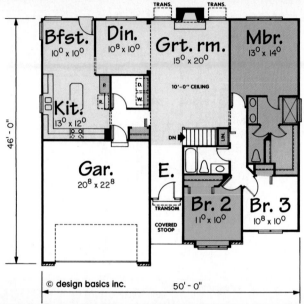

TRANS. | TRANS.

Bfst.
10⁰ x 10⁰

Din.
10⁸ x 10⁰

Grt. rm.
15⁰ x 20⁰

Mbr.
13⁰ x 14⁰

10'-0" CEILING

Kit.
13⁰ x 12⁰

DN
LIN.

Gar.
20⁸ x 22⁸

E.

TRANSOM

COVERED STOOP

Br. 2
11⁰ x 10⁰

Br. 3
10⁸ x 10⁰

46' - 0"

© design basics inc.   50' - 0"

the
Leighton
2377-9JJ
pricecode 16

Total Square Ft. **1636**

Standard Foundation: Basement

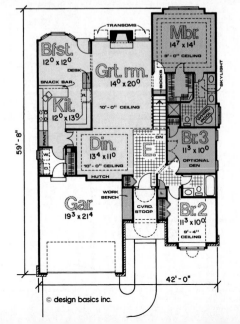

Bfst.
12⁰ x 12⁰

DESK

Grt. rm.
14⁰ x 20⁰

TRANSOMS

Mbr.
14⁷ x 14¹
9'-0" CEILING

SKYLIGHT

SNACK BAR

Kit.
12⁰ x 13⁰

10'-0" CEILING

BOOKS

PANT.

Din.
13⁴ x 11⁰
10'-0" CEILING

HUTCH

DN

E.

Br.3
11³ x 10⁰

OPTIONAL DEN

W.D.

WORK BENCH

Gar.
19³ x 21⁴

CVRD. STOOP

Br 2
11³ x 10⁰
9'-4" CEILING

59' - 8"

42' - 0"

© design basics inc.

www.designbasics.com/9JJ

the
Somerdale
5466-9JJ
pricecode 16

Total Square Ft.   **1636**

Standard Foundation: Basement

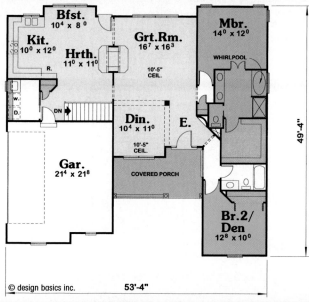

Bfst.
10⁴ x 8⁰

Kit.
10⁰ x 12⁰

Hrth.
11⁰ x 11⁰

Grt.Rm.
16⁷ x 16³

10'-5"
CEIL.

Mbr.
14⁰ x 12⁰

WHIRLPOOL

Din.
10⁴ x 11⁰

10'-5"
CEIL.

DN

W.
D.

Gar.
21⁴ x 21⁸

COVERED PORCH

E.

**Br.2/
Den**
12⁸ x 10⁰

49'-4"

53'-4"

© design basics inc.

the
Orchard
2818-9JJ
pricecode 16

Total Square Ft.   **1651**

Standard Foundation: Basement

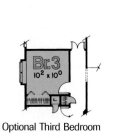

Br.3
10² x 10⁰

Optional Third Bedroom

WHIRLPOOL

LIN.

Mbr.
14⁰ x 13⁰

9'-0" CEILING

Den
10² x 10⁰

OPTIONAL
BEDROOM

WET BAR

Br.2
11⁰ x 10⁰

10'-0"
CLG.

TRANSOMS

Grt. rm.
17⁰ x 17⁰

10'-0" CEILING

DN

E.

SERVERY

Din.
12⁰ x 11⁰

9'-0" CEILING

COVERED
PORCH

TRANSOMS

Bfst.
11⁰ x 11⁰

10'-0" CEILING

SNACK BAR

Kit.
13⁰ x 11⁸

P.

COVERED
PORCH

Gar.
30⁰ x 20⁸

56'-0"

62'-0"

© design basics inc.

800.947.7526

the
Ashley
2907-9JJ
pricecode 16

Total Square Ft. **1658**

Standard Foundation: Basement

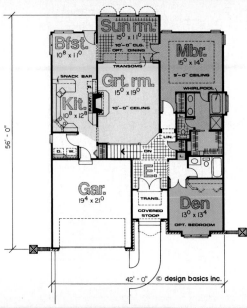

Sun rm.
15⁰ x 11⁰
10'-0" CLG.
OPT. DINING

Bfst.
10⁸ x 11⁰

TRANSOMS

Mbr.
15⁰ x 14⁰
5'-0" CEILING

SNACK BAR

Grt. rm.
15⁰ x 19⁰
10'-0" CEILING

WHIRLPOOL

Kit.
10⁸ x 12⁸

LIN.

D. W.

DN

Gar.
19⁴ x 21⁰

56'-0"

E

TRANS.

COVERED
STOOP

Den
13⁰ x 13⁴

OPT. BEDROOM

42'-0"   © design basics inc.

---

the
Monterey
2290-9JJ
pricecode 16

Total Square Ft. **1666**

Standard Foundation: Basement

TRANSOMS

COVERED
PORCH

Din.
12⁰ x 10⁴
8'-8" CLG.

Grt. rm.
15⁰ x 21⁸
10'-0" CEILING

Mbr.
15⁰ x 12⁰
8'-6" CLG.

WHIRLPOOL

Bfst.
10⁰ x 10⁰
8'-8" CLG.

Kit.
14³ x 13³

SNACK BAR

W. D.   P.

DN   LIN.

E

Gar.
19⁷ x 23⁰

48'-0"

Br.3
11⁰ x 11⁰

Br.2
11⁰ x 11⁰
10'-0" CLG.

COVERED
STOOP

55'-4"   © design basics inc.

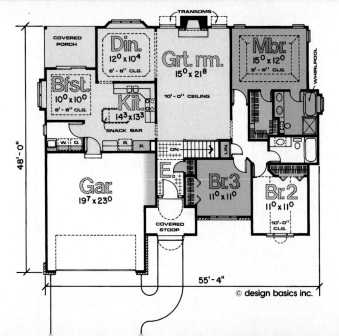

Livability
at a Glance™

Storing
Entertaining
Flexible Living
De-Stressing

46

www.designbasics.com/9JJ

the
Jennys Brook
8016-9JJ
price code 16

Total Square Ft. **1691**

Standard Foundation: Basement

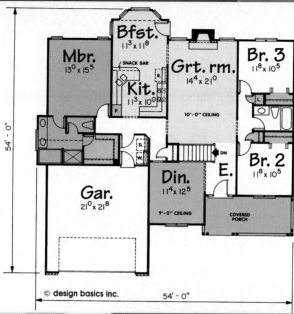

Mbr.
13⁰ x 15⁵

Bfst.
11³ x 11⁸

SNACK BAR

Kit.
11³ x 10⁰

Grt. rm.
14⁴ x 21⁰

10'-0" CEILING

Br. 3
11⁸ x 10⁵

Br. 2
11⁸ x 10⁵

54' - 0"

Gar.
21⁰ x 21⁸

Din.
11⁴ x 12⁵

9'-0" CEILING

E.

COVERED PORCH

DN

© design basics inc.

54' - 0"

the
Monte Vista
1032-9JJ
price code 16

Total Square Ft. **1697**

Standard Foundation: Basement

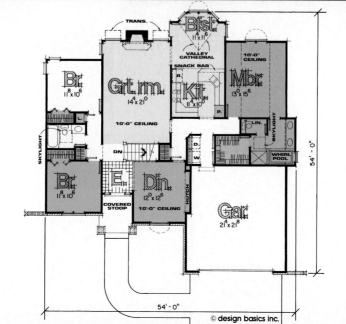

TRANS.

Bfst.
11⁴ x 11⁶

VALLEY CATHEDRAL

10'-0" CEILING

SNACK BAR

Br.
11⁸ x 10⁶

Grt. rm.
14⁴ x 21⁰

10'-0" CEILING

Kit.
11⁴ x 10⁰

Mbr.
13⁰ x 15⁶

LIN.

SKYLIGHT

WHIRL POOL

54' - 0"

DN

Br.
11⁸ x 10⁶

E.

Din.
12⁰ x 12⁶

10'-0" CEILING

COVERED STOOP

HUTCH

Gar.
21⁴ x 21⁴

54' - 0"

© design basics inc.

Livability
at a Glance™
Storing
Entertaining
Flexible Living
De-Stressing

800.947.7526

47

the
North Cliffs
8078-9JJ
pricecode 17

Total Square Ft. **1707**

Standard Foundation: Basement

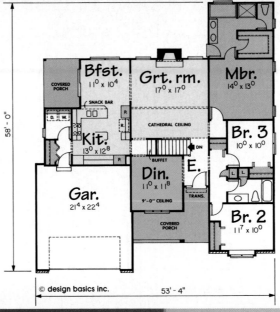

Bfst.
11⁰ x 10⁴

COVERED PORCH

SNACK BAR

D. W.

Kit.
13⁰ x 12⁸

Grt. rm.
17⁰ x 17⁰

CATHEDRAL CEILING

Mbr.
14⁰ x 13⁰

Br. 3
10⁰ x 10⁰

BUFFET

DN

E.

Gar.
21⁴ x 22⁴

Din.
11⁰ x 11⁸

9'-0" CEILING

TRANS.

COVERED PORCH

Br. 2
11⁷ x 10⁰

58' - 0"

53' - 4"

© design basics inc.

---

the
Waverly
2355-9JJ
pricecode 17

Total Square Ft. **1710**

Standard Foundation: Basement

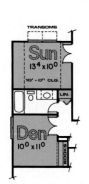

TRANSOMS

Sun
13⁴ x 10⁰

10'-0" CLG.

LIN.

Den
10⁰ x 11⁰

Sun Room/Den Option

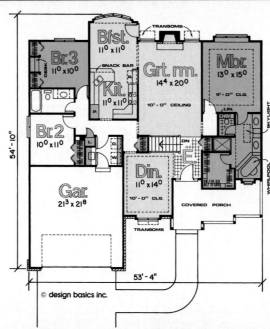

TRANSOMS

Br 3
11⁰ x 10⁰

DESK

Bfst.
11⁰ x 11⁰

SNACK BAR

TRANSOMS

Grt. rm.
14⁴ x 20⁰

10'-0" CEILING

Mbr.
13⁰ x 15⁰

9'-0" CLG.

Kit.
11⁰ x 11⁰

LIN.

SKYLIGHT

Br 2
10⁰ x 11⁰

DN

E.

WHIRLPOOL

Gar.
21³ x 21⁸

Din.
11⁰ x 14⁰

10'-0" CLG.

COVERED PORCH

TRANSOMS

54' - 10"

53' - 4"

© design basics inc.

Livability
at a Glance™

Storing
Entertaining
Flexible Living
De-Stressing

www.designbasics.com/9JJ

the
Carthage
43007-9JJ
price code 17

Total Square Ft. **1719**

Standard Foundation: Slab

Mbr.
13⁰ x 15⁰

Family Room
15⁰ x 17⁰

Dining Room
12⁸ x 11⁰

Kit.
12⁸ x 12⁴

WIC

W D

WIC L

WIC

DROP ZONE

R

P

STORAGE

Br.2
11⁸ x 13⁰

Br.3
11³ x 13⁰

Garage
21⁴ x 25⁸

© dbi

52'-0"

50'-0"

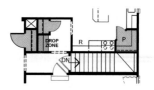

DROP ZONE

R

P

DN

Optional Basement Stair Location
adds 87 Sq. Ft.

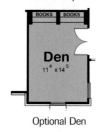

BOOKS BOOKS

Den
11⁴ x 14⁵

Optional Den

the
Laundale
43008-9JJ
price code 17

Total Square Ft. **1719**

Standard Foundation: Slab

Mbr.
13⁰ x 15⁰

Family Room
15⁰ x 17⁰

Dining Room
12⁸ x 11⁰

Kit.
12⁸ x 12⁴

WIC

W D

WIC L

WIC

DROP ZONE

R

P

STORAGE

Br.2
11⁸ x 13⁰

Br.3
11³ x 13⁰

Garage
21⁴ x 25⁸

© dbi

52'-0"

50'-0"

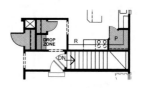

DROP ZONE

R

P

DN

Optional Basement Stair Location
adds 87 Sq. Ft.

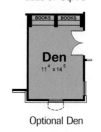

BOOKS BOOKS

Den
11⁴ x 14⁵

Optional Den

Livability
at a Glance™

Storing
Entertaining
Flexible Living
De-Stressing

the Seville
2212-9JJ
pricecode 17

Total Square Ft. **1735**

Standard Foundation: Basement

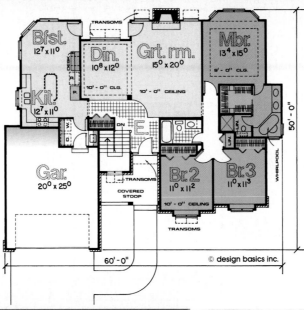

Bfst. 12⁷ x 11⁰
Din. 10⁸ x 12⁰ 10'-0" CLG.
Grt. rm. 15⁰ x 20⁰ 10'-0" CEILING
Mbr. 13⁴ x 15⁰ 9'-0" CLG.
Kit. 12⁷ x 11⁰
TRANSOMS
DESK
P.
DN
D. W.
Gar. 20⁰ x 25⁰
TRANSOMS
COVERED STOOP
Br. 2 11⁰ x 11² 10'-0" CEILING
Br. 3 11⁰ x 11³
LIN LIN
WHIRLPOOL
TRANSOMS
50'-0"
60'-0"

© design basics inc.

---

the Bay Hill
43016-9JJ
pricecode 17

Total Square Ft. **1755**

Standard Foundation: Slab

Family Room 15⁰ x 24⁴ CATHEDRAL CEILING
Kit. 12⁰ x 12⁰
R
P

Optional Kitchen

Dining Room 12⁰ x 12⁰
ENT CENTER
BOOKS
Family Room 15⁰ x 24⁴ CATHEDRAL CEILING
Mbr. 14⁸ x 13⁰
WIC
Kit. 12⁰ x 12⁰
DROP ZONE
SEAT
WIC
Br. 2 12² x 10⁰
STORAGE
W D
SEAT
L
Garage 33⁴ x 24⁰
Br. 3 12⁸ x 11⁰
© dbi
56'-0"
64'-0"

SEAT
WIC
DN

Optional Basement Stair Location

Livability at a Glance™
Storing
Entertaining
Flexible Living
De-Stressing

www.designbasics.com/9JJ

the Saugatuck
43017-9JJ
pricecode 17

Total Square Ft. **1755**

Standard Foundation: Slab

Kit.
12⁰ x 12⁰

Optional Kitchen

Optional Basement Stair Location

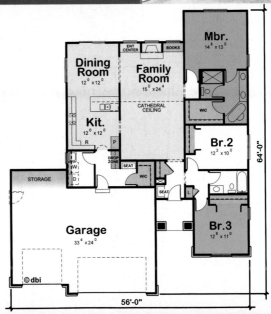

Dining Room
12⁰ x 12⁰

Family Room
15⁰ x 24⁴
CATHEDRAL CEILING

Mbr.
14⁸ x 13⁰

Kit.
12⁰ x 12⁰

Br.2
12² x 10⁰

STORAGE

Garage
33⁴ x 24⁰

Br.3
12⁸ x 11⁰

©dbi

56'-0"

64'-0"

the Bradbury
4948-9JJ
pricecode 17

Total Square Ft. **1758**

Standard Foundation: Basement

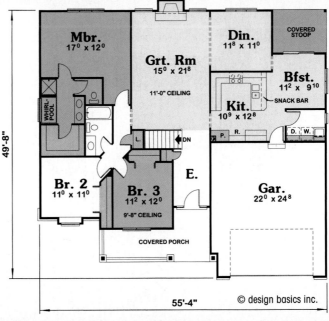

Mbr.
17⁰ x 12⁰

Grt. Rm
15⁰ x 21⁸
11'-0" CEILING

Din.
11⁸ x 11⁰

COVERED STOOP

WHIRL-POOL

Bfst.
11² x 9¹⁰

Kit.
10⁹ x 12⁸
SNACK BAR

Br. 2
11⁰ x 11⁰

Br. 3
11² x 12⁰
9'-8" CEILING

E.

Gar.
22⁰ x 24⁸

DN

COVERED PORCH

49'-8"

55'-4"

© design basics inc.

Livability at a Glance™

Storing
Entertaining
Flexible Living
De-Stressing

the Tuxford
24003-9JJ
pricecode 17

Total Square Ft. **1762**

Standard Foundation: Slab

46'

BEDROOM 2
11'4" X 10'6"

FAMILY ROOM
20'10" X 16'8"
11' CLG.

MASTER SUITE
12'6" x 16'6"
10' CLG.

VAULT

VAULT

OPTIONAL
BASEMENT
STAIRS

EATING BAR

BEDROOM 3
11'4" X 10'8"

ARCH

KITCHEN
15'6" X 13'

ISLAND

W
D

AC   WH

PANTRY

10' CLG.

ARCH

ARCH

NOOK
9'8" X 9'8"

GARAGE
18'4" X 20'8"

DINING ROOM
11'4" X 11'6"

10' CLG.

OPTIONAL
LIVING ROOM

PORCH

58'

© W. L. Martin Designs

the James
24185-9JJ
pricecode 17

Total Square Ft. **1768**

Standard Foundation: Slab

49'

Shelves

SCREEN
PORCH
15' x 12'
9' Ceiling

PORCH
9' Ceiling

BED #2
12' x 11'
9' Ceiling

BED #1
16' x 12'
9' Ceiling

LIVING
20' x 15'
14' Ceiling

NOOK
11' x 10'
9' Ceiling

BED #3
11' x 11'
9' Ceiling

STUDY
11' x 12'
9' Ceiling

Raised
Eating Bar

KIT
13'-6" x 10'

W
D

Pantry

R.

FOYER
11' Clg

UP

Storage

A.C.

DINING
14' x 11'
11' Ceiling

PORCH

Arch

Seat

To Attic/
Optional
Basement
Stairs

GARAGE
22' x 22'

66'

© W. L. Martin Designs

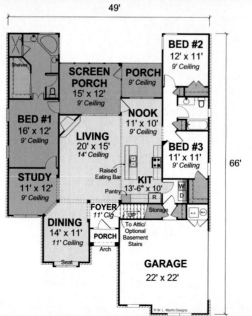

Livability
at a Glance™

Storing
Entertaining
Flexible Living
De-Stressing

www.designbasics.com/9JJ

the
Bennett
3577-9JJ
pricecode 17

Total Square Ft. **1782**

Standard Foundation: Basement

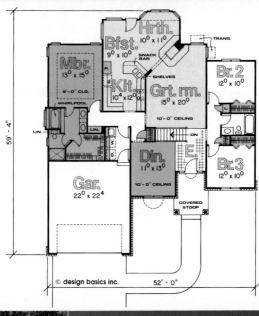

Mbr.
13⁰ x 15⁰
9'-0" CLG.

WHIRLPOOL

LIN.

LIN.

Bfst.
9⁰ x 10⁰

Hrth.
10⁰ x 11⁰

TRANS.

SNACK BAR

P.

SHELVES

Kit.
10⁴ x 12⁰

Grt. rm.
15⁰ x 20⁰
10'-0" CEILING

Br. 2
12⁰ x 10⁰

DN

Din.
11⁰ x 13⁰
10'-0" CEILING

E.

Br. 3
12⁰ x 10⁰

Gar.
22⁰ x 22⁴

COVERED STOOP

59' - 4"

© design basics inc.   52' - 0"

the
Christine
5465-9JJ
pricecode 17

Total Square Ft. **1790**

Standard Foundation: Basement

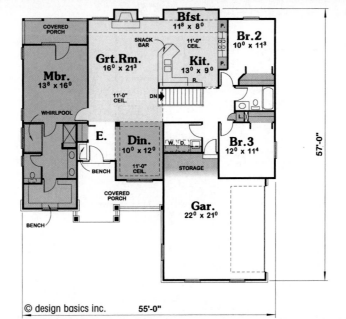

COVERED PORCH

Mbr.
13⁸ x 16⁰

WHIRLPOOL

E.

BENCH

Grt.Rm.
16⁰ x 21³
11'-0" CEIL.

Bfst.
11⁸ x 8⁰

SNACK BAR

11'-0" CEIL.

Kit.
13⁰ x 9⁰

DN

R.

Br. 2
10⁰ x 11³

Din.
10⁰ x 12⁰
11'-0" CEIL.

W. D.

STORAGE

Br. 3
12⁰ x 11⁴

BENCH

COVERED PORCH

Gar.
22⁰ x 21⁰

57'-0"

BENCH

© design basics inc.   55'-0"

the Charleston
3587-9JJ
pricecode 17

Total Square Ft. **1796**

Standard Foundation: Basement

Mbr.
13⁰ x 16⁰
9'-0" CLG.

Grt. rm.
15⁰ x 18⁰
10'-0" CEILING

SCREEN PORCH

TRANSOMS

SNACK COUNTER

Hrth.
11⁰ x 20⁰

Kit.
12⁰ x 16⁰

SNACK BAR

WHIRL-POOL

BOOKS

PANT.

Br. 2
11⁴ x 13⁰
9'-0" CEILING

DN

Din.
11⁰ x 14²
10'-0" CLG.

ENT. CENTER

W. D.

STORAGE

Gar.
20⁰ x 22⁴

CVRD. STOOP

OPTIONAL DEN

TRANS.

COURTYARD

58' - 0"

58' - 0"

© design basics inc.

---

the Grayson
3006-9JJ
pricecode 18

Total Square Ft. **1806**

Standard Foundation: Basement

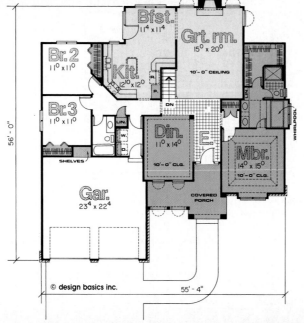

Bfst.
11⁴ x 11⁴

Grt. rm.
15⁰ x 20⁰
10'-0" CEILING

Br. 2
11⁰ x 11⁰

Kit.
12¹⁰ x 12⁰

Br. 3
11⁰ x 11⁰

LIN.

DN

P.

W. D.

SHELVES

Din.
11⁰ x 14⁰
10'-0" CLG.

E.

WHIRLPOOL

Mbr.
14⁰ x 15⁰
10'-0" CLG.

Gar.
23⁴ x 22⁴

COVERED PORCH

56' - 0"

55' - 4"

© design basics inc.

the
Westlake
24206-9JJ
pricecode 18

Total Square Ft.   **1807**

Standard Foundation: Slab

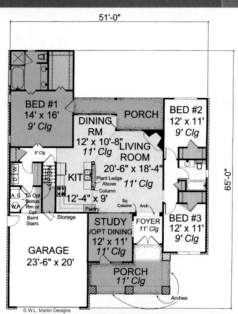

51'-0"

65'-0"

BED #1
14' x 16'
9' Clg

DINING
RM
12' x 10'-8"
11' Clg

PORCH

LIVING
ROOM
20'-6" x 18'-4"
11' Clg

BED #2
12' x 11'
9' Clg

9' Clg

KIT
Plant Ledge
Above
Column
12'-4" x 9'

Sq
Column

Arch

Pantry

Storage

A.C.
W.H.
To Opt
Bonus
Rm or
Opt
Bsmt
Stairs

STUDY
/OPT DINING
12' x 11'
11' Clg

FOYER
11' Clg

BED #3
12' x 11'
9' Clg

GARAGE
23'-6" x 20'

PORCH
11' Clg

Arches

© W.L. Martin Designs

DN

Access
Panel

Vault   Vault

**OPT
GAME
ROOM**
23'-6" x 12'

Arch

Optional Game Room
adds 293 Sq. Ft.

the
Bancroft
1559-9JJ
pricecode 18

Total Square Ft.   **1808**

Standard Foundation: Basement

TRANSOMS

WET
BAR

Br
11 x 11

Grt. rm.
14⁰ x 20⁰

Bfst
11 x 11

DESK

SNACK BAR

Kit
19⁰ x 12⁷

10'-0" CEILING

Br
12⁹ x 10²

P.   R.

STORAGE

LIN.

DN

F.

W.D.

Mbr
13⁴ x 15⁰

E

Gar
21⁴ x 25⁰

WHIRL-
POOL

10'-0"
CEILING

COVERED
PORCH

44'-0"

64'-0"

© design basics inc.

Livability
at a Glance™

Storing
Entertaining
Flexible Living
De-Stressing

the Madeline
24212-9JJ
pricecode 18

Total Square Ft. **1812**

Standard Foundation: Slab

46'-0"

64'-6"

BED #1
14' x 16'
9' Clg

SCREENED PORCH
11' X 10'
9' Clg

DINING
15' x 10'-8"
11' Clg

LIVING ROOM
18' x 18'
11' Clg

Slope

Eating Bar

KIT
12'-8" x 10'

BED #2
12' x 11'-4"
9' Clg

D W
Pantry
W.H. A C
OPTION

Opt Bonus Rm or Bsmt Stairs

GARAGE
23' x 21'

FOYER
9' Clg

BED #3
12' x 12'
9' Clg

PATIO
10' Clg

© W.L. Martin Designs

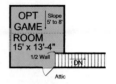

OPT GAME ROOM
15' x 13'-4"
1/2 Wall

Slope 5' to 8'

DN

Attic

Optional Game Room
adds 210 Sq. Ft.

---

the Corridon
43058-9JJ
pricecode 18

Total Square Ft. **1820**

Standard Foundation: Slab

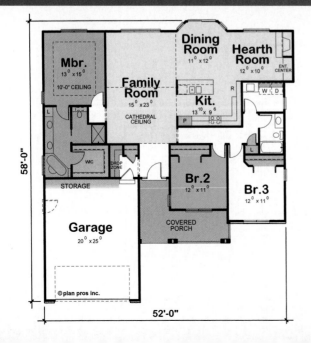

58'-0"

52'-0"

Mbr.
13⁰ x 15⁰
10'-0" CEILING

Family Room
15⁰ x 23⁰
CATHEDRAL CEILING

Dining Room
11⁰ x 12⁰

Hearth Room
12⁰ x 10⁰
ENT CENTER

Kit.
13¹⁰ x 9⁰

R
W D
P

L
WIC
DROP ZONE
STORAGE

Br.2
12⁰ x 11⁰

Br.3
12⁰ x 11⁰

L

Garage
20⁰ x 25⁰

COVERED PORCH

© plan pros inc.

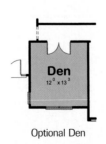

Den
12⁰ x 13³

Optional Den

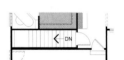

DN

Optional Basement Stair Location
adds 83 Sq. Ft.

Livability
at a Glance™

Storing
Entertaining
Flexible Living
De-Stressing

www.designbasics.com/9JJ

the Farrington
42001-9JJ
price code 18

Total Square Ft. **1820**

Standard Foundation: Basement

- COVERED PORCH
- **Dining Room** 10³ x 12⁶
- **Mbr.** 14³ x 17³ 10'-0" CEILING
- COMP DESK
- **Kit.** 11⁶ x 14³
- UP
- R
- **Great Room** 16⁴ x 19⁰ CATHEDRAL CEILING
- BOOKS
- L
- DN
- W/D
- SEAT
- **Garage** 22⁴ x 24⁴
- **Br.2** 11⁰ x 11⁰
- **Br.3** 11⁰ x 11⁰
- COVERED PORCH
- ©dbi
- 53'-0"
- 62'-0"

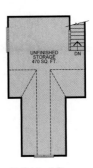

UNFINISHED STORAGE 470 SQ. FT.

DN

Unfinished Storage
adds 470 Sq. Ft.

the Goodman
43059-9JJ
price code 18

Total Square Ft. **1820**

Standard Foundation: Slab

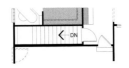

DN

Optional Basement Stair Location
adds 83 Sq. Ft.

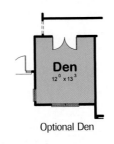

Den 12⁰ x 13³

Optional Den

- **Mbr.** 13⁰ x 15⁰ 10'-0" CEILING
- **Dining Room** 11⁰ x 12⁰
- **Hearth Room** 12⁰ x 10⁰
- ENT CENTER
- **Family Room** 15⁰ x 23⁰ CATHEDRAL CEILING
- **Kit.** 13¹⁰ x 9⁶
- R
- W D
- P
- L
- WIC
- DROP ZONE
- STORAGE
- COV. STOOP
- **Br.2** 12⁰ x 11⁰ 10'-0" CEILING
- **Br.3** 12⁰ x 11⁰ 11'-0" CEILING
- **Garage** 20⁰ x 25⁰
- ©plan pros inc.
- 58'-0"
- 52'-0"

Livability
at a Glance™
- Storing
- Entertaining
- Flexible Living
- De-Stressing

the Everton
24140-9JJ
pricecode 18

Total Square Ft. **1842**

Standard Foundation: Slab

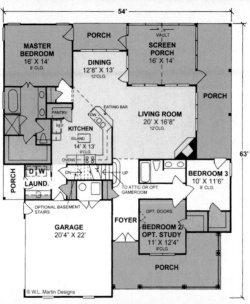

MASTER BEDROOM 16' X 14' 9' CLG.

PORCH

VAULT

SCREEN PORCH 16' X 14'

DINING 12'8" X 13' 12' CLG.

PORCH

PANTRY

EATING BAR

LIVING ROOM 20' X 16'8" 12' CLG.

REF

KITCHEN

ISLAND 14' X 13' 9' CLG.

OVENS

BEDROOM 3 10' X 11'6" 9' CLG.

D W

LAUND.

PORCH

DN

UP

TO ATTIC OR OPT. GAMEROOM

OPTIONAL BASEMENT STAIRS

GARAGE 20'4" X 22'

FOYER

OPT. DOORS

BEDROOM 2/ OPT. STUDY 11' X 12'4" 9' CLG.

PORCH

© W.L. Martin Designs

54'

63'

DN

OPTIONAL GAMEROOM 20'4" X 16'

Optional Game Room adds 386 Sq. Ft.

the Indian Springs
8059-9JJ
pricecode 18

Total Square Ft. **1842**

Standard Foundation: Basement

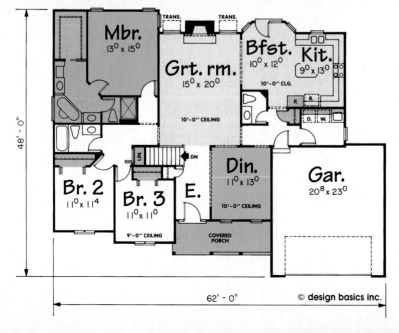

TRANS.

TRANS.

Mbr. 13⁰ x 15⁰

Grt. rm. 15⁰ x 20⁰

Bfst. 10⁰ x 12⁰

Kit. 9⁰ x 13⁰

10'-0" CLG.

10'-0" CEILING

LIN.

DN

Br. 2 11⁰ x 11⁴

Br. 3 11⁰ x 11⁰

E.

Din. 11⁰ x 13⁰

Gar. 20⁸ x 23⁰

9'-0" CEILING

10'-0" CEILING

COVERED PORCH

48' - 0"

62' - 0"

© design basics inc.

Livability
at a Glance™

Storing
Entertaining
Flexible Living
De-Stressing

www.designbasics.com/9JJ

the Shawnee
2461-9JJ
price code 18

Total Square Ft. **1850**

Standard Foundation: Basement

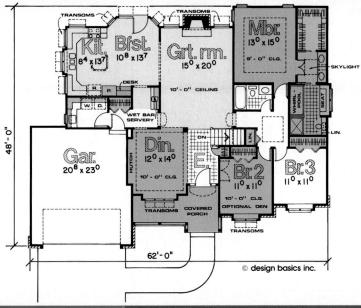

© design basics inc.

the Hawthorne
2799-9JJ
price code 18

Total Square Ft. **1887**

Standard Foundation: Basement

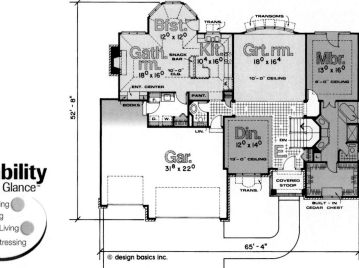

© design basics inc.

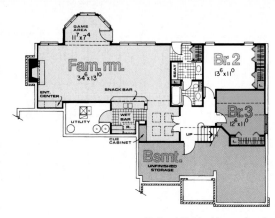

Optional Finished Lower Level
adds 1338 Sq. Ft.

Livability
at a Glance™

Storing
Entertaining
Flexible Living
De-Stressing

the
Carrigan
30016-9JJ
pricecode 18

Total Square Ft. **1899**

Standard Foundation: Basement

Mbr.
14⁴ x 12⁴
10'-0" CEILING

Great
Room
18⁰ x 16⁴
10'-0" CEILING

Eating
Area
14¹⁰ x 10⁰
10'-0" CEILING

Kit.
13⁰ x 11⁰
10'-0" CEILING

COVERED
PORCH

Den
10⁶ x 10⁰

DESK

Dining
Room
12⁰ x 10¹⁰

COVERED
PORCH

Br.2
11⁰ x 10⁰

Garage
30⁰ x 26⁰

©dbi

62'-0"

68'-8"

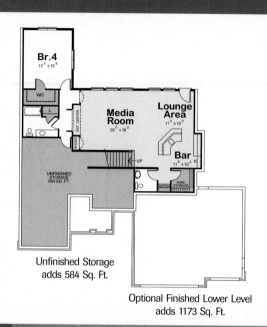

Br.4
13² x 15⁶

WIC

Media
Room
20⁰ x 16⁰

Lounge
Area
11⁰ x 10⁰

Bar
11⁸ x 10⁴

UP

UNFINISHED
STORAGE
584 SQ. FT.

Unfinished Storage
adds 584 Sq. Ft.

Optional Finished Lower Level
adds 1173 Sq. Ft.

the
Rayford
8516-9JJ
pricecode 19

Total Square Ft. **1902**

Standard Foundation: Basement

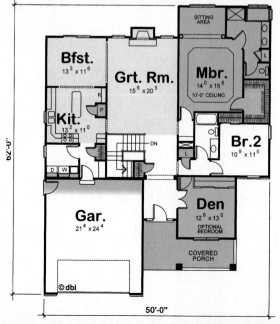

Bfst.
13² x 11⁶

Grt. Rm.
15⁶ x 20⁵

SITTING
AREA

Mbr.
14⁰ x 15⁶
10'-0" CEILING

Kit.
13² x 11⁰

DN

Br.2
10⁹ x 11⁰

D W

Gar.
21⁴ x 24⁴

Den
12⁸ x 13⁰
OPTIONAL
BEDROOM

COVERED
PORCH

©dbi

50'-0"

29'-0"

Livability
at a Glance™

Storing
Entertaining
Flexible Living
De-Stressing

www.designbasics.com/9JJ

the Sinclair
1748-9JJ
pricecode 19

Total Square Ft. **1911**

Standard Foundation: Basement

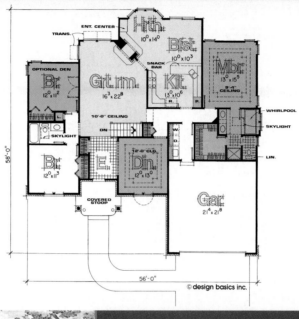

© design basics inc.

the Hunters Crossing
8019-9JJ
pricecode 19

Total Square Ft. **1919**

Standard Foundation: Basement

Livability
at a Glance

- Storing
- Entertaining
- Flexible Living
- De-Stressing

© design basics inc.

800.947.7526

61

the
JONESVILLE
3031-9JJ
pricecode 19

Total Square Ft. **1978**

Standard Foundation: Basement

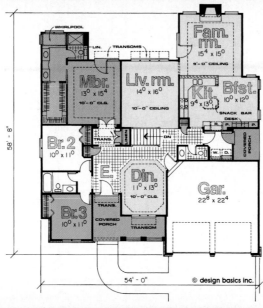

WHIRLPOOL

Fam. rm.
15⁴ x 15⁰
9'-0" CEILING

LIN. TRANSOMS

Mbr.
13⁰ x 15⁴
10'-0" CLG.

Liv. rm.
14⁰ x 16⁰
10'-0" CEILING

Kit.
9⁴ x 13⁰

Bfst.
10⁰ x 12⁰

SNACK BAR

DESK

Br. 2
10⁰ x 11⁰

TRANS. LINEN

UP DN

COVERED PORCH

W. D.

E.

Din.
11⁰ x 13⁰
10'-0" CLG.

Gar.
22⁸ x 22⁴

Br. 3
10⁰ x 11⁰

TRANS.

COVERED PORCH

TRANSOM

58' - 8"

54' - 0"

© design basics inc.

---

the
Hardwick
24203-9JJ
pricecode 19

Total Square Ft. **1985**

Standard Foundation: Slab

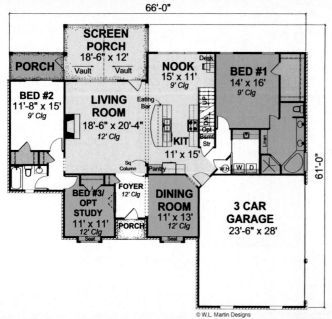

66'-0"

SCREEN PORCH
18'-6" x 12'
Vault   Vault

PORCH

NOOK
15' x 11'
9' Clg

Desk

BED #1
14' x 16'
9' Clg

BED #2
11'-8" x 15'
9' Clg

LIVING ROOM
18'-6" x 20'-4"
12' Clg

Eating Bar

KIT
11' x 15'

Opt Bsmt
Str

Linen

BED #3/
OPT STUDY
11' x 11'
12' Clg

FOYER
12' Clg

Sq Column

Pantry

DINING ROOM
11' x 13'
12' Clg

3 CAR GARAGE
23'-6" x 28'

WH   W   D

PORCH

Seat

Seat

61'-0"

© W.L. Martin Designs

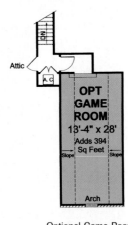

DN

Attic

A.C.

OPT GAME ROOM
13'-4" x 28'
Adds 394 Sq Feet
Slope   Slope

Arch

Optional Game Room
adds 394 Sq. Ft.

Livability
at a Glance™

Storing
Entertaining
Flexible Living
De-Stressing

www.designbasics.com/9JJ

the Mansfield
1539-9JJ
pricecode 19

Total Square Ft. **1996**

Standard Foundation: Basement

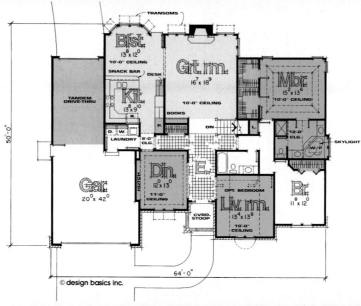

Bfst.
13⁸ x 12⁰
10'-0" CEILING

SNACK BAR

DESK

TRANSOMS

Grt. rm.
16⁷ x 18⁹
10'-0" CEILING

Mbr.
15² x 13⁶
10'-0" CEILING

TANDEM
DRIVE-THRU

Kit.
13 x 9⁰

BOOKS

P.

DN

L.

12'-0"
CLG.

SKYLIGHT

W/D

D. W.

R.

9'-0"
CLG.

LAUNDRY

50'-0"

Gar.
20⁰ x 42⁰

HUTCH

Dn.
12⁰ x 13
11'-0"
CEILING

OPT. BEDROOM

Br.
11 x 12

CVRD.
STOOP

Liv. rm.
13⁴ x 13⁸
10'-0"
CEILING

© design basics inc.

64'-0"

the Dekyan
29501-9JJ
pricecode 20

Total Square Ft. **2038**

Standard Foundation: Slab

Entry
6⁸ x 9⁶
11'-0"
CEILING

DN

Optional Basement
Stair Location

STORAGE

Optional Study

Study
12⁴ x 12⁴
11'-0" CEILING

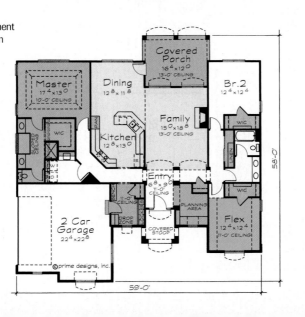

Master
17⁴ x 13⁰
10'-0" CEILING

SLOPED CEILING

WIC

Dining
12⁸ x 11⁸

Covered
Porch
16⁴ x 12⁰
13'-0" CEILING

Br.2
12⁴ x 12⁴

PAN.

Kitchen
12⁸ x 13⁰

Family
15⁰ x 18⁰
13'-0" CEILING

WIC

Entry
6⁸ x 9⁰
11'-0"
CEILING

WIC

2 Car
Garage
22⁴ x 22⁸

DROP
ZONE

PLANNING
AREA

Flex
12⁴ x 12⁴
11'-0" CEILING

COVERED
STOOP

© prime designs, inc.

59'-0"

58'-0"

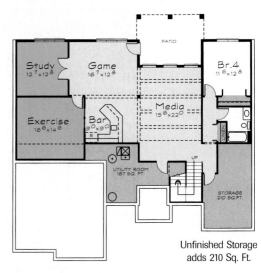

Study
12⁷ x 12⁸

Game
16⁷ x 12⁸

PATIO

Br.4
11⁶ x 12⁸

Exercise
16⁶ x 14⁶

Bar
9⁰ x 9⁰

Media
15⁶ x 22⁰

LINEN

UTILITY ROOM
187 SQ. FT.

UP

STORAGE
210 SQ. FT.

Unfinished Storage
adds 210 Sq. Ft.

Optional Finished Lower Level
adds 1487 Sq. Ft.

Livability
at a Glance™

Storing
Entertaining
Flexible Living
De-Stressing

the Westcott Manor
9171-9JJ
price code 20

Total Square Ft. **2040**

Standard Foundation: Slab

Floor plan labels:
- 9' CH
- PORCH
- BEDROOM 3 12'-0" x 11'-0" 9'-11" CH
- BATH 3 CATH CLG
- CLO
- BREAKFAST 11'-7" x 10'-0" 9' CH
- BEDROOM 2 12'-6" x 11'-0" 9' CH
- CLO
- UP TO OPT ATTIC
- MASTER BEDROOM 13'-0" x 15'-0" 9'-11" CH
- FAMILY ROOM 17'-0" x 16'-0" CATH CLG 9'-15' CH
- KITCHEN 11'-7" x 14'-10" 9' CH
- GARAGE 21'-6" x 21'-8" 9' CH
- DOWN TO BSMNT
- MASTER BATH
- BATH 2 9' CH
- DINING ROOM 11'-0" x 12'-0" 9' CH
- PAN
- UTILITY
- MASTER CLOSET
- CLO
- ENTRY 9' CH
- W D
- COAT CLO
- CLO
- STUDY / BEDROOM 4 11'-2" x 11'-0" 9' CH
- PORCH 9' CH

63'-6"

69'-5"

© CARMICHAEL & DAME DESIGNS, INC.

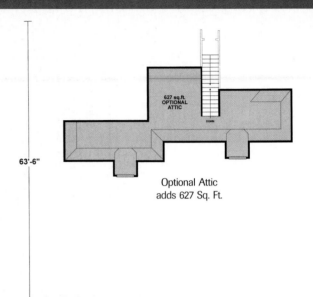

627 sq.ft. OPTIONAL ATTIC

DOWN

Optional Attic adds 627 Sq. Ft.

the Alberta Falls
8122-9JJ
price code 20

Total Square Ft. **2042**

Standard Foundation: Basement

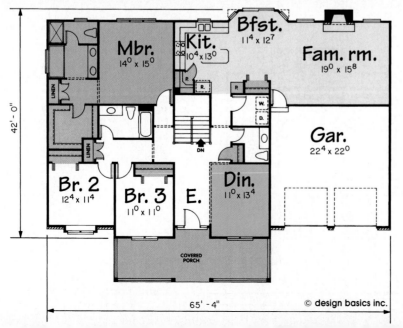

Floor plan labels:
- Mbr. 14⁰ x 15⁰
- Kit. 10⁴ x 13⁰
- Bfst. 11⁴ x 12⁷
- Fam. rm. 19⁰ x 15⁸
- LINEN
- P.
- R.
- P.
- W.
- D.
- Gar. 22⁴ x 22⁰
- DN
- LINEN
- Br. 2 12⁴ x 11⁴
- Br. 3 11⁰ x 11⁰
- E.
- Din. 11⁰ x 13⁴
- COVERED PORCH

42'-0"

65'-4"

© design basics inc.

Livability at a Glance™
- Storing
- Entertaining
- Flexible Living
- De-Stressing

www.designbasics.com/9JJ

the Creighton
4208-9JJ
pricecode 20

Total Square Ft. **2057**

Standard Foundation: Basement

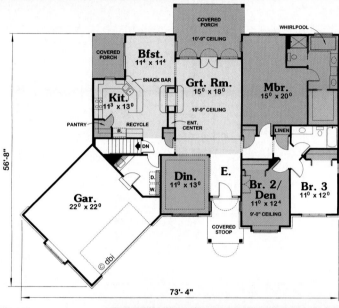

Floor plan labels:
- COVERED PORCH
- Bfst. 11⁴ x 11⁴
- COVERED PORCH 10'-9" CEILING
- WHIRLPOOL
- SNACK BAR
- Grt. Rm. 15⁰ x 18⁰ 10'-9" CEILING
- Mbr. 15⁰ x 20⁰
- Kit. 11³ x 13⁰
- PANTRY
- RECYCLE
- R.
- ENT. CENTER
- LINEN
- DN
- Din. 11⁰ x 13⁰
- E.
- Br. 2/ Den 11⁰ x 12⁴ 9'-0" CEILING
- Br. 3 11⁰ x 12⁰
- D. W.
- Gar. 22⁰ x 22⁰
- COVERED STOOP
- 56'-8"
- 73'-4"
- © dbi

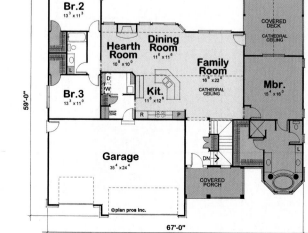

the Gammon
29095-9JJ
pricecode 20

Total Square Ft. **2065**

Standard Foundation: Basement

Floor plan labels:
- Br.2 13³ x 11³
- Hearth Room 10⁸ x 10⁰
- Dining Room 11⁰ x 11⁸
- COVERED DECK CATHEDRAL CEILING
- Family Room 16⁸ x 22⁰ CATHEDRAL CEILING
- Br.3 13³ x 11⁰
- D. W.
- Kit. 11⁶ x 12⁸
- DROP ZONE
- R
- P
- Mbr. 15⁴ x 16⁰
- Garage 35⁴ x 24⁴
- DN
- COVERED PORCH
- 59'-0"
- 67'-0"
- ©plan pros inc.

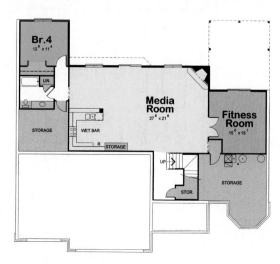

Lower level labels:
- Br.4 12⁸ x 11⁴
- LIN.
- STORAGE
- WET BAR
- STORAGE
- R
- Media Room 27⁸ x 21⁸
- Fitness Room 15⁰ x 15⁷
- UP
- STOR.
- STORAGE

Optional Finished Lower Level
adds 1446 Sq. Ft.

Livability
at a Glance™

- Storing
- Entertaining
- Flexible Living
- De-Stressing

the Plainview
2222-9JJ
pricecode 20

Total Square Ft. **2068**

Standard Foundation: Basement

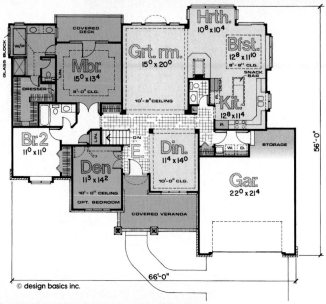

Covered Deck

Hrth. 10⁸ x 10⁴

Grt. rm. 15⁰ x 20⁰
10'-8" CEILING

Bfst. 12⁸ x 11¹⁰
8' - 8" CLG.

Mbr. 15⁰ x 13⁴
9'-0" CLG.

SNACK BAR

Kit. 12⁸ x 11⁴

DRESSER

LIN

W/P

GLASS BLOCK

Br 2 11⁰ x 11⁰

LIN

DN

Den 11³ x 14²
10'-0" CEILING
OPT. BEDROOM

Din. 11⁴ x 14⁰
10'-0" CLG.

W. D.

STORAGE

Gar. 22⁰ x 21⁴

56'-0"

66'-0"

COVERED VERANDA

© design basics inc.

the Rigby
43031-9JJ
pricecode 20

Total Square Ft. **2069**

Standard Foundation: Slab

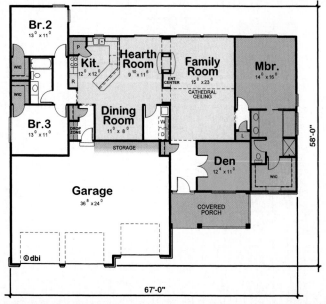

Br.2 13⁰ x 11⁰

WIC

Kit. 12⁰ x 12⁰

P

Hearth Room 9¹⁰ x 11⁸

Family Room 15⁰ x 23⁰
CATHEDRAL CEILING

Mbr. 14⁰ x 16⁰

ENT CENTER

WIC

Br.3 13⁰ x 11⁰

DROP ZONE

Dining Room 11⁰ x 8⁰

W D

STORAGE

Den 12⁴ x 11⁰

WIC

Garage 36⁸ x 24⁰

COVERED PORCH

58'-0"

67'-0"

© dbi

Optional Basement Stair Location

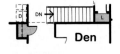

D | DN → | L

Den

Guest Suite 13⁰ x 16⁸

Optional Guest Suite
adds 208 Sq. Ft.

Livability at a Glance™

Storing
Entertaining
Flexible Living
De-Stressing

www.designbasics.com/9JJ

the West Forks
43032-9JJ
price code 20

Total Square Ft. **2081**

Standard Foundation: Slab

Br.2
13⁰ x 11⁰

P

Kit.
12⁰ x 12⁰

Hearth Room
9¹⁰ x 11⁶

Family Room
15⁰ x 23⁰

ENT CENTER

CATHEDRAL CEILING

Mbr.
14⁰ x 16⁰

R

WIC

WIC

Br.3
13⁰ x 11⁰

DROP ZONE

Dining Room
11⁰ x 8⁰

W
D

STORAGE

10'-0" CEILING

Den
12⁴ x 13⁰
10'-0" CEILING

L

WIC

Garage
36⁸ x 24⁰

© dbi

58'-0"

67'-0"

Guest Suite
13⁰ x 16⁰

Optional Guest Suite
adds 208 Sq. Ft.

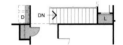

D DN → L

Optional Basement Stair Location

the Clarkson
24038-9JJ
price code 21

Total Square Ft. **2126**

Standard Foundation: Slab

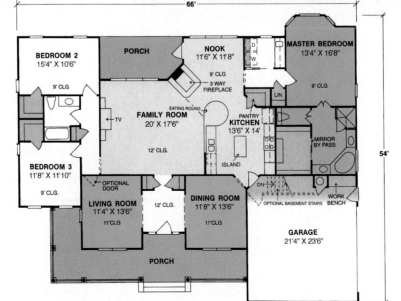

66'

BEDROOM 2
15'4" X 10'6"

9' CLG

PORCH

NOOK
11'6" X 11'8"

D
W

MASTER BEDROOM
13'4" X 16'8"

9' CLG

9' CLG
3 WAY FIREPLACE

LIN

TV

FAMILY ROOM
20' X 17'6"

EATING ROUND

KITCHEN
13'6" X 14'

PANTRY

MIRROR BY PASS

12' CLG.

ISLAND

BEDROOM 3
11'8" X 11'10"

9' CLG.

OPTIONAL DOOR

LIVING ROOM
11'4" X 13'6"

11'CLG

12' CLG.

DINING ROOM
11'8" X 13'6"

11'CLG

DN

OPTIONAL BASEMENT STAIRS

WORK BENCH

54'

GARAGE
21'4" X 23'6"

PORCH

Livability
at a Glance™

- Storing
- Entertaining
- Flexible Living
- De-Stressing

© W. L. Martin Designs

the
Concorde
3597-9JJ
price**code** 21

Total Square Ft. **2132**

Standard Foundation: Basement

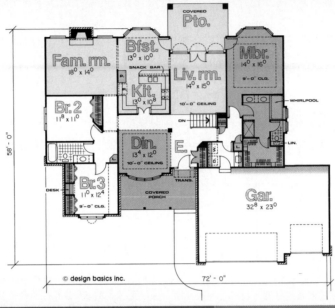

© design basics inc.

the
Newman
1689-9JJ
price**code** 21

Total Square Ft. **2133**

Standard Foundation: Basement

© design basics inc.

Livability
at a Glance™

Storing
Entertaining
Flexible Living
De-Stressing

www.designbasics.com/9JJ

the Inglenook
24210-9JJ
price code 21

Total Square Ft. **2140**

Standard Foundation: Slab

68'-0"

58'-0"

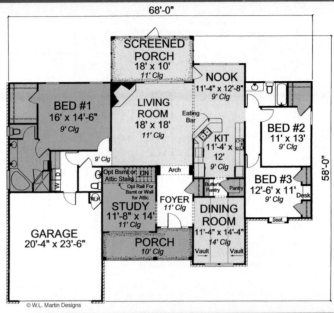

SCREENED PORCH 18' x 10' 11' Clg

NOOK 11'-4" x 12'-8" 9' Clg

BED #1 16' x 14'-6" 9' Clg

LIVING ROOM 18' x 18' 11' Clg

Eating Bar

KIT 11'-4" x 12' 9' Clg

BED #2 11' x 13' 9' Clg

9' Clg

Opt Bsmt or Attic Stairs

DN

Opt Rail For Bsmt or Wall for Attic

Arch

Butler's Pantry

Pantry

BED #3 12'-6" x 11' 9' Clg

Desk

STUDY 11'-8" x 14' 11' Clg

FOYER 11' Clg

DINING ROOM 11'-4" x 14'-4" 14' Clg

Seat

W/D

W.I.C.

GARAGE 20'-4" x 23'-6"

PORCH 10' Clg

Vault

Vault

© W.L. Martin Designs

the Essex
2213-9JJ
price code 21

Total Square Ft. **2149**

Standard Foundation: Basement

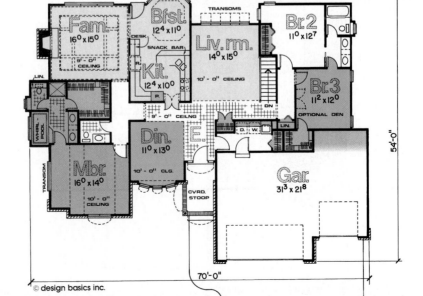

54'-0"

70'-0"

Fam. 16⁰ x 15⁰ 9'-0" CEILING

Bfst. 12⁴ x 11⁰

DESK

TRANSOMS

Br. 2 11⁰ x 12⁷

SNACK BAR

Kit. 12⁴ x 10⁰

Liv. rm. 14⁰ x 15⁰ 10'-0" CEILING

Br. 3 11² x 12⁰ OPTIONAL DEN

LIN.

WHIRL-POOL

P.

9'-0" CEILING

DN

LIN.

D. W.

Din. 11⁰ x 13⁰ 10'-0" CLG.

E.

Gar. 31³ x 21⁸

TRANSOM

Mbr. 16⁰ x 14⁰ 10'-0" CEILING

CVRD. STOOP

© design basics inc.

Livability
at a Glance™
- Storing
- Entertaining
- Flexible Living
- De-Stressing

800.947.7526

69

the Coopers Farm
8045-9JJ
pricecode 21

Total Square Ft. **2151**

Standard Foundation: Basement

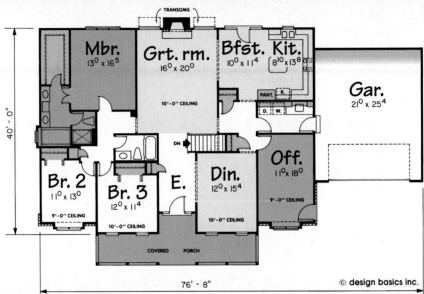

TRANSOMS

Mbr.
13⁰ x 16⁵

Grt. rm.
16⁰ x 20⁰
10'-0" CEILING

Bfst.
10⁰ x 11⁴

Kit.
8¹⁰ x 13⁸

PANT.   R.

D. W.

Gar.
21⁰ x 25⁴

Br. 2
11⁰ x 13⁰
9'-0" CEILING

Br. 3
12⁰ x 11⁴
10'-0" CEILING

E.

DN

Din.
12⁰ x 15⁴
10'-0" CEILING

Off.
11⁰ x 18⁰
9'-0" CEILING

COVERED   PORCH

40' - 0"

76' - 8"

© design basics inc.

the Cameron
5036-9JJ
pricecode 21

Total Square Ft. **2167**

Standard Foundation: Basement

OPEN TO BELOW

DN

Bfst.
16¹¹ x 13⁴

10'-0" CEILING

BUILT-IN

3-SIDED FIREPLACE

Grt. Rm.
17⁰ x 17⁰
10'-0" CEILING

Kit.
14³ x 14⁴

P.

R.

Br.2
11⁰ x 11⁰

Br.3
11⁰ x 11⁰

W.

D.

WHIRL-POOL

Mbr.
14⁰ x 17²

E.

Den
11⁰ x 13⁰
OPT. DINING RM.

Gar.
22⁸ x 22⁴

61'-4"

© design basics inc.   55'-4"

Livability
at a Glance™

Storing
Entertaining
Flexible Living
De-Stressing

www.designbasics.com/9JJ

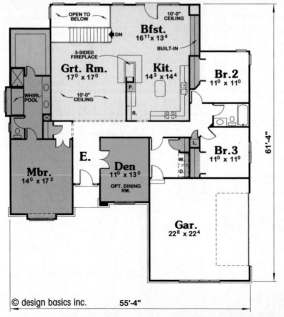

the Greensboro
2326-9JJ
pricecode 21

Total Square Ft. **2172**

Standard Foundation: Basement

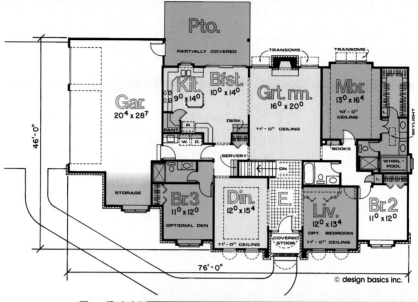

Gar. 20⁴ x 28⁷

Pto. PARTIALLY COVERED

Kit. 9⁰ x 14⁰

Bfst. 10⁰ x 14⁰

Grt. rm. 16⁰ x 20⁰
11'-0" CEILING

Mbr. 13⁰ x 16⁴
10'-0" CEILING

TRANSOMS   TRANSOMS

SKYLIGHT

PANT.

DESK

BOOKS

SERVERY

W. D.

DN

WHIRL-POOL

STORAGE

Br.3 11⁰ x 12⁰
OPTIONAL DEN

Din. 12⁰ x 15⁴
11'-0" CEILING

E

COVERED STOOP

Liv. 12⁰ x 13⁴
11'-0" CEILING

OPT. BEDROOM

Br.2 11⁰ x 12⁰

46'-0"

76'-0"

© design basics inc.

the Mallory
29157-9JJ
pricecode 21

Total Square Ft. **2173**

Standard Foundation: Basement

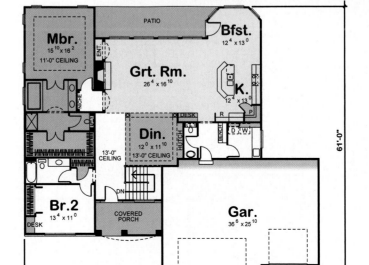

PATIO

Mbr. 15¹⁰ x 16²
11'-0" CEILING

NICHE

Grt. Rm. 26⁴ x 16¹⁰

Bfst. 12⁴ x 13⁰

K. 12⁴ x 13⁰

DESK

R   P

BENCH   D   W

Din. 12⁰ x 11¹⁰
13'-0" CEILING

HUTCH

13'-0" CEILING

DN

Br.2 13⁴ x 11⁰

DESK

COVERED PORCH

Gar. 36⁶ x 25¹⁰

61'-0"

69'-0"

© Advanced Designs Inc.

Livability
at a Glance™
- Storing
- Entertaining
- Flexible Living
- De-Stressing

800.947.7526

71

the
Wrenwood
3005-9JJ
price code 21

Total Square Ft.   **2186**

Standard Foundation: Basement

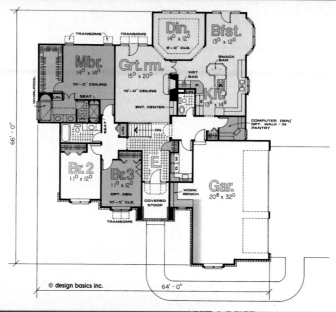

TRANSOMS   TRANSOMS

Din.
14⁰ x 12⁰
9'-0" CLG.

Bfst.
13 x 12⁰

Mbr.
14⁰ x 14⁰
10'-0" CEILING
SEAT

Grt. rm.
15⁰ x 20⁰
10'-0" CEILING
ENT. CENTER

SNACK BAR
WET BAR
Kit.
13⁶ x 14⁸

WHIRLPOOL   LIN   SEAT   DN

66'-0"

COMPUTER DEN/
OPT. WALK-IN
PANTRY

Br. 2
11⁰ x 12⁰

Br. 3
11⁰ x 12⁰
OPT. DEN
10'-0" CLG.

COVERED STOOP

WORK BENCH

Gar.
20⁸ x 32⁰

TRANSOMS

© design basics inc.

64'-0"

the
Longvale
24215-9JJ
price code 21

Total Square Ft.   **2194**

Standard Foundation: Slab

66'-0"

BED #2
15'-4" x 10'-6"
9' Clg

SCREENED PORCH
16' x 12'
11' Clg

Slope

BED #1
13'-4" x 17'-4"
9' Clg

NOOK
11'-6" x 11'-8"
11' Clg

W/D

FAMILY ROOM
20' x 17'-6"
11' Clg

Eating Bar

PANTRY

KIT
13'-6" x 14'
Island
11' Clg

Dresser

BED #3
11'-8" x 14'
9' Clg

Barrel Arch

Opt Door

LIVING ROOM
Opt Bed #4
11'-4" x 13'-6"
9' Clg

FOYER
10' Clg

DINING ROOM
11'-8" x 13'-6"
10' Clg

Opt Wall & Door w/Bsmt

DN

Opt Bsmt Stairs

W.H.

Work bench

62'-0"

3 CAR GARAGE
21'-4" x 30'-6"

PORCH
9' Clg

© W.L. Martin Designs

Livability
at a Glance™

Storing
Entertaining
Flexible Living
De-Stressing

www.designbasics.com/9JJ

The Moment of Discovery

by Erika Woelfel

Who knew plain old blue had a *cousin called Periwinkle,*

Erika Woelfel understands the importance of color in the home. She is Senior Color Designer of the Colwell Color Studio, a company that produces color merchandising tools for the decorative products industry.

Do you remember as a child when you graduated from the box of 8 crayon colors to the box of 48?

If you're like me, your memory probably doesn't go back that far. What I do recall is the new color possibilities seemed endless and I couldn't wait to try them all. Who knew red with just a touch of blue could be transformed into a brilliant new shade called Magenta? Or that plain old blue had a cousin called Periwinkle? Or that green had a neighbor called Lime?

My mother saved my box of 48 colors from when I was in elementary school. When I opened it to see what crayon I used the most, brown was a stump with no wrapper – (the best color to use for drawing horses) – green was broken in half and taped back together, and purple was virtually non-existent because it was applied to everything. Once you determine your palette of personal favorites, I think you carry that with you throughout your entire life. For example, I love wearing purple, and there is lots of green in my house.

So this is my question: As adults, how did we become so cautious about using color?

Think of your home as a giant coloring project. Paint, wallpaper, window treatments, carpet, upholstery and tile are your crayons, your tools. All of these products come in a universe of colors. The disappointing fact is most manufacturers admit their number one selling SKUs are shades of white or beige. My philosophy is this: Somewhere between being a kid secretly trying on mom's hot pink lipstick and as an adult, moving into that first apartment, we lost our nerve when it came to using color!

Don't worry; catching the color fever is quite contagious. Once you start experimenting with your favorites, it's hard to stop. I like to tell people: Use as much or as little as you are comfortable with. Some people approach color by researching all the rules; others break them with wild abandon. The only rule I can think of is: Use colors you enjoy! It makes them much more fun to live with!

If you think you've forgotten the joy of discovering color, the solution is simple. Try opening a box of crayons and pick your favorite. I guarantee it will put a smile on your face – and the crayon you pick won't be white!

Will the RIGHT COLOR *please* Come Forward?

Sometimes discovering which colors are right for expressing your personality is as simple as asking a few questions. Take the quiz below by circling your first choice answer. Refer to the chart (right) to find your perfect color match!

The words that best describe my personal style would be:
- D) bold and daring
- C) eclectic and chic
- M) sophisticated and precise
- T) formal and classic
- R) pretty and romantic

I would prefer which activity:
- C) a nature walk
- R) a candlelight dinner for two
- M) attending a cultural event
- T) lunch at the country club
- D) throwing a wild party

I feel great when wearing:
- D) bright, flashy accessory colors
- R) feminine floral prints
- C) blue jeans and tennis shoes
- M) basic black, gray
- T) navy and khaki

I would like my kitchen to feel:
- M) clean and streamlined
- R) light and airy
- C) chic and functional
- T) traditional
- D) lively and fun

I would like my living room to feel:
- T) dignified
- D) vibrant
- R) cozy
- M) uncluttered
- C) laid back and comfortable

My bedroom should be:
- M) clean-lined
- T) tasteful
- D) passionate
- C) peaceful
- R) romantic

The furnishings I have in my home are:
- R) nostalgic, with soft detailing
- C) like old friends, easy to live with
- T) antique
- D) whimsical
- M) contemporary

Dynamic
If you circled mostly D's, then you are an out-going, active person. You have no problem trying new colors. Bright red and sunflower yellow best fit your personality for the kitchen. Hot pink and chartreuse are fun colors for the living room, and try living it up a little with periwinkle blue and deep violet in the bedroom!

Modern
If you circled M's, you are probably a color purist who prefers crisp white, sharp black and complex neutrals in all ranges from sage green to warm sand. For a dramatic feature wall, try using an accent of celadon green, chili pepper red, or chocolate brown and dark teal.

Casual Chic
If you circled more C's, you probably like colors from a natural setting, whether you live in the mountains or near the ocean. Jade blues, sage greens, caramel brown, camel, and sunset violets best represent your unfussy, but fun sense of style.

Romantic
If you circled mostly R's, then you are most likely a romantic: soft poetic colors suit you well... pastels in pale pink, sky blue, dinner mint green, downy yellow and fresh apricot create great backdrop hues for floral prints.

Timeless
If you circled T's, you tend to be more traditional in your color style: navy blue, shadowy green, and burnished gold fit your tailored sense of style. Jeweltones add a touch of luxury to your home in hues ranging from amethyst to sapphire to emerald and ruby red.

the
Britebay
24159-9JJ
pricecode 22

Total Square Ft. **2218**

Standard Foundation: Slab

Livability
at a Glance™
- Storing
- Entertaining
- Flexible Living
- De-Stressing

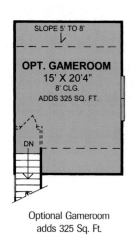

SLOPE 5' TO 8'

OPT. GAMEROOM
15' X 20'4"
8' CLG.
ADDS 325 SQ. FT.

DN

Optional Gameroom
adds 325 Sq. Ft.

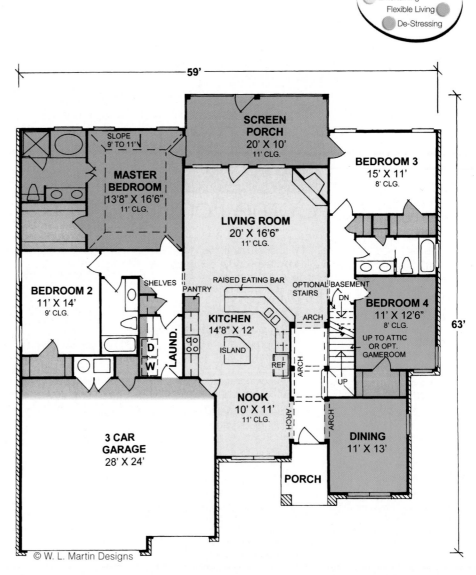

59'

63'

SLOPE 9' TO 11'

SCREEN PORCH
20' X 10'
11' CLG.

BEDROOM 3
15' X 11'
8' CLG.

MASTER BEDROOM
13'8" X 16'6"
11' CLG.

LIVING ROOM
20' X 16'6"
11' CLG.

SHELVES

PANTRY

RAISED EATING BAR

OPTIONAL BASEMENT STAIRS

BEDROOM 2
11' X 14'
9' CLG.

KITCHEN
14'8" X 12'

ISLAND

ARCH

DN

BEDROOM 4
11' X 12'6"
8' CLG.

UP TO ATTIC OR OPT. GAMEROOM

REF

ARCH

D W

LAUND.

ARCH

UP

NOOK
10' X 11'
11' CLG.

ARCH

3 CAR GARAGE
28' X 24'

ARCH

DINING
11' X 13'

PORCH

© W. L. Martin Designs

www.designbasics.com/9JJ

the
Baywood
6672-9JJ
pricecode 22

Total Square Ft. **2223**

Standard Foundation: Basement

Livability
at a Glance™

- Storing
- Entertaining
- Flexible Living
- De-Stressing

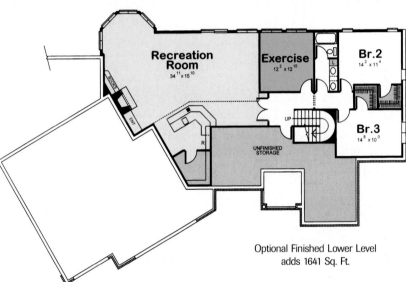

Recreation Room
34¹¹ x 15¹⁰

Exercise
12² x 12¹⁰

Br.2
14² x 11⁴

Br.3
14⁸ x 10⁰

UNFINISHED STORAGE

UP

R

ENT

Optional Finished Lower Level
adds 1641 Sq. Ft.

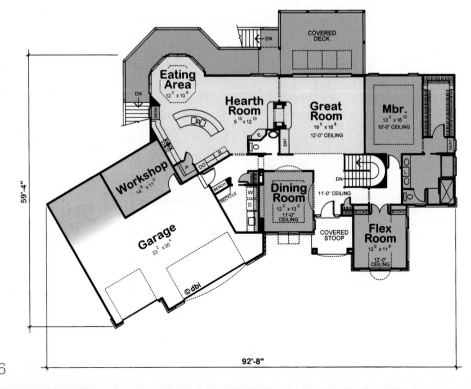

COVERED DECK

DN

Eating Area
12⁰ x 10⁶

DN

DESK

Hearth Room
9¹⁰ x 12¹⁰

Great Room
19⁰ x 16⁸
12'-0" CEILING

ENT

E

Mbr.
13⁰ x 16¹⁰
10'-0" CEILING

SEAT

Workshop
14⁸ x 11⁰

P

DO

BENCH

RECYCLE

W D

Dining Room
12⁰ x 13⁰
11'-0" CEILING

DN

11'-0" CEILING

BOOKS

Garage
33² x 30⁴

COVERED STOOP

Flex Room
12⁰ x 11⁸
12'-0" CEILING

© dbi

59'-4"

92'-8"

the Enfield
5141-9JJ

price code 22

Total Square Ft. **2242**

Standard Foundation: Basement

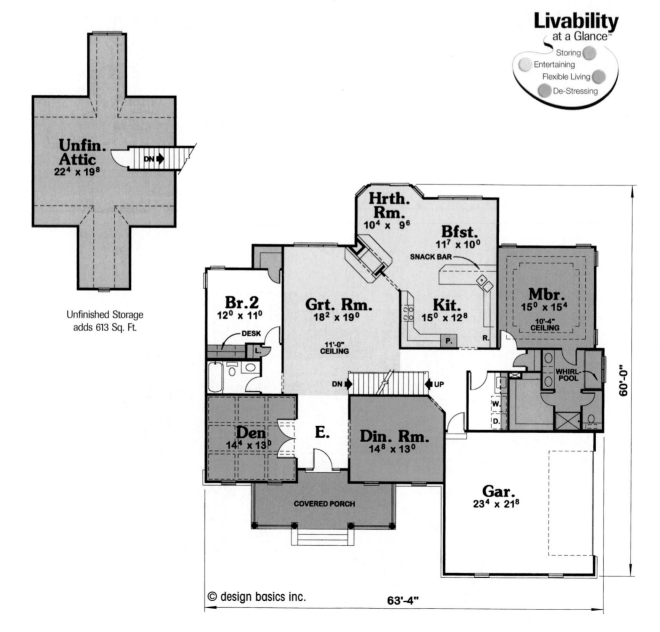

Livability
at a Glance™

Storing
Entertaining
Flexible Living
De-Stressing

Unfin. Attic
22⁴ x 19⁸

DN

Unfinished Storage
adds 613 Sq. Ft.

Hrth. Rm.
10⁴ x 9⁶

Bfst.
11⁷ x 10⁰

SNACK BAR

Br. 2
12⁰ x 11⁰

DESK

Grt. Rm.
18² x 19⁰

11'-0"
CEILING

Kit.
15⁰ x 12⁸

Mbr.
15⁰ x 15⁴

10'-4"
CEILING

P.   R.

DN   UP

WHIRL-POOL

W.
D.

Den
14⁴ x 13⁰

E.

Din. Rm.
14⁸ x 13⁰

Gar.
23⁴ x 21⁸

COVERED PORCH

60'-0"

63'-4"

© design basics inc.

the
Tiffany
Brooke
29510-9JJ
price**code** 22

Total Square Ft. **2242**

Standard Foundation: Slab

Livability
at a Glance™

- Storing
- Entertaining
- Flexible Living
- De-Stressing

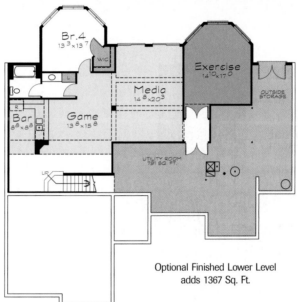

Optional Finished Lower Level
adds 1367 Sq. Ft.

Optional Basement Stair Location
adds 65 Sq. Ft.

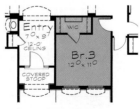

Optional Third Bedroom

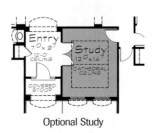

Optional Study

the
Stokley
29097-9JJ
pricecode 22

Total Square Ft. **2255**

Standard Foundation: Slab

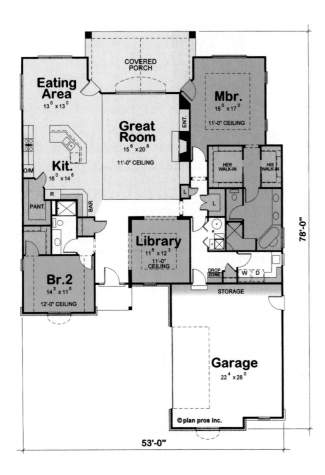

Eating Area 13⁰ x 13⁰

COVERED PORCH

Mbr. 15⁰ x 17⁰ 11'-0" CEILING

Great Room 15⁶ x 20⁸ 11'-0" CEILING

Kit. 16⁰ x 14⁸

HER WALK-IN | HIS WALK-IN

PANT.

BAR

R

Library 11⁶ x 12³ 11'-0" CEILING

DROP ZONE | W | D

Br.2 14³ x 11⁰ 12'-0" CEILING

STORAGE

78'-0"

Garage 22⁴ x 28⁰

© plan pros inc.

53'-0"

Livability
at a Glance™

Storing
Entertaining
Flexible Living
De-Stressing

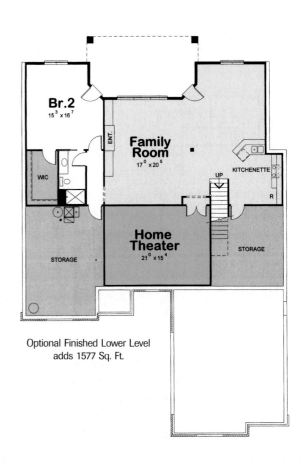

Br.2 15³ x 16⁷

WIC

ENT.

Family Room 17⁰ x 20⁵

KITCHENETTE

R

UP

STORAGE

Home Theater 21⁰ x 15⁴

STORAGE

Optional Finished Lower Level
adds 1577 Sq. Ft.

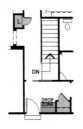

DN

DROP ZONE

Optional Basement
Stair Location

www.designbasics.com/9JJ

the
Kathryn
42025-9JJ
pricecode 22

Total Square Ft. **2274**

Standard Foundation: Slab

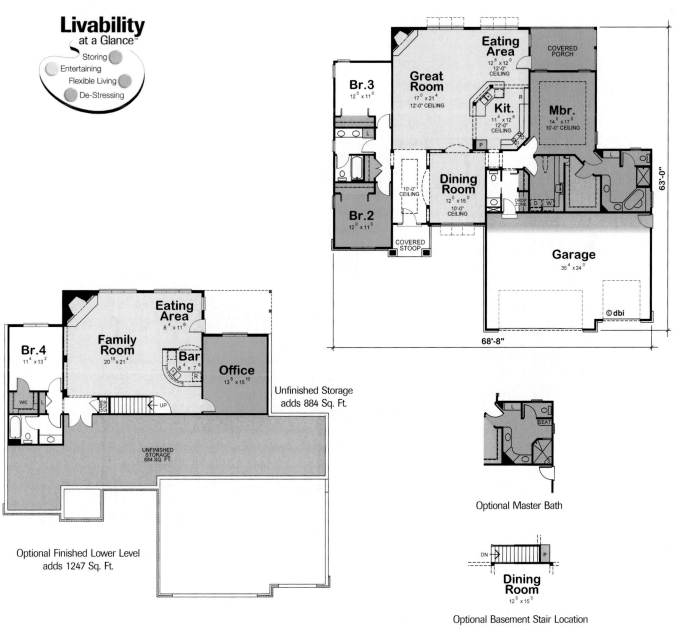

Livability at a Glance™

- Storing
- Entertaining
- Flexible Living
- De-Stressing

Br. 3
12⁰ x 11⁰

Great Room
17⁰ x 21⁴
12'-0" CEILING

Eating Area
12⁸ x 12⁰
12'-0" CEILING

COVERED PORCH

Kit.
11⁴ x 12⁸
12'-0" CEILING

Mbr.
14⁰ x 17⁰
10'-0" CEILING

Dining Room
12⁰ x 15⁰
10'-0" CEILING

10'-0" CEILING

DROP ZONE

Br. 2
12⁰ x 11⁰

COVERED STOOP

Garage
35⁴ x 24⁰

©dbi

63'-0"

68'-8"

Br. 4
11⁴ x 13²

Family Room
20¹⁰ x 21⁴

Eating Area
8⁴ x 11⁶

Bar
8⁴ x 7⁶

Office
13⁸ x 15¹⁰

Unfinished Storage adds 884 Sq. Ft.

UP

UNFINISHED STORAGE 884 SQ. FT.

Optional Finished Lower Level adds 1247 Sq. Ft.

SEAT

Optional Master Bath

DN

Dining Room
12⁰ x 15⁰

Optional Basement Stair Location

the
Aberdeen
2321-9JJ
pricecode 22

Total Square Ft. **2276**

Standard Foundation: Basement

Livability at a Glance™

- Storing
- Entertaining
- Flexible Living
- De-Stressing

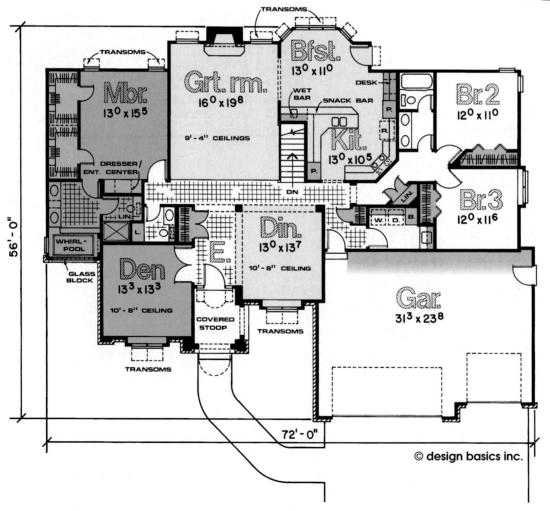

TRANSOMS

TRANSOMS

Mbr.
13⁰ x 15⁵

Grt. rm.
16⁰ x 19⁸

9'-4" CEILINGS

Bfst.
13⁰ x 11⁰

DESK

WET BAR

SNACK BAR

Br. 2
12⁰ x 11⁰

Kit.
13⁰ x 10⁵

DRESSER / ENT. CENTER

DN

LIN.

P.

R.

P.

LIN.

W. D.

B.

Br. 3
12⁰ x 11⁶

WHIRL- POOL

L.

Din.
13⁰ x 13⁷

10'-8" CEILING

GLASS BLOCK

Den
13³ x 13³

10'-8" CEILING

Gar.
31³ x 23⁸

COVERED STOOP

TRANSOMS

TRANSOMS

56'-0"

72'-0"

© **design basics inc.**

the Montgomery
3058-9JJ
price code 23

Total Square Ft. **2311**

Standard Foundation: Basement

Livability
at a Glance™

- Storing
- Entertaining
- Flexible Living
- De-Stressing

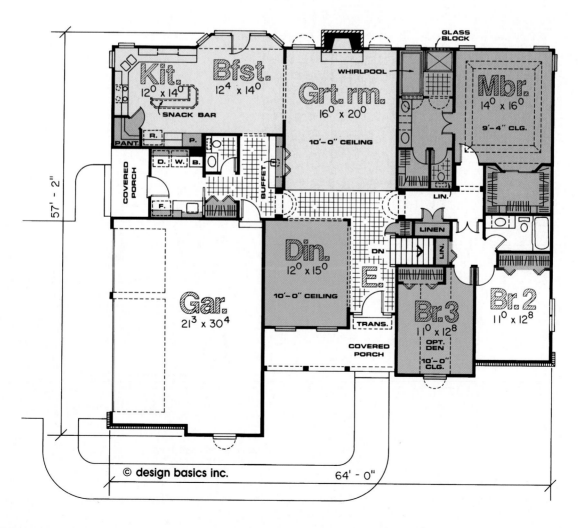

Kit.
12⁰ x 14⁰

Bfst.
12⁴ x 14⁰

SNACK BAR

PANT.

R.

P.

D. W. B.

F.

COVERED PORCH

Grt. rm.
16⁰ x 20⁰
10'-0" CEILING

WHIRLPOOL

GLASS BLOCK

Mbr.
14⁰ x 16⁰
9'-4" CLG.

BUFFET

LIN.

LINEN

Din.
12⁰ x 15⁰
10'-0" CEILING

DN

LIN.

Gar.
21³ x 30⁴

TRANS.

Br. 3
11⁰ x 12⁸
OPT. DEN
10'-0" CLG.

Br. 2
11⁰ x 12⁸

COVERED PORCH

57' - 2"

64' - 0"

© design basics inc.

the
Fairway
2651-9JJ
pricecode 23

Total Square Ft. **2317**

Standard Foundation: Basement

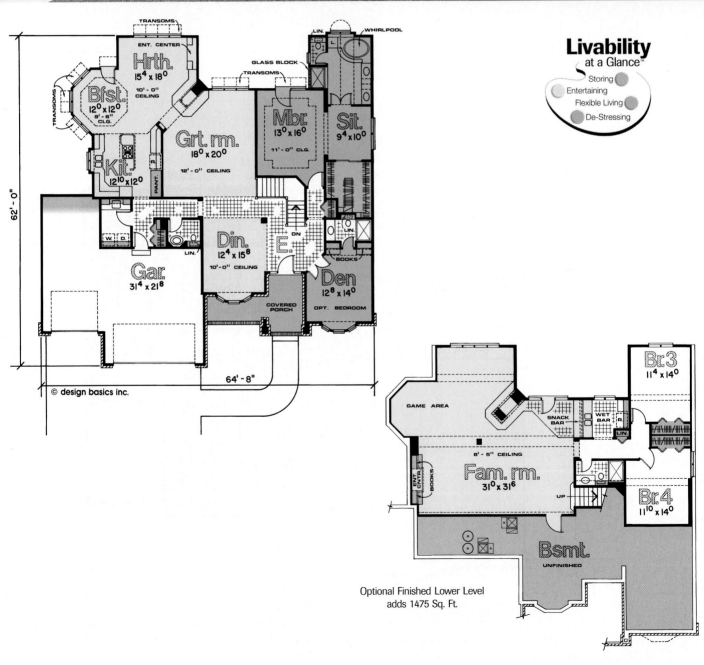

Livability
at a Glance™
- Storing
- Entertaining
- Flexible Living
- De-Stressing

© design basics inc.

Optional Finished Lower Level
adds 1475 Sq. Ft.

www.designbasics.com/9JJ

the
Briar Manor
9207-9JJ
pricecode 23

Total Square Ft. **2331**

Standard Foundation: Slab

Livability
at a Glance™

- Storing
- Entertaining
- Flexible Living
- De-Stressing

BATH 2

BEDROOM 2
11'-0" x 16'-0"
9' CH

CLOSET

BEDROOM 3
11'-0" x 11'-0"
9' CH

CLO

FAMILY ROOM
15'-0" x 15'-0"
9'-11' CH

F.P.

CLO

1-CAR GARAGE
11'-0" x 22'-0"
9' CH

9' CH

9' CH

UTIL
6'-4" x 8'-0"
9' CH

D
W

KITCHEN
14'-7" x 14'-0"
11' CH

R

DN CLO

9' CH

P

BRKFST
6'-6" x 11'-0"
9' CH

PORCH
11' CH

MASTER BEDROOM
14'-0" x 15'-0"
9'-10' CH

MSTR. BATH
9' CH

DINING/ LIVING ROOM
18'-9" x 13'-0"
11' CH

F.P.

CLO

PDR
9' CH

CLO
6'-0" x 12'-0"

68'-9 1/2"

ENTRY
11' CH

STUDY
13'-0" x 13'-0"
9' CH

PORCH
11' CH

2-CAR GARAGE
22' x 23'-8"
9' CH

© CARMICHAEL & DAME DESIGNS, INC.

74'-11"

the
Montana
24205-9JJ
pricecode 23

Total Square Ft. **2340**

Standard Foundation: Slab

Livability
at a Glance™

- Storing
- Entertaining
- Flexible Living
- De-Stressing

Slope

OPT GAME ROOM
15' X 19'-8"
8' Clg

Slope

DN

Optional Game Room
adds 296 Sq. Ft.

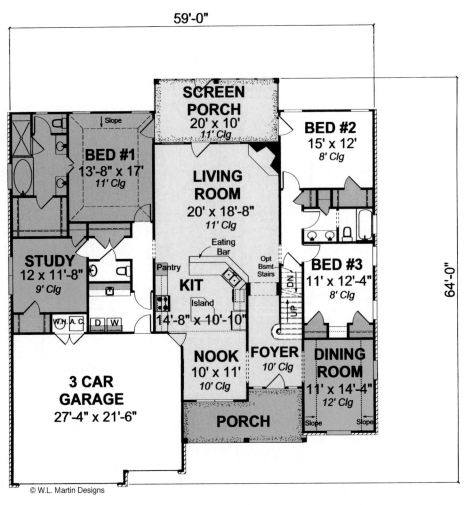

59'-0"

64'-0"

Slope

SCREEN PORCH
20' x 10'
11' Clg

BED #2
15' x 12'
8' Clg

BED #1
13'-8" x 17'
11' Clg

LIVING ROOM
20' x 18'-8"
11' Clg

Eating Bar

Opt Bsmt Stairs

BED #3
11' x 12'-4"
8' Clg

STUDY
12 x 11'-8"
9' Clg

Pantry

KIT
14'-8" x 10'-10"

Island

DN

UP

W.H. A.C. D W

NOOK
10' x 11'
10' Clg

FOYER
10' Clg

DINING ROOM
11' x 14'-4"
12' Clg

3 CAR GARAGE
27'-4" x 21'-6"

PORCH

Slope   Slope

© W.L. Martin Designs

the
Richgrove
24207-9JJ

pricecode 23

Total Square Ft. **2354**

Standard Foundation: Slab

Livability
at a Glance™

- Storing
- Entertaining
- Flexible Living
- De-Stressing

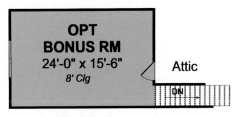

OPT BONUS RM
24'-0" x 15'-6"
8' Clg

Attic

DN

Optional Bonus Room
adds 374 Sq. Ft.

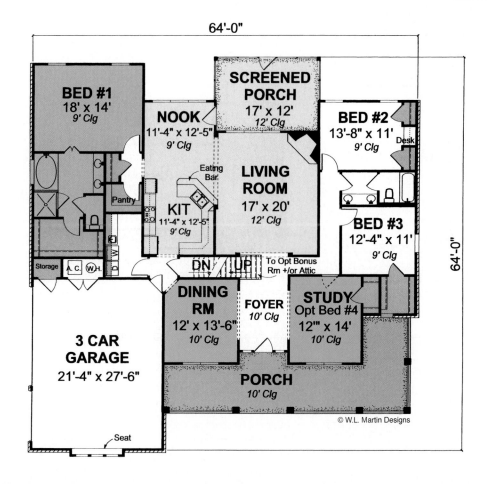

64'-0"

64'-0"

BED #1
18' x 14'
9' Clg

NOOK
11'-4" x 12'-5"
9' Clg

Pantry

Eating Bar

KIT
11'-4" x 12'-5"
9' Clg

SCREENED PORCH
17' x 12'
12' Clg

LIVING ROOM
17' x 20'
12' Clg

BED #2
13'-8" x 11'
9' Clg

Desk

BED #3
12'-4" x 11'
9' Clg

Storage A.C. W.H. D W

DN UP

To Opt Bonus Rm +/or Attic

DINING RM
12' x 13'-6"
10' Clg

FOYER
10' Clg

STUDY
Opt Bed #4
12'" x 14'
10' Clg

3 CAR GARAGE
21'-4" x 27'-6"

PORCH
10' Clg

Seat

© W.L. Martin Designs

the
Hennessey
42026-9JJ
pricecode 23

Total Square Ft. **2390**

Standard Foundation: Basement

Livability
at a Glance™

Storing
Entertaining
Flexible Living
De-Stressing

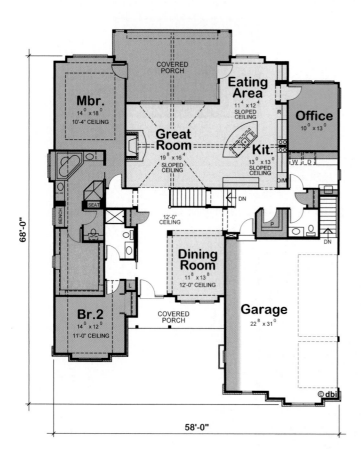

COVERED PORCH

Mbr.
14⁰ x 18⁰
10'-4" CEILING

Eating Area
11⁴ x 12⁴
SLOPED CEILING

Office
10⁰ x 13⁰

Great Room
19⁸ x 16⁴
SLOPED CEILING

Kit.
13⁰ x 13⁰
SLOPED CEILING

W D

DN

D/W

12'-0" CEILING

P

DN

Dining Room
11⁸ x 13⁸
12'-0" CEILING

Garage
22⁸ x 31⁰

Br.2
14⁰ x 12⁰
11'-0" CEILING

COVERED PORCH

68'-0"

58'-0"

SEAT
BENCH

©dbi

COVERED PATIO

Br.
13² x 11⁶

Recreation Room
32⁸ x 16⁰

Bar
9¹⁰ x 11¹⁰

WINE STORAGE

R

UP

Br.
13² x 11⁶

UP

UNFINISHED STORAGE
894 SQ. FT.

Optional Finished Lower Level
adds 1322 Sq. Ft.

the
West University Manor
9264-9JJ

pricecode 24

Total Square Ft. **2430**

Standard Foundation: Slab

Livability
at a Glance™

- Storing
- Entertaining
- Flexible Living
- De-Stressing

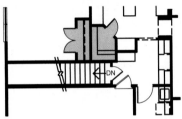

Optional Basement Stair Location
adds 57 Sq. Ft.

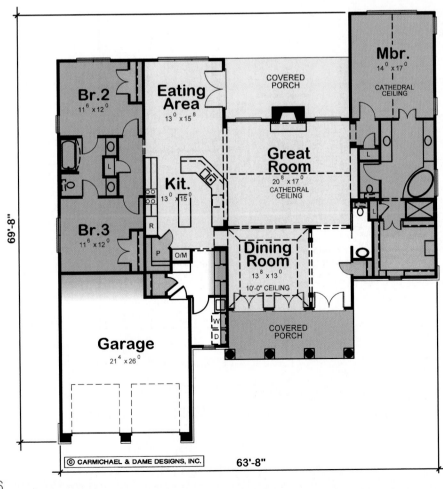

Br.2
11⁶ x 12⁰

Eating Area
13⁰ x 15⁸

COVERED PORCH

Mbr.
14⁰ x 17⁰
CATHEDRAL CEILING

Kit.
13⁰ x 15⁰

Great Room
20⁸ x 17⁰
CATHEDRAL CEILING

Br.3
11⁶ x 12⁰

Dining Room
13⁸ x 13⁰
10'-0" CEILING

Garage
21⁴ x 26⁰

COVERED PORCH

69'-8"

63'-8"

© CARMICHAEL & DAME DESIGNS, INC.

the
Comstock
2778-9JJ

pricecode 24

Total Square Ft. **2456**

Standard Foundation: Basement

Livability
at a Glance™

Storing
Entertaining
Flexible Living
De-Stressing

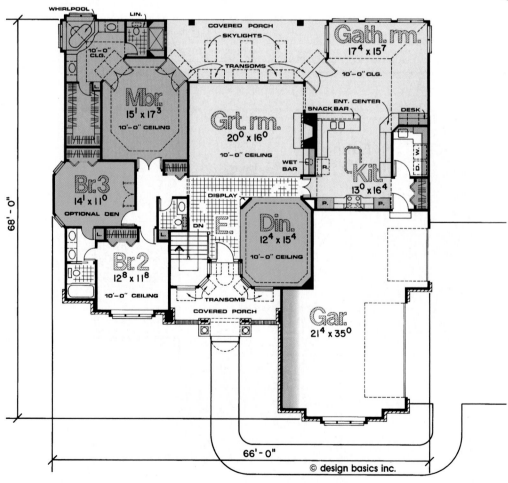

WHIRLPOOL   LIN.

COVERED PORCH
SKYLIGHTS

TRANSOMS

Gath. rm.
17⁴ x 15⁷

10'-0" CLG.

10'-0"
CLG.

Mbr.
15¹ x 17³
10'-0" CEILING

Grt. rm.
20⁰ x 16⁰

10'-0" CEILING

ENT. CENTER

SNACK BAR

DESK

WET
BAR

Kit.
13⁰ x 16⁴

Br.3
14¹ x 11⁰

OPTIONAL DEN

DISPLAY

DN

Din.
12⁴ x 15⁴

10'-0" CEILING

Br.2
12⁸ x 11⁸

10'-0" CEILING

TRANSOMS

COVERED PORCH

Gar.
21⁴ x 35⁰

68' - 0"

66' - 0"

© design basics inc.

the
Maribel
24109-9JJ
pricecode 24

Total Square Ft. **2462**

Standard Foundation: Slab

Livability at a Glance™

- Storing
- Entertaining
- Flexible Living
- De-Stressing

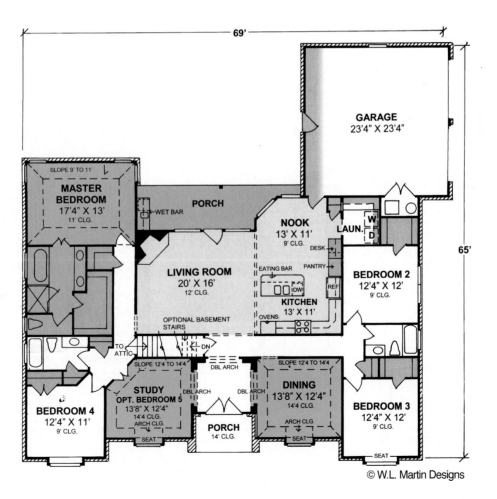

69'

65'

GARAGE
23'4" X 23'4"

MASTER BEDROOM
17'4" X 13'
11' CLG.

SLOPE 9' TO 11'

PORCH

WET BAR

NOOK
13' X 11'
9' CLG.

LAUN.

W
D

LIVING ROOM
20' X 16'
12' CLG.

DESK

EATING BAR

PANTRY

BEDROOM 2
12'4" X 12'
9' CLG.

DW

REF

KITCHEN
13' X 11'

OVENS

OPTIONAL BASEMENT STAIRS

TO ATTIC

DN

SLOPE 12'4 TO 14'4

DBL ARCH

DBL ARCH

DBL ARCH

DBL ARCH

SLOPE 12'4 TO 14'4

STUDY
OPT. BEDROOM 5
13'8" X 12'4"
14'4 CLG.
ARCH CLG.

DINING
13'8" X 12'4"
14'4 CLG.

ARCH CLG.

BEDROOM 4
12'4" X 11'
9' CLG.

BEDROOM 3
12'4" X 12'
9' CLG.

PORCH
14' CLG.

SEAT

SEAT

SEAT

SEAT

© W.L. Martin Designs

the
Hawkesbury
2206-9JJ
pricecode 24

Total Square Ft. **2498**

Standard Foundation: Basement

Livability
at a Glance™

Storing
Entertaining
Flexible Living
De-Stressing

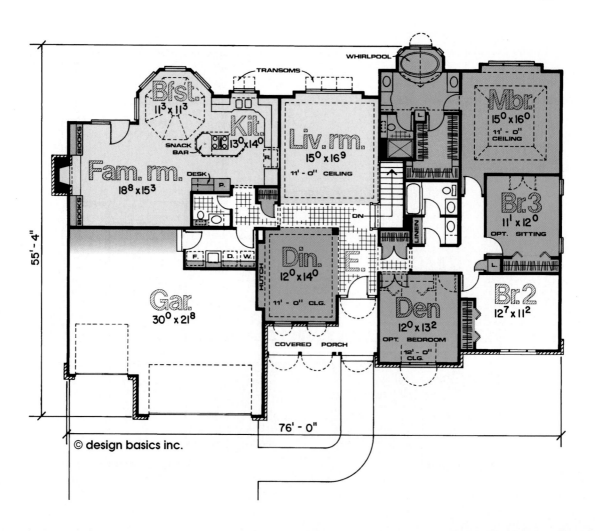

WHIRLPOOL

TRANSOMS

Bfst.
11³ x 11³

Mbr.
15⁰ x 16⁰
11'-0"
CEILING

Kit.
13⁰ x 14⁰

Liv. rm.
15⁰ x 16⁹
11'-0" CEILING

SNACK
BAR

Fam. rm.
18⁸ x 15³

DESK

P.

Br.3
11¹ x 12⁰
OPT. SITTING

BOOKS

DN

LINEN

F.   D.   W.

Din.
12⁰ x 14⁰
11'-0" CLG.

E.

Br.2
12⁷ x 11²

HUTCH

Gar.
30⁰ x 21⁸

Den
12⁰ x 13²
OPT. BEDROOM
12'-0"
CLG.

55'-4"

COVERED   PORCH

76'-0"

© design basics inc.

the
Hallmark
3535-9JJ
pricecode 25

Total Square Ft. **2504**

Standard Foundation: Basement

Livability
at a Glance™

- Storing
- Entertaining
- Flexible Living
- De-Stressing

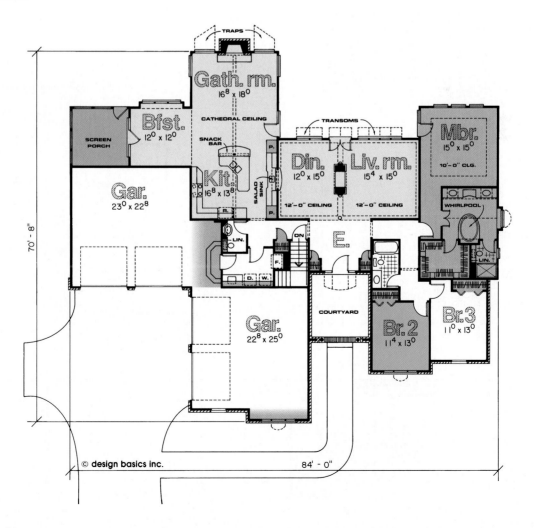

TRAPS

Gath. rm.
16⁸ x 18⁰

CATHEDRAL CEILING

Bfst.
12⁰ x 12⁰

SCREEN PORCH

SNACK BAR

TRANSOMS

Mbr.
15⁰ x 15⁰

10'-0" CLG.

Kit.
16⁸ x 13⁸

SALAD SINK

Din.
12⁰ x 15⁰

Liv. rm.
15⁴ x 15⁰

12'-0" CEILING

12'-0" CEILING

WHIRLPOOL

Gar.
23⁰ x 22⁸

LIN.

DN

E.

LIN.

70'-8"

D. W.

F.

Gar.
22⁸ x 25⁰

COURTYARD

Br. 2
11⁴ x 13⁰

Br. 3
11⁰ x 13⁰

© design basics inc.

84'-0"

the
Heatherstone
42002-9JJ
price code 25

Total Square Ft. **2506**

Standard Foundation: Basement

COVERED DECK

Mbr.
13⁰ x 17⁰
10'-0" CEILING

Great Room
19⁰ x 19⁰
13'-0" CEILING

Br.2
13⁸ x 12⁰

DN

12'-0" CEILING

Br.3
11⁶ x 13⁰

Eating Area
15⁰ x 12⁰

Dining Room
10⁹ x 19⁸
10'-0" CEILING

COVERED PORCH

READING ALCOVE

Kit.
15⁰ x 12⁷

O/M

W D

PLANNING CENTER

R P

Garage
33⁴ x 29⁰

© dbi

88'-0"

59'-4"

Livability
at a Glance™

Storing
Entertaining
Flexible Living
De-Stressing

Optional Finished Lower Level
adds 1541 Sq. Ft.

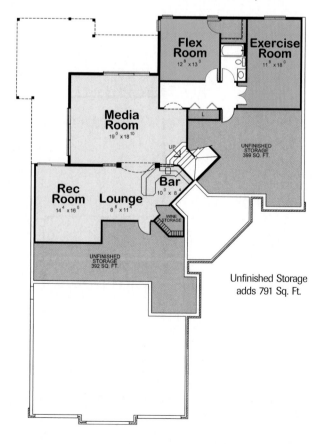

Flex Room
12⁸ x 13⁰

Exercise Room
11⁸ x 18⁰

Media Room
19⁰ x 18¹⁰

UNFINISHED STORAGE
399 SQ. FT.

UP

L

Bar
10⁰ x 8⁰

Rec Room
14⁴ x 16⁰

Lounge
8⁸ x 11⁰

WINE STORAGE

UNFINISHED STORAGE
392 SQ. FT.

Unfinished Storage
adds 791 Sq. Ft.

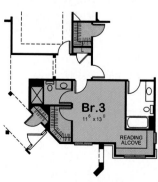

Br.3
11⁶ x 13⁰

READING ALCOVE

Optional Third Bedroom

www.designbasics.com/9JJ

the
Lawrence
2652-9JJ
pricecode 25

Total Square Ft. **2512**

Standard Foundation: Basement

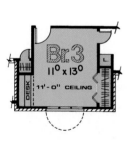

Livability
at a Glance™

- Storing
- Entertaining
- Flexible Living
- De-Stressing

Br. 3
11⁰ x 13⁰
11'-0" CEILING

Optional Third Bedroom

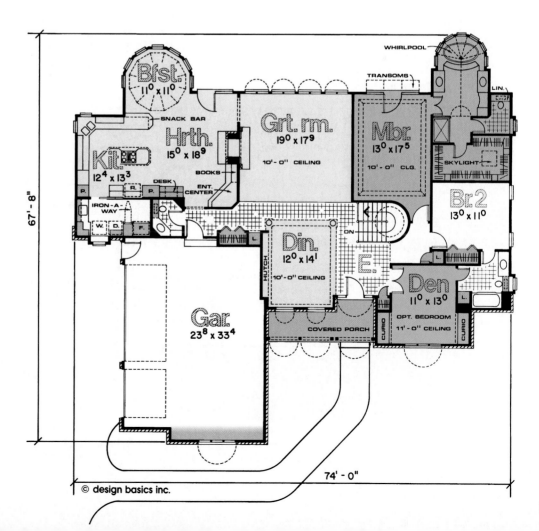

Bfst.
11⁰ x 11⁰

WHIRLPOOL

TRANSOMS

LIN.

SNACK BAR

Grt. rm.
19⁰ x 17⁹
10'-0" CEILING

Mbr.
13⁰ x 17⁵
10'-0" CLG.

Hrth.
15⁰ x 18⁹

SKYLIGHT

Kit.
12⁴ x 13³

BOOKS

DESK

P.

R.

P.

ENT.
CENTER

Br. 2
13⁰ x 11⁰

IRON-A-WAY

W. D. F.

HUTCH

Din.
12⁰ x 14¹
10'-0" CEILING

DN

Den
11⁰ x 13⁰
OPT. BEDROOM
11'-0" CEILING

CURIO

CURIO

Gar.
23⁸ x 33⁴

COVERED PORCH

67'-8"

74'-0"

© design basics inc.

the
Kingwood
Showcase
9199-9JJ

pricecode 25

Total Square Ft. **2517**

Standard Foundation: Slab

Livability
at a Glance™

- Storing
- Entertaining
- Flexible Living
- De-Stressing

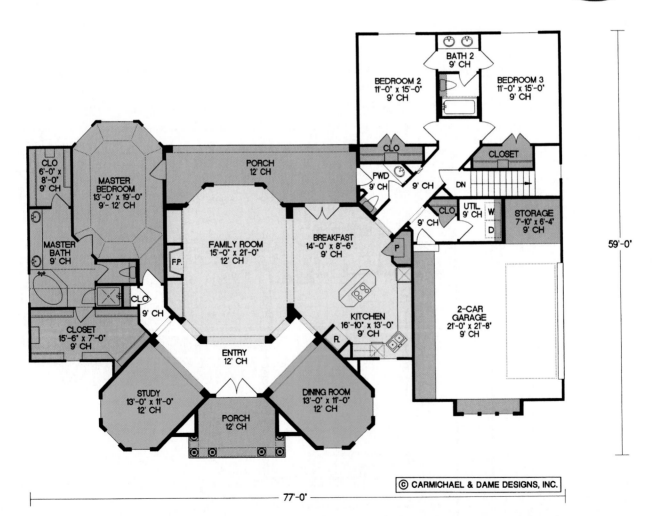

© CARMICHAEL & DAME DESIGNS, INC.

the
Ascott
3057-9JJ
pricecode 25

Total Square Ft. **2538**

Standard Foundation: Basement

Livability
at a Glance™

Storing
Entertaining
Flexible Living
De-Stressing

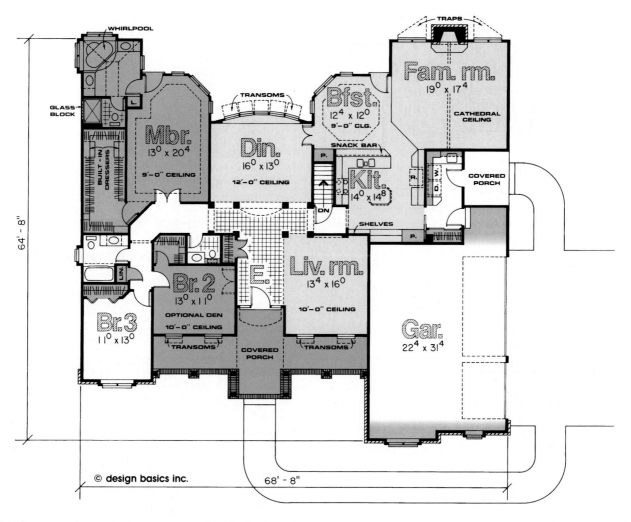

WHIRLPOOL

TRAPS

GLASS BLOCK

Fam. rm.
19⁰ x 17⁴

CATHEDRAL CEILING

Mbr.
13⁰ x 20⁴

Bfst.
12⁴ x 12⁰
9'-0" CLG.

TRANSOMS

9'-0" CEILING

Din.
16⁰ x 13⁰

SNACK BAR

Kit.
14⁰ x 14⁸

COVERED PORCH

BUILT-IN DRESSERS

12'-0" CEILING

P.

R.

D.W.

DN

SHELVES

P.

64' - 8"

LIN.

Br. 2
13⁰ x 11⁰

Liv. rm.
13⁴ x 16⁰

Gar.
22⁴ x 31⁴

OPTIONAL DEN
10'-0" CEILING

10'-0" CEILING

Br. 3
11⁰ x 13⁰

TRANSOMS

COVERED PORCH

TRANSOMS

© design basics inc.

68' - 8"

the McAllister
42027-9JJ
price code 25

Total Square Ft. **2598**

Standard Foundation: Slab

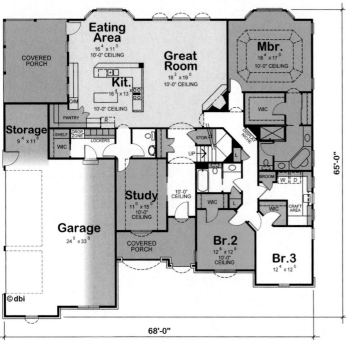

Eating Area 16⁴ x 11⁰ 10'-0" CEILING

Great Room 18² x 19⁰ 10'-0" CEILING

Mbr. 18⁴ x 17⁰ 10'-0" CEILING

Kit. 16⁴ x 13⁸ 10'-0" CEILING

COVERED PORCH

Storage 9⁴ x 11⁰

PANTRY
SHELF
DROP ZONE
LOCKERS
WIC
WIC

Study 11⁰ x 15⁰ 10'-0" CEILING

Garage 24⁰ x 33⁰

10'-0" CEILING

COVERED PORCH

Br.2 12⁸ x 12⁸ 10'-0" CEILING

Br.3 12⁴ x 12⁰

WIC
CRAFT AREA
BROOM
W D
STOR.
UP

© dbi

65'-0"

68'-0"

DN
UP

Optional Basement Stair Location

Dining Room 11⁰ x 16⁰ 10'-0" CEILING

Optional Dining Room

Livability
at a Glance™
- Storing
- Entertaining
- Flexible Living
- De-Stressing

Optional Finished Lower Level
adds 1543 Sq. Ft.

Rec. Room 15⁴ x 17⁰

Media Room 18⁴ x 22⁰

Br.4 13⁰ x 11⁰

Bar 11⁰ x 11⁰

Exercise Room 16⁸ x 12⁰

UP

UNFINISHED STORAGE 931 SQ. FT.

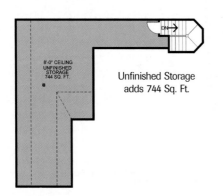

8'-0" CEILING
UNFINISHED STORAGE 744 SQ. FT.

DN

Unfinished Storage
adds 744 Sq. Ft.

96

www.designbasics.com/9JJ

the
Georgetown
Showcase
9262-9JJ

price code 26

Total Square Ft. **2640**

Standard Foundation: Basement

Livability
at a Glance™

- Storing
- Entertaining
- Flexible Living
- De-Stressing

Optional Finished Lower Level
adds 696 Sq. Ft.

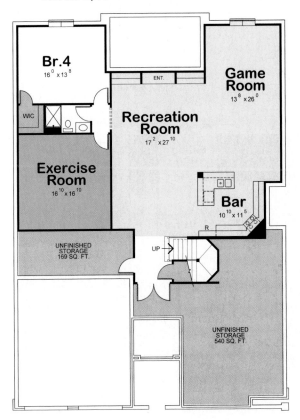

Br. 4
16⁰ x 13⁸

WIC

Game
Room
13⁸ x 26⁰

ENT.

Recreation
Room
17² x 27¹⁰

Exercise
Room
16¹⁰ x 16¹⁰

Bar
10¹⁰ x 11⁵

R

UP

UNFINISHED
STORAGE
169 SQ. FT.

UNFINISHED
STORAGE
540 SQ. FT.

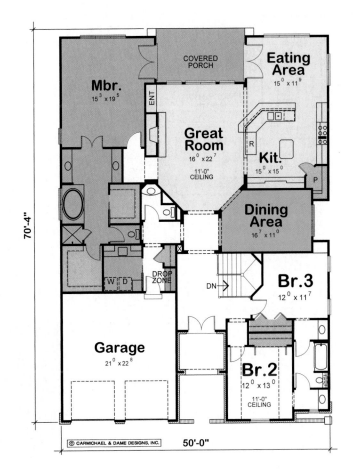

COVERED
PORCH

Eating
Area
15⁰ x 11⁹

Mbr.
15³ x 19⁵

ENT

Great
Room
16⁰ x 22⁷
11'-0"
CEILING

Kit.
15⁰ x 15⁰

R

P

Dining
Area
16⁷ x 11⁰

W D

DROP
ZONE

DN

Br. 3
12⁰ x 11⁷

Garage
21⁰ x 22⁸

Br. 2
12⁰ x 13⁰
11'-0"
CEILING

70'-4"

50'-0"

© CARMICHAEL & DAME DESIGNS, INC.

the
Haskell
42006-9JJ
pricecode 26

Total Square Ft.   **2641**

Standard Foundation: Slab

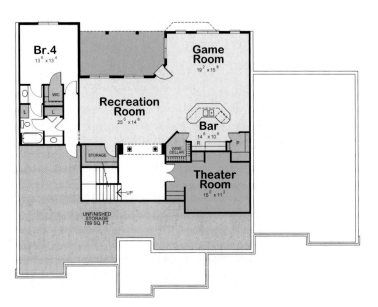

Optional Finished Lower Level
adds 1692 Sq. Ft.

Livability
at a Glance™

Storing
Entertaining
Flexible Living
De-Stressing

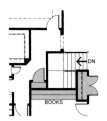

Optional Basement
Stair Location

Optional Fourth Bedroom

www.designbasics.com/9JJ

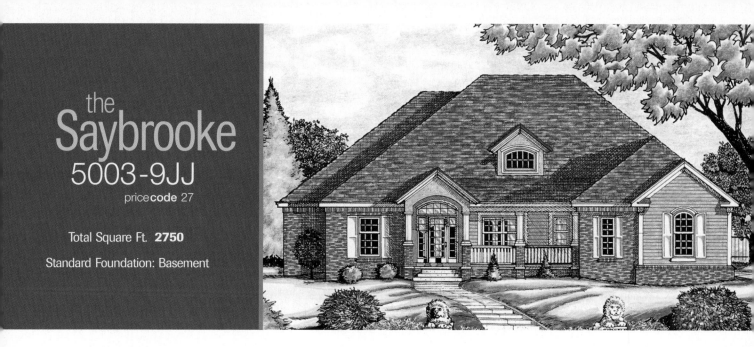

the
Saybrooke
5003-9JJ
price code 27

Total Square Ft. **2750**

Standard Foundation: Basement

Livability
at a Glance™

- Storing
- Entertaining
- Flexible Living
- De-Stressing

11'-0" CEILING
Bfst.
12⁰ x 12⁴

Br.2
12⁰ x 12⁰

Grt. Rm.
16⁰ x 23⁴

DESK
SNACK BAR

Kit.
14⁰ x 14⁴

Mbr.
17⁰ x 14⁷

11'-0" CEILING

P.

P.

R.

P.

Br.3
12⁰ x 12⁰

L.

WHIRL-POOL

DN

L.

W.
D.

11'-0" CEILING
E.

**Br.4/
Opt. Den**
12⁰ x 14⁰

Din. Rm.
12⁰ x 16⁰

COVERED PORCH

Gar.
22⁰ x 31⁰

72'-8"

66'-8"

© design basics inc.

the
Palomar
24208-9JJ
price code 27

Total Square Ft. **2766**

Standard Foundation: Slab

Livability
at a Glance™
- Storing
- Entertaining
- Flexible Living
- De-Stressing

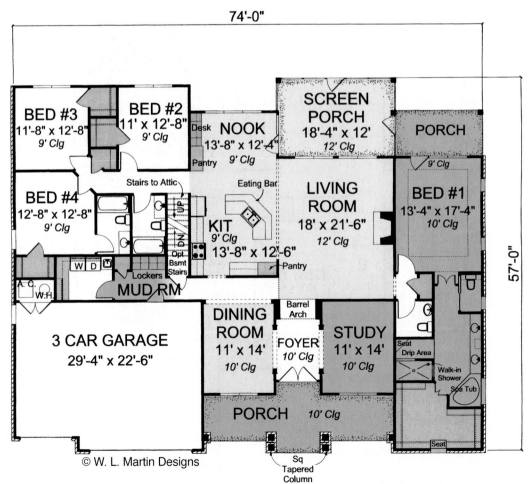

74'-0"

57'-0"

BED #3
11'-8" x 12'-8"
9' Clg

BED #2
11' x 12'-8"
9' Clg

Desk

NOOK
13'-8" x 12'-4"
9' Clg

Pantry

SCREEN
PORCH
18'-4" x 12'
12' Clg

PORCH
9' Clg

Stairs to Attic

BED #4
12'-8" x 12'-8"
9' Clg

Eating Bar

UP
DN

Opt
Bsmt
Stairs

KIT
9' Clg
13'-8" x 12'-6"

Pantry

LIVING
ROOM
18' x 21'-6"
12' Clg

BED #1
13'-4" x 17'-4"
10' Clg

W D

Lockers

MUD RM

A. C.
W.H.

3 CAR GARAGE
29'-4" x 22'-6"

DINING
ROOM
11' x 14'
10' Clg

Barrel
Arch

FOYER
10' Clg

STUDY
11' x 14'
10' Clg

Seat
Drip Area

Walk-in
Shower

Spa Tub

Seat

PORCH   10' Clg

Seat

© W. L. Martin Designs

Sq
Tapered
Column

the
Behrens Court

29509-9JJ

pricecode 29

Total Square Ft. **2956**

Standard Foundation: Slab

Livability
at a Glance™

- Storing
- Entertaining
- Flexible Living
- De-Stressing

Family 16⁰×16⁰ 13'-0 CEILING

Covered Patio

Sitting 7⁹×10⁰

Master 18⁸×15⁹ 12'-0 CEILING

Morning 13⁰×12⁰

Living 21⁴×18⁰

HIS WIC

HER WIC

Kitchen 13⁸×13⁸

CATHEDRAL CEILING

Entry 7⁸×11⁰ 13'-0 CEILING

Garage 23⁴×18⁴

3 Car Garage 23⁴×45⁰

WIC

Dining 12⁰×14⁰ 13'-0 CEILING

Flex 12⁰×15⁰ 13'-0 CEILING

Covered Stoop

©prime designs, inc.

78'-4"

108'-9"

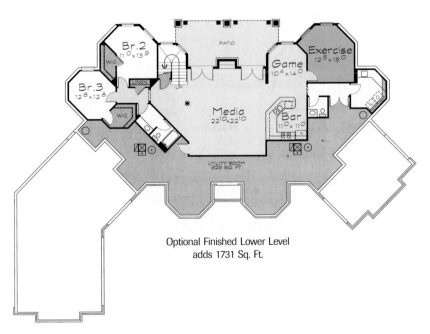

Br. 2 11⁰×13⁹

WIC

Patio

Game 10⁴×14⁰

Exercise 12⁵×15⁰

Br. 3 12⁸×12⁸

LINEN

WIC

Media 22¹⁰×22¹⁰

Bar 11⁰×11⁰

UTILITY ROOM 928 SQ. FT.

Optional Finished Lower Level
adds 1731 Sq. Ft.

Optional Basement
Stair Location

DN

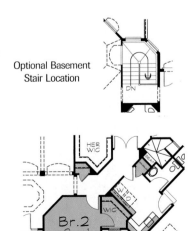

HER WIC

WIC

Br. 2 12⁰×15¹ 13'-0" CEILING

Optional Second Bedroom

800.947.7526

101

the Proel
29096-9JJ
pricecode 29

Total Square Ft. **2962**

Standard Foundation: Basement

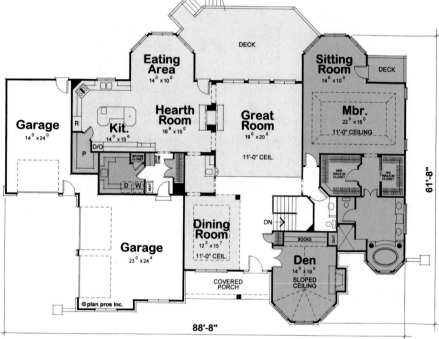

Garage
14⁰ x 24⁰

Kit.
14⁰ x 15⁰

Eating Area
14⁰ x 10⁰

Hearth Room
16⁹ x 15⁰

DECK

Great Room
19⁰ x 20⁰
11'-0" CEIL.

Sitting Room
14⁰ x 10⁰

DECK

Mbr.
22⁵ x 15⁰
11'-0" CEILING

HER WALK-IN CLOSET

HIS WALK-IN CLOSET

BROOM CLOSET

D W SEAT

P

D/O

R

61'-8"

Garage
23⁰ x 24⁴

Dining Room
12³ x 15⁷
11'-0" CEIL.

DN

BOOKS

SEAT

Den
14⁰ x 19⁰
SLOPED CEILING

COVERED PORCH

© plan pros inc.

88'-8"

Livability at a Glance

Storing
Entertaining
Flexible Living
De-Stressing

Optional Finished Lower Level
adds 2268 Sq. Ft.

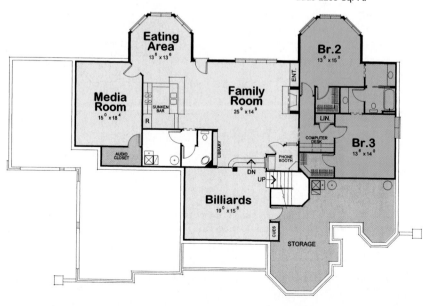

Eating Area
13⁶ x 13⁶

Media Room
15⁰ x 18⁴

SUNKEN BAR

R

AUDIO CLOSET

Family Room
25⁰ x 14⁰

LIBRARY

ENT.

LIN.

Br.2
13⁶ x 15⁰

COMPUTER DESK

PHONE BOOTH

DN

UP

Br.3
13⁶ x 14⁰

Billiards
19⁰ x 15⁸

CUES

STORAGE

www.designbasics.com/9JJ

the
Whitmore
9120-9JJ
pricecode 33

Total Square Ft. **3312**

Standard Foundation: Slab

Livability
at a Glance™

- Storing
- Entertaining
- Flexible Living
- De-Stressing

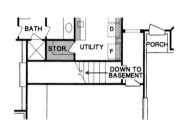

Optional Basement
Stair Location
adds 89 Sq. Ft.

BATH

STOR. UTILITY

D
F

PORCH

DOWN TO
BASEMENT

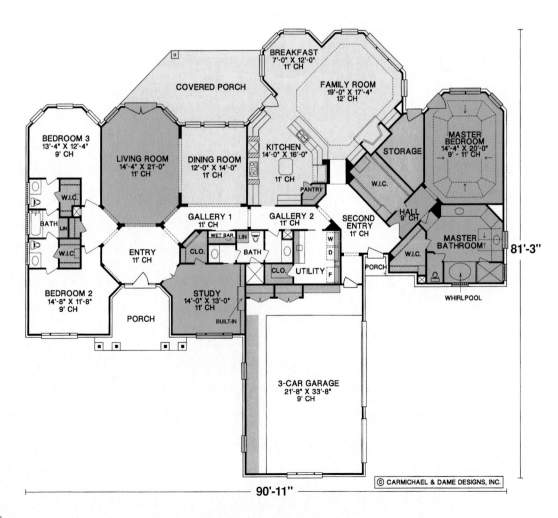

BREAKFAST
7'-0" X 12'-0"
11' CH

FAMILY ROOM
19'-0" X 17'-4"
12' CH

COVERED PORCH

BEDROOM 3
13'-4" X 12'-4"
9' CH

LIVING ROOM
14'-4" X 21'-0"
11' CH

DINING ROOM
12'-0" X 14'-0"
11' CH

KITCHEN
14'-0" X 16'-0"
11' CH

STORAGE

MASTER BEDROOM
14'-4" X 20'-0"
9' - 11' CH

W.I.C.

BATH LIN

W.I.C.

PANTRY

GALLERY 1
11' CH

GALLERY 2
11' CH

WET BAR LIN

BATH

SECOND ENTRY
11' CH

HALL
9' CH

ENTRY
11' CH

CLO.

CLO.

W
D
F

W.I.C.

MASTER BATHROOM

W.I.C.

UTILITY

PORCH

BEDROOM 2
14'-8" X 11'-8"
9' CH

STUDY
14'-0" X 13'-0"
11' CH

BUILT-IN

PORCH

WHIRLPOOL

81'-3"

3-CAR GARAGE
21'-8" X 33'-8"
9' CH

© CARMICHAEL & DAME DESIGNS, INC.

90'-11"

Getting Away
Without Leaving HOME

It's great to live at a time when women can have it all: career, home and family. But let's face it, there are times when we feel like a piece of taffy being pulled in every direction at the same time. Our need to retreat from all of the pressures – to relax and rejuvenat – has created a demand for special places to "get away to" for mini vacations – without leaving home.

As a receptionist, Marilyn has contact with the public all day long. So after she comes home and has dinner, she appreciates some solitude in her sewing room. "Several years ago, I took up quilting," Marilyn remarks. "I've made a quilt for my own bed and the bed in the guest room, plus quilts for my grown children and grandchildren. So much of what women do has to be redone and redone. But quilting provides a sense of accomplishment, something concrete to show for my time."

When planning a new home, we usually consider how the home lives, whether the traffic flows well and how functional the kitchen, baths and laundry room are. But it's also important to look at how we can carve out a place for ourselves in the home...a special private area that will serve as a personal refuge from a hectic, pressure-laden lifestyle.

To help you consider the type of "me" space you may want to incorporate in your new home, *Her Home* recently talked with six women about the special places they escape to.

At the end of a demanding day as a corporate lawyer, Jane enjoys a quiet evening reading in her den. "The wood paneling gives the room a quiet sense that is perfect for reading," Jane says. "On cooler evenings, I sit in the chair closest to the fireplace, cover up with my favorite afghan and sink into a captivating novel – while my husband watches football or basketball games in the family room."

With two active teenage children, Nancy and her husband have a lively household – filled with the sounds of computer games, action movies, "music," and groups of friends playing pool or foosball. "We love having the children close at hand," Nancy says, "but there are times when we need to get our privacy, peace and quiet. The sitting room in our master bedroom has been such a blessing – our own spot to talk or read before turning in for the night."

Delores teaches English and remedial reading in middle school. "Some days are very rewarding...when a dyslexic student grasps a way of interpreting the mixed signals he sees or a group of kids sees the relevancy in a piece of classic literature," Delores comments. "Then there are the days when a class is bored, apathetic or disruptive. Those are the times I can't wait to come home and let the jets in my whirlpool soothe my tight muscles."

Heather also has two active, noisy children: a one-year-old and a three-year-old. They keep her constantly on the go – except when her husband takes over and she escapes to her shady porch. Heather explains what makes her porch special: "I love breathing the fresh air, watching the squirrel that lives in our big oak tree and reading something besides Dr. Seuss."

Julie is a wife and mom who works full time while taking classes toward a degree in business. A sunroom in the back of her home serves as her place of refuge. "Caring for my assortment of plants and being surrounded by living things is very calming," Julie comments. "And even on cold, wintry days, I can sit and bask in the sunshine."

Joyce Vollmer Brown writes on homebuilding topics and is the author of several inspirational books including *Snapshots of Heaven*.

As you plan your new home, don't forget to carefully consider what type of quiet haven will best refresh your spirit – a sunroom, a den, a hobby room, a master bath, a sitting room or a porch?

Each of these women are fortunate enough to have carved out a spot in their homes, just for them. But what if your home, or even the one you're planning to build, doesn't include a designated "get-away" space such as a library or sunroom? Don't despair. With a bit of out-of-the-box creativity, you may discover an overlooked nook or cranny that can become your private refuge. Here are a few spots to consider:

• The space underneath a staircase for a cozy reading nook.
• An unused, or under-utilized walk-in closet for a craft area.
• Attic space that begs to be finished as a sewing room or studio.
• A small walk-up closet can become a computer nook by removing the doors.
• A decorative screen or partial wall can provide a private space at the end of a long room.

the Bethany
3123-9JJ
price**code** 15

Main Level	**1191**
Second Level	**405**
Total Square Ft.	**1596**

Standard Foundation: Basement

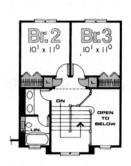

© design basics inc. 50' - 0"

48' - 0"

Mbr. 15⁰ x 12⁰ — 9'-0" CEILING
Kit. 10⁰ x 12⁰
Bfst. 10⁰ x 11²
Grt. rm. 13⁸ x 19⁴ — 10'-0" CEILING
SNACK BAR
Gar. 20⁸ x 21⁰
COVERED PORCH
TRANSOMS
TRANS.

Br. 2 10¹ x 11⁰
Br. 3 10¹ x 11⁰
OPEN TO BELOW

the Ellies Knoll
8027-9JJ
price**code** 16

Main Level	**1210**
Second Level	**405**
Total Square Ft.	**1615**

Standard Foundation: Basement

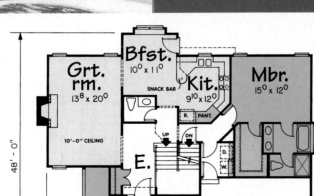

© design basics inc. 50' - 0"

48' - 0"

Grt. rm. 13⁸ x 20⁰ — 10'-0" CEILING
Bfst. 10⁰ x 11⁰
SNACK BAR
Kit. 9¹⁰ x 12⁰
Mbr. 15⁰ x 12⁰
Gar. 20⁸ x 21⁰
COVERED PORCH
E.
R. PANT.

Br. 3 10² x 11⁰
Br. 2 10² x 11⁰
OPEN TO BELOW

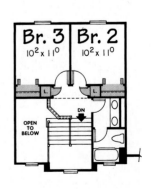

Livability
at a Glance
- Storing
- Entertaining
- Flexible Living
- De-Stressing

the Catalina
5475-9JJ
pricecode 16

Main Level	1138
Second Level	479
Total Square Ft.	1617

Standard Foundation: Basement

Mbr. 14⁰ x 12⁰
Bfst. 14⁷ x 9³
UP
SNACK BAR
Kit. 11⁰ x 11⁰
Grt.Rm. 12⁷ x 19³
DN
R.
STORAGE
W. D.
BENCH
COVERED PORCH
Gar. 21⁴ x 22⁴

54'-8"
46'-8"

© design basics inc.

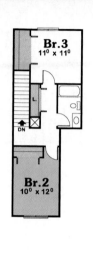

Br.3 11⁰ x 11⁰
DN
Br.2 10⁰ x 12⁰

the Millhome
24083-9JJ
pricecode 16

Main Level	1101
Second Level	527
Total Square Ft.	1628

Standard Foundation: Slab

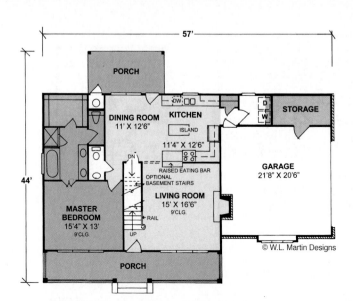

57'
44'

PORCH
DINING ROOM 11' X 12'6"
KITCHEN 11'4" X 12'6"
DW
STORAGE
D W
ISLAND
RAISED EATING BAR
OPTIONAL BASEMENT STAIRS
DN
GARAGE 21'8" X 20'6"
LIVING ROOM 15' X 16'6" 9'CLG.
MASTER BEDROOM 15'4" X 13' 9'CLG.
RAIL
UP
PORCH

© W.L. Martin Designs

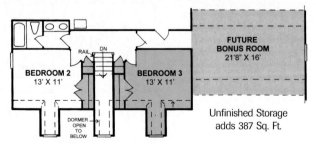

BEDROOM 2 13' X 11'
RAIL
DN
BEDROOM 3 13' X 11'
FUTURE BONUS ROOM 21'8" X 16'
DORMER OPEN TO BELOW

Unfinished Storage adds 387 Sq. Ft.

Livability at a Glance™

- Storing
- Entertaining
- Flexible Living
- De-Stressing

the Limington
43037-9JJ
price code 16

Main Level	1173
Second Level	465
Total Square Ft.	1638

Standard Foundation: Slab

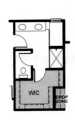

Optional Master Bath

48'-0"

42'-0"

© dbi

Mbr. 13⁰ x 15⁰
Dining Room 9⁴ x 13⁰
Kit. 8⁴ x 13⁰
WIC
L
DROP ZONE
W D
STORAGE
UP
BRM
UP
Family Room 14⁰ x 18⁰
SLOPED CEILING
ENT CENTER
Garage 19⁴ x 26⁰
R
P

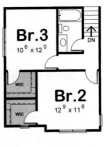

Br.3 10⁶ x 12⁰
Br.2 12⁹ x 11⁶
WIC
WIC
DN

UP
DN
UP
Family Room 14⁰ x 18⁰

Optional Basement Stair Location

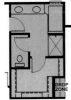

Optional Master Bath

the Tillamook
43038-9JJ
price code 16

Main Level	1173
Second Level	465
Total Square Ft.	1638

Standard Foundation: Slab

Mbr. 13⁰ x 15⁰
Dining Room 9⁴ x 13⁰
Kit. 8⁴ x 13⁰
L
DROP ZONE
W D
STORAGE
UP
BRM
UP
Family Room 14⁰ x 18⁰
SLOPED CEILING
ENT CENTER
Garage 19⁴ x 26⁰
R
P
48'-0"
42'-0"
© dbi

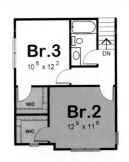

Br.3 10⁶ x 12²
Br.2 12⁹ x 11⁶
WIC
WIC
DN

UP
DN
UP
Family Room 14⁰ x 18⁰

Optional Basement Stair Location

Livability at a Glance™
Storing
Entertaining
Flexible Living
De-Stressing

the
Bellamy
3121-9JJ
price code 16

Main Level	1265
Second Level	395
Total Square Ft.	1660

Standard Foundation: Basement

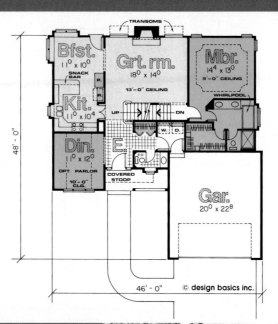

the
Maplehurst
24096-9JJ
price code 16

Main Level	1087
Second Level	584
Total Square Ft.	1671

Standard Foundation: Slab

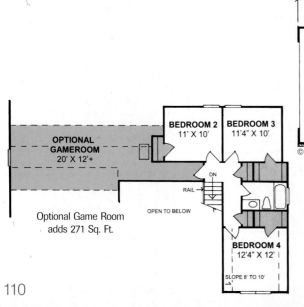

Optional Game Room
adds 271 Sq. Ft.

Livability
at a Glance

- Storing
- Entertaining
- Flexible Living
- De-Stressing

www.designbasics.com/9JJ

the Moore
24132-9JJ
pricecode 16

Main Level	**1297**
Second Level	**391**
Total Square Ft.	**1688**

Standard Foundation: Slab

Optional Gameroom
adds 236 Sq. Ft.

© W. L. Martin Designs

the Sun Valley
8095-9JJ
pricecode 16

Main Level	**1298**
Second Level	**396**
Total Square Ft.	**1694**

Standard Foundation: Basement

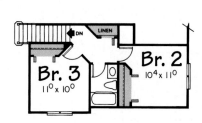

Livability
at a Glance

- Storing
- Entertaining
- Flexible Living
- De-Stressing

© design basics inc.

800.947.7526

111

the
Parnell
3089-9JJ
pricecode 17

Main Level	**1316**
Second Level	**396**
Total Square Ft.	**1712**

Standard Foundation: Basement

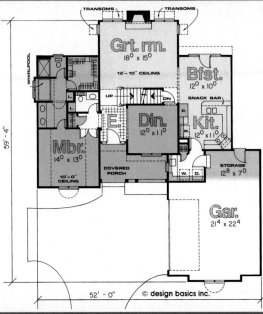

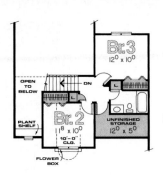

Unfinished Storage
adds 65 Sq. Ft.

the
Angel Cove
8094-9JJ
pricecode 17

Main Level	**1324**
Second Level	**391**
Total Square Ft.	**1715**

Standard Foundation: Basement

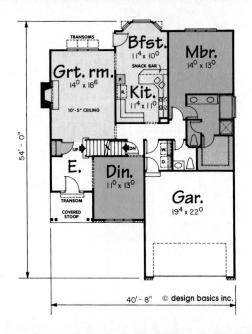

Optional Bonus Room
adds 212 Sq. Ft.

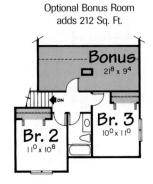

Livability
at a Glance™

- Storing
- Entertaining
- Flexible Living
- De-Stressing

www.designbasics.com/9JJ

the Sedona
5151-9JJ
pricecode 17

Main Level	**1331**
Second Level	**424**
Total Square Ft.	**1755**

Standard Foundation: Basement

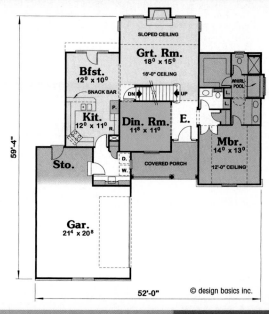

Floor plan labels:
- SLOPED CEILING
- Grt. Rm. 18⁰ x 15⁰ / 18'-0" CEILING
- Bfst. 12⁰ x 10⁰
- SNACK BAR
- Kit. 12⁰ x 11⁰
- Din. Rm. 11⁸ x 11⁰
- Sto.
- Gar. 21⁴ x 20⁸
- Mbr. 14⁰ x 13⁰ / 12'-0" CEILING
- COVERED PORCH
- WHIRLPOOL
- DN / UP
- E.
- 59'-4"
- 52'-0"
- © design basics inc.

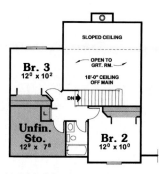

Second floor labels:
- SLOPED CEILING
- OPEN TO GRT. RM.
- 18'-0" CEILING OFF MAIN
- Br. 3 12⁰ x 10²
- Unfin. Sto. 12⁹ x 7⁸
- Br. 2 12⁰ x 10⁰
- DN

Unfinished Storage adds 121 Sq. Ft.

the Marcell
4133-9JJ
pricecode 17

Main Level	**1314**
Second Level	**458**
Total Square Ft.	**1772**

Standard Foundation: Basement

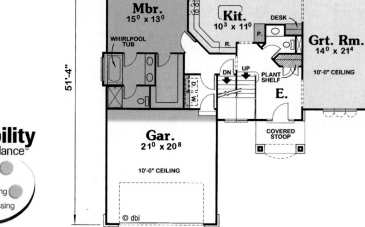

Floor plan labels:
- Bfst. 11⁰ x 13⁸
- Mbr. 15⁰ x 13⁰
- WHIRLPOOL TUB
- Kit. 10³ x 11⁰
- DESK
- Grt. Rm. 14⁰ x 21⁴ / 10'-0" CEILING
- PLANT SHELF
- E.
- DN / UP
- Gar. 21⁰ x 20⁸ / 10'-0" CEILING
- COVERED STOOP
- 51'-4"
- 52'-0"
- © dbi

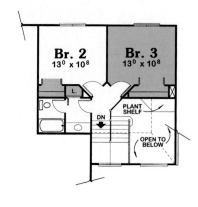

Second floor labels:
- Br. 2 13⁰ x 10⁸
- Br. 3 13⁰ x 10⁸
- PLANT SHELF
- DN
- OPEN TO BELOW

Livability at a Glance™
- Storing
- Entertaining
- Flexible Living
- De-Stressing

the Ingram
2281-9JJ
pricecode 17

Main Level	**1348**
Second Level	**430**
Total Square Ft.	**1778**

Standard Foundation: Basement

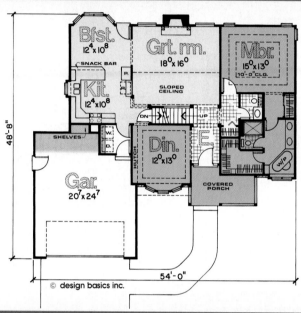

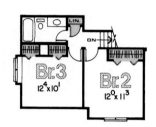

© design basics inc.

the Brittany
3385-9JJ
pricecode 17

Main Level	**1191**
Second Level	**597**
Total Square Ft.	**1788**

Standard Foundation: Basement

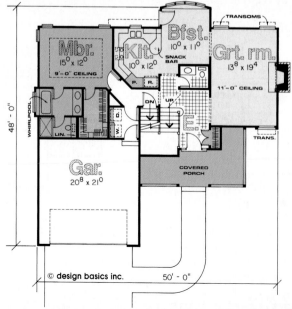

© design basics inc.

Livability at a Glance™
- Storing
- Entertaining
- Flexible Living
- De-Stressing

www.designbasics.com/9JJ

the Kelvington

5463-9JJ

pricecode 17

Main Level 1379

Second Level 419

Total Square Ft. 1798

Standard Foundation: Basement

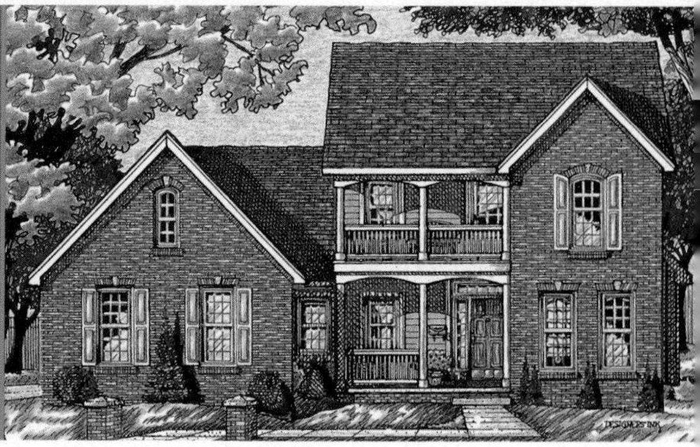

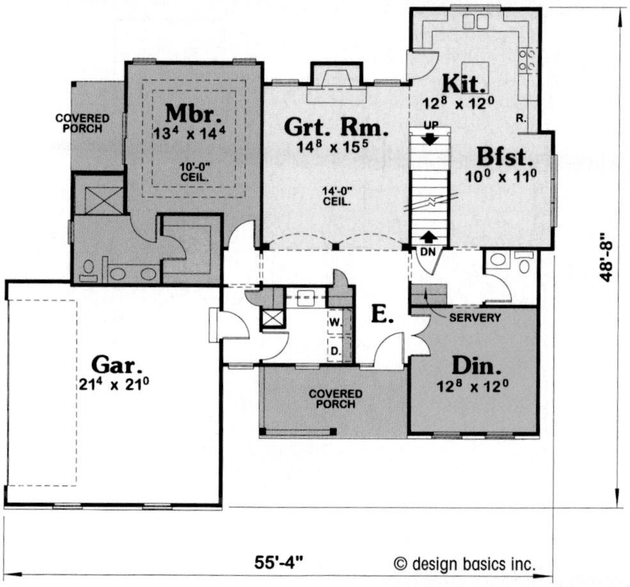

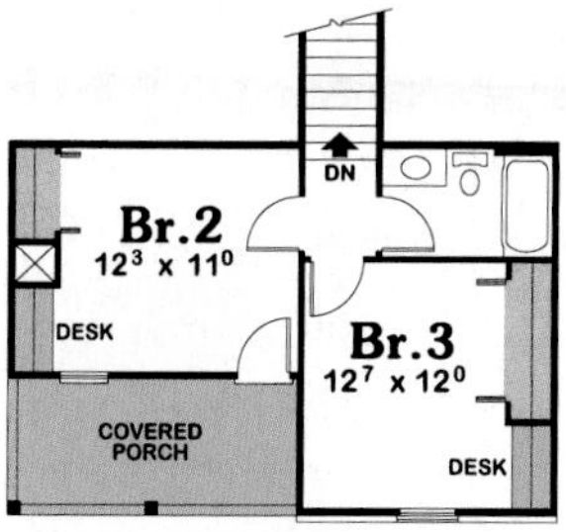

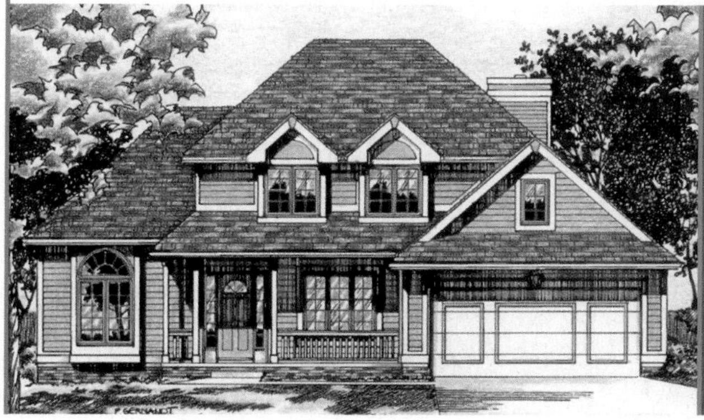

the Sayler

3076-9JJ

pricecode 17

Main Level 1348

Second Level 450

Total Square Ft. 1798

Standard Foundation: Basement

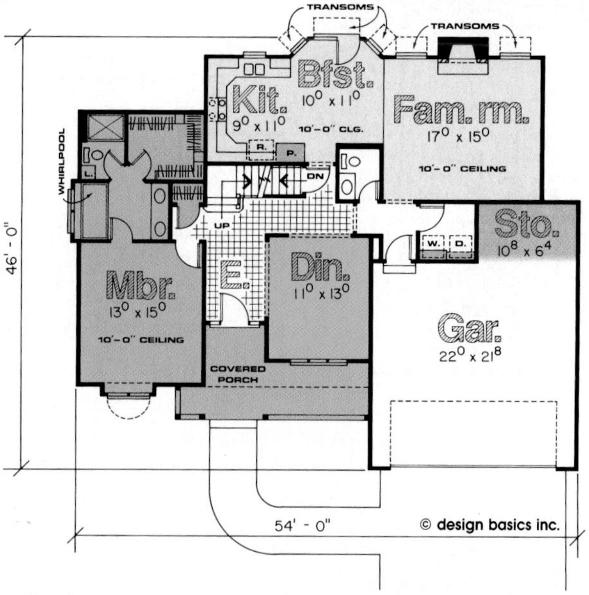

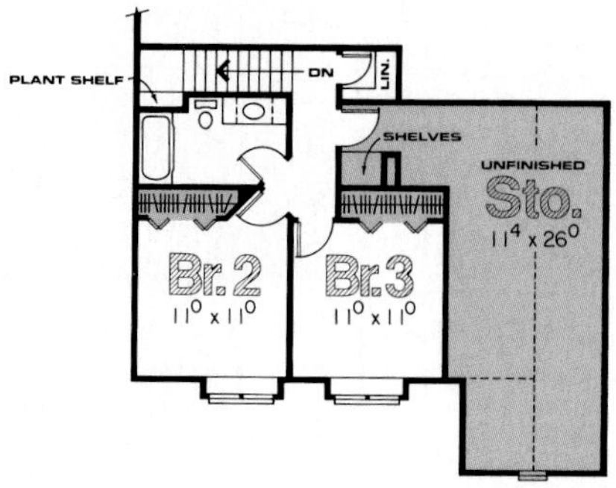

Unfinished Storage adds 351 Sq. Ft.

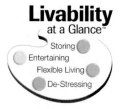

Livability at a Glance™

Storing

Entertaining

Flexible Living

De-Stressing

the Finley
5462-9JJ
price code 17

Main Level	**1331**
Second Level	**468**
Total Square Ft.	**1799**

Standard Foundation: Basement

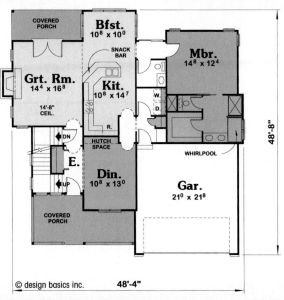

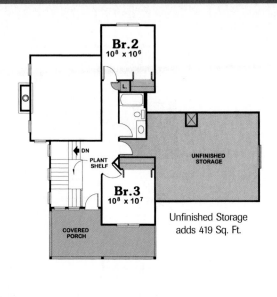

Unfinished Storage adds 419 Sq. Ft.

© design basics inc.

---

the Carriage Hills
8037-9JJ
price code 18

Main Level	**1284**
Second Level	**518**
Total Square Ft.	**1802**

Standard Foundation: Basement

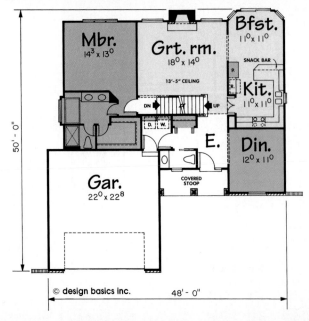

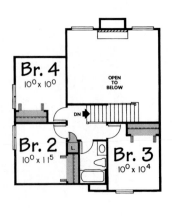

© design basics inc.

Livability
at a Glance™

Storing
Entertaining
Flexible Living
De-Stressing

www.designbasics.com/9JJ

the Weaver
8509-9JJ
price code 18

Main Level	**1302**
Second Level	**516**
Total Square Ft.	**1818**

Standard Foundation: Basement

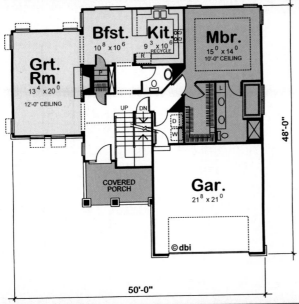

Bfst. 10⁸ x 10⁶
Kit. 9³ x 10⁶ RECYCLE
Mbr. 15⁰ x 14⁰ 10'-0" CEILING
Grt. Rm. 13⁴ x 20⁰ 12'-0" CEILING
UP DN
COVERED PORCH
Gar. 21⁸ x 21⁰
© dbi
48'-0"
50'-0"

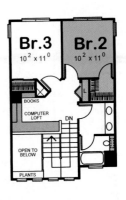

Br.3 10² x 11⁰
Br.2 10² x 11⁰
BOOKS
COMPUTER LOFT
DN
OPEN TO BELOW
PLANTS

the Pine Ridge
8096-9JJ
price code 18

Main Level	**1412**
Second Level	**425**
Total Square Ft.	**1837**

Standard Foundation: Basement

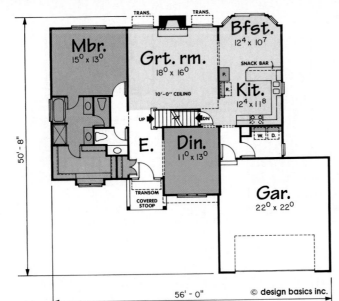

TRANS. TRANS.
Mbr. 15⁰ x 13⁰
Grt. rm. 18⁰ x 16⁰ 10'-0" CEILING
Bfst. 12⁴ x 10⁷
SNACK BAR
Kit. 12⁴ x 11⁸
UP DN
E.
Din. 11⁰ x 13⁰
W. D.
TRANSOM
COVERED STOOP
Gar. 22⁰ x 22⁰
50' - 8"
56' - 0"
© design basics inc.

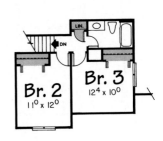

LIN.
DN
Br. 2 11⁰ x 12⁰
Br. 3 12⁴ x 10⁰

Livability at a Glance™
Storing
Entertaining
Flexible Living
De-Stressing

800.947.7526

the
Kirkwood
4646-9JJ
pricecode 18

Main Level	**1285**
Second Level	**568**
Total Square Ft.	**1853**

Standard Foundation: Basement

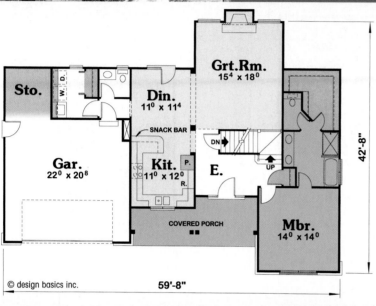

Sto.

W.D.

Din.
11⁰ x 11⁴

Grt.Rm.
15⁴ x 18⁰

SNACK BAR

Gar.
22⁰ x 20⁸

Kit.
11⁰ x 12⁰

P. R.

E.

DN

UP

42'-8"

COVERED PORCH

Mbr.
14⁰ x 14⁰

© design basics inc.

59'-8"

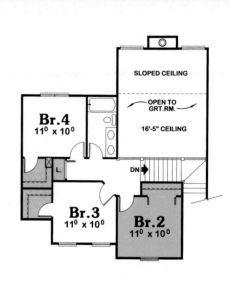

SLOPED CEILING

Br.4
11⁰ x 10⁰

OPEN TO GRT.RM.

16'-5" CEILING

L.

DN

Br.3
11⁰ x 10⁰

Br.2
11⁰ x 10⁰

the
Bermier
2236-9JJ
pricecode 18

Main Level	**1297**
Second Level	**558**
Total Square Ft.	**1855**

Standard Foundation: Basement

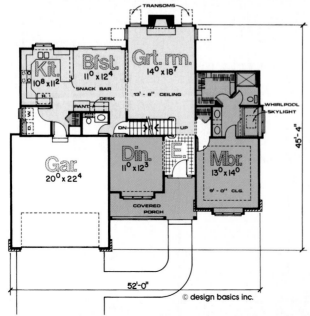

TRANSOMS

Kit.
10⁸ x11²

Bfst.
11⁰ x 12⁴

Grt. rm.
14⁰ x 18⁷

SNACK BAR

13'-8" CEILING

PANT.

DESK

D W

Gar.
20⁰ x 22⁴

Din.
11⁰ x 12³

E.

DN

UP

WHIRLPOOL SKYLIGHT

Mbr.
13⁰ x 14⁰

9'-0" CLG.

COVERED PORCH

45'-4"

52'-0"

© design basics inc.

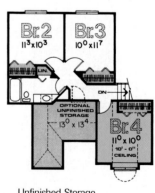

Br.2
11³x10³

Br.3
10⁰ x11⁷

LIN.

DN

OPTIONAL UNFINISHED STORAGE
13⁰ x 13⁴

Br.4
11⁰ x 10⁰
10'-0" CEILING

Unfinished Storage
adds 141 Sq. Ft.

Livability
at a Glance™

Storing
Entertaining
Flexible Living
De-Stressing

www.designbasics.com/9JJ

the Meadow Creek
8077-9JJ
pricecode 18

Main Level	**1405**
Second Level	**453**
Total Square Ft.	**1858**

Standard Foundation: Basement

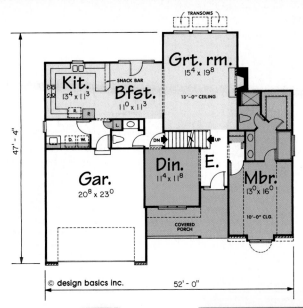

Kit.
13⁴ x 11³

SNACK BAR

Bfst.
11⁰ x 11³

Grt. rm.
15⁴ x 19⁸

13'-0" CEILING

TRANSOMS

Gar.
20⁸ x 23⁰

Din.
11⁴ x 11⁸

E.

DN UP

Mbr.
13⁰ x 16⁰

10'-0" CLG.

COVERED PORCH

47' - 4"

52' - 0"

© design basics inc.

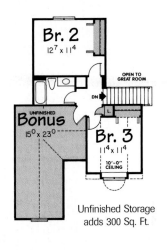

Br. 2
12⁷ x 11⁴

OPEN TO GREAT ROOM

DN

Bonus
UNFINISHED
15⁰ x 23⁰

Br. 3
11⁴ x 11⁴
10'-0" CEILING

Unfinished Storage
adds 300 Sq. Ft.

the Brook Valley
8084-9JJ
pricecode 18

Main Level	**1301**
Second Level	**564**
Total Square Ft.	**1865**

Standard Foundation: Basement

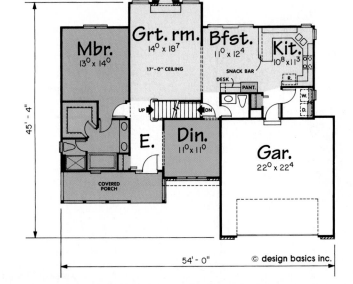

Mbr.
13⁰ x 14⁰

Grt. rm.
14⁰ x 18⁷
17'-0" CEILING

Bfst.
11⁰ x 12⁴

SNACK BAR

Kit.
10⁸ x 11³

DESK

PANT.

UP   DN

E.

Din.
11⁰ x 11⁰

Gar.
22⁰ x 22⁴

COVERED PORCH

TRANS.   TRANS.

45' - 4"

54' - 0"

© design basics inc.

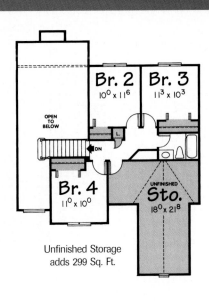

OPEN TO BELOW

Br. 2
10⁰ x 11⁶

Br. 3
11³ x 10³

DN

Br. 4
11⁰ x 10⁰

Sto.
UNFINISHED
18⁰ x 21⁸

Unfinished Storage
adds 299 Sq. Ft.

Livability
at a Glance™

- Storing
- Entertaining
- Flexible Living
- De-Stressing

the Largo
24146-9JJ
pricecode 18

Main Level	**1375**
Second Level	**492**
Total Square Ft.	**1867**

Standard Foundation: Slab

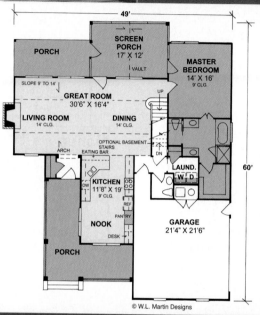

© W.L. Martin Designs

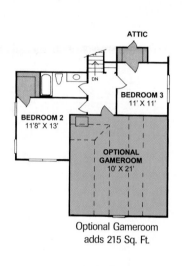

Optional Gameroom
adds 215 Sq. Ft.

the Trenton
1330-9JJ
pricecode 18

Main Level	**1421**
Second Level	**448**
Total Square Ft.	**1869**

Standard Foundation: Basement

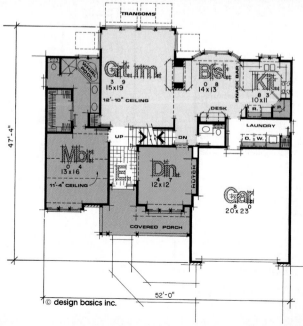

© design basics inc.

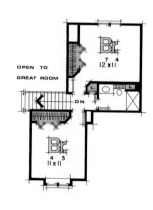

Livability
at a Glance™

- Storing
- Entertaining
- Flexible Living
- De-Stressing

www.designbasics.com/9JJ

the
Barons
24016-9JJ
pricecode 18

Main Level	**1448**
Second Level	**449**
Total Square Ft.	**1897**

Standard Foundation: Slab

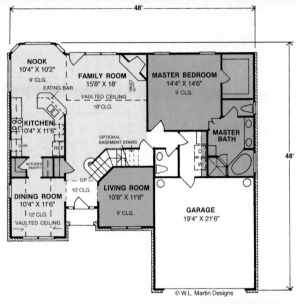

NOOK
10'4" X 10'2"
9' CLG.

EATING BAR

FAMILY ROOM
15'8" X 18'
VAULTED CEILING
18' CLG.

MASTER BEDROOM
14'4" X 14'6"
9' CLG.

KITCHEN
10'4" X 11'6"

DESK REF.

OPTIONAL
BASEMENT STAIRS

MASTER
BATH

BUTLER'S
PANTRY

UP

10' CLG.

DINING ROOM
10'4" X 11'6"
12' CLG.
VAULTED CEILING

LIVING ROOM
10'8" X 11'6"
9' CLG.

GARAGE
19'4" X 21'6"

48'

48'

© W.L. Martin Designs

BEDROOM 2
11'8" X 10'8"

OPEN TO BELOW

DN

BEDROOM 3
10'6" X 11'10"

ATTIC

the
Girard
2551-9JJ
pricecode 19

Main Level	**1486**
Second Level	**441**
Total Square Ft.	**1927**

Standard Foundation: Basement

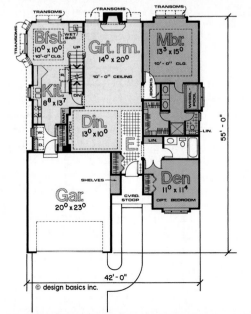

TRANSOMS

TRANSOMS

TRANSOMS

Bfst.
10⁰ x 10⁰
10'-0" CLG.

WET
BAR

Grt. rm.
14⁰ x 20⁰
10'-0" CEILING

Mbr.
13³ x 15⁰
10'-0" CLG.

Kit.
8⁸ x 13⁷

UP
DN

Din.
13⁰ x 10⁰

WHIRL
POOL

LIN.

SHELVES

Gar.
20⁰ x 23⁰

CVRD.
STOOP

Den
11⁰ x 11⁴
OPT. BEDROOM

55' - 0"

42' - 0"

© design basics inc.

Br. 3
10⁰ x 12⁰

DN

Br. 2
13² x 11¹

SEAT

Livability
at a Glance™

- Storing
- Entertaining
- Flexible Living
- De-Stressing

800.947.7526

121

the Lansing
2554-9JJ
pricecode 19

Main Level	**1517**
Second Level	**431**
Total Square Ft.	**1948**

Standard Foundation: Basement

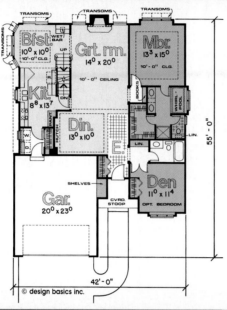

© design basics inc.

the Taylor
3063-9JJ
pricecode 19

Main Level	**1348**
Second Level	**609**
Total Square Ft.	**1957**

Standard Foundation: Basement

© design basics inc.

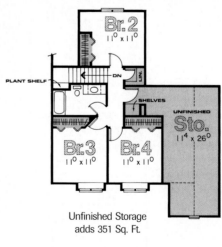

Unfinished Storage
adds 351 Sq. Ft.

Livability
at a Glance™

Storing
Entertaining
Flexible Living
De-Stressing

www.designbasics.com/9JJ

the Holly Mills
8076-9JJ
pricecode 19

Main Level	1534
Second Level	439
Total Square Ft.	1973

Standard Foundation: Basement

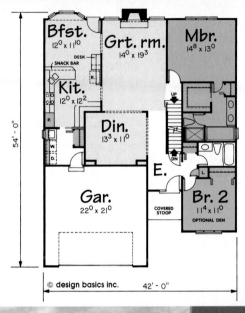

54' - 0"

42' - 0"

© design basics inc.

Bfst. 12⁰ x 11¹⁰
Grt. rm. 14⁰ x 19³
Mbr. 14⁸ x 13⁰
Kit. 12⁰ x 12²
SNACK BAR
DESK
Din. 13³ x 11⁰
UP
W. D.
Gar. 22⁰ x 21⁰
E.
DN
COVERED STOOP
Br. 2 11⁴ x 11⁰
OPTIONAL DEN
L.

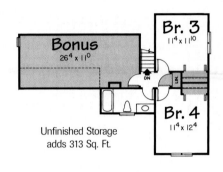

Bonus 26⁴ x 11⁰
Br. 3 11⁴ x 11¹⁰
DN
LIN.
Br. 4 11⁴ x 12⁴

Unfinished Storage
adds 313 Sq. Ft.

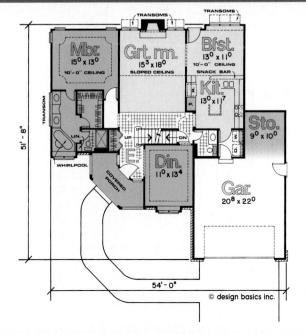

the Eldorado
2719-9JJ
pricecode 19

Main Level	1413
Second Level	563
Total Square Ft.	1976

Standard Foundation: Basement

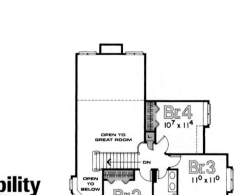

OPEN TO GREAT ROOM
Br. 4 10⁷ x 11⁴
DN
OPEN TO BELOW
Br. 2 11⁰ x 11⁰
Br. 3 11⁰ x 11⁰

Livability
at a Glance™
Storing
Entertaining
Flexible Living
De-Stressing

TRANSOMS
Mbr. 15⁰ x 13⁰ 10'-0" CEILING
Grt. rm. 15³ x 18⁰ SLOPED CEILING
Bfst. 13⁰ x 11⁰ 10'-0" CEILING SNACK BAR
Kit. 13⁰ x 11⁷
Sto. 9⁰ x 10⁰
LIN.
UP
E.
DN
WHIRLPOOL
COVERED PORCH
Din. 11⁰ x 13⁴
Gar. 20⁸ x 22⁰
TRANSOM
51' - 8"
54' - 0"
© design basics inc.

the Stendal
24154-9JJ
price code 19

Main Level	1467
Second Level	513
Total Square Ft.	1980

Standard Foundation: Slab

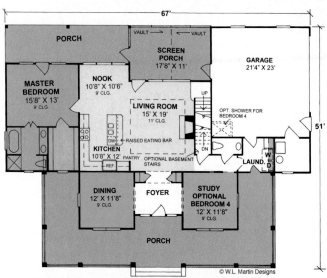

67'

PORCH

VAULT → ← VAULT

SCREEN PORCH
17'8" X 11'

GARAGE
21'4" X 23'

MASTER BEDROOM
15'8" X 13'
9' CLG.

NOOK
10'8" X 10'6"
9' CLG.

LIVING ROOM
15' X 19'
11' CLG.

UP

OPT. SHOWER FOR BEDROOM 4

51'

KITCHEN
10'8" X 12'

RAISED EATING BAR

DW
REF
PANTRY

DN

LAUND.
W D

OPTIONAL BASEMENT STAIRS

DINING
12' X 11'8"
9' CLG.

FOYER

STUDY OPTIONAL BEDROOM 4
12' X 11'8"
9' CLG.

PORCH

© W.L. Martin Designs

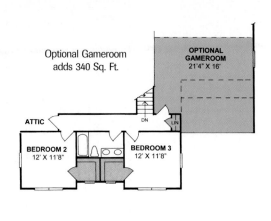

Optional Gameroom adds 340 Sq. Ft.

OPTIONAL GAMEROOM
21'4" X 16'

ATTIC

DN

LIN

BEDROOM 2
12' X 11'8"

BEDROOM 3
12' X 11'8"

---

the Buckland Showcase
9170-9JJ
price code 19

Main Level	1487
Second Level	497
Total Square Ft.	1984

Standard Foundation: Slab

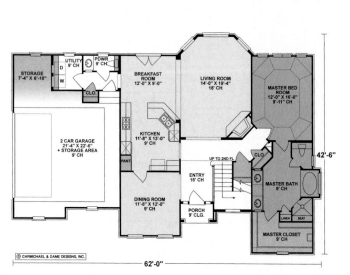

STORAGE
7'-4" X 6'-10"

UTILITY
9' CH
D W

PDWR
9' CH

CLO

BREAKFAST ROOM
12'-0" X 9'-0"

LIVING ROOM
14'-0" X 19'-4"
18' CH

MASTER BED ROOM
12'-0" X 16'-0"
9'-11" CH

2 CAR GARAGE
21'-4" X 22'-6"
+ STORAGE AREA
9' CH

KITCHEN
11'-8" X 13'-0"
9' CH

PANT

UP TO 2ND FL

CLO

ENTRY
18' CH

DINING ROOM
11'-8" X 12'-0"
9' CH

PORCH
9' CLG.

MASTER BATH
9' CH

LINEN SEAT

MASTER CLOSET
9' CH

42'-6"

62'-0"

® CARMICHAEL & DAME DESIGNS, INC.

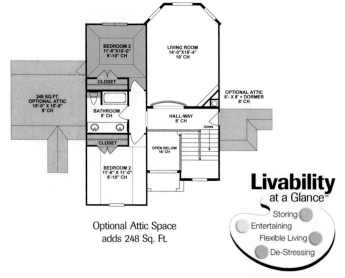

BEDROOM 3
11'-8"X10'-0"
8'-10" CH

LIVING ROOM
14'-0"X19'-4"
18' CH

CLOSET

248 SQ.FT.
OPTIONAL ATTIC
15'-0" X 15'-0"
8' CH

BATHROOM
8' CH

HALL-WAY
8' CH

OPTIONAL ATTIC
8'- X 8' + DORMER
8' CH

CLOSET

OPEN BELOW
18' CH

DOWN

BEDROOM 2
11'-8" X 11'-0"
8'-10" CH

Optional Attic Space adds 248 Sq. Ft.

Livability
at a Glance™

- Storing
- Entertaining
- Flexible Living
- De-Stressing

the Middlebury
42004-9JJ
pricecode 19

Main Level	1619
Second Level	372
Total Square Ft.	1991

Standard Foundation: Basement

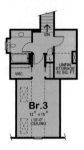

Unfinished Storage
adds 82 Sq. Ft.

Optional Finished Lower Level
adds 708 Sq. Ft.

Optional Dining Room

Optional Fourth Bedroom

© dbi

70'-8"

44'-8"

the Timber Point
8075-9JJ
pricecode 19

Main Level	1426
Second Level	568
Total Square Ft.	1994

Standard Foundation: Basement

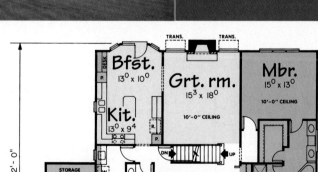

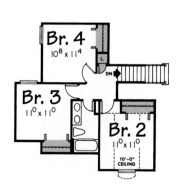

52' - 0"

54' - 8"

© design basics inc.

Livability
at a Glance™

- Storing
- Entertaining
- Flexible Living
- De-Stressing

the Stevens Woods
8053-9JJ
price code 19

Main Level	**1398**
Second Level	**598**
Total Square Ft.	**1996**

Standard Foundation: Basement

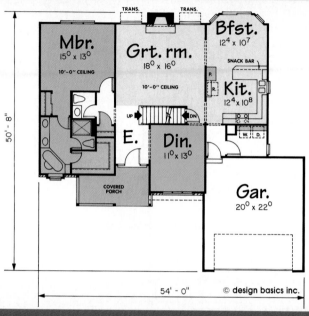

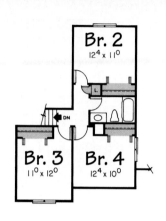

© design basics inc.

---

the Andover
1863-9JJ
price code 19

Main Level	**1421**
Second Level	**578**
Total Square Ft.	**1999**

Standard Foundation: Basement

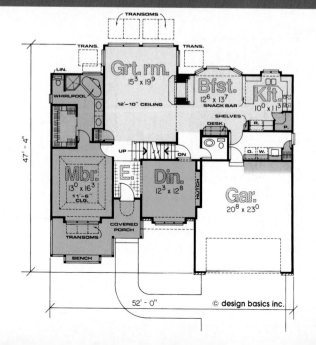

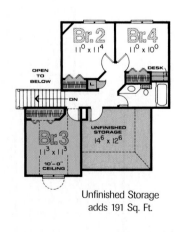

Unfinished Storage
adds 191 Sq. Ft.

© design basics inc.

Livability at a Glance™
- Storing
- Entertaining
- Flexible Living
- De-Stressing

www.designbasics.com/9JJ

the Paterson
1380-9JJ
pricecode 19

Main Level	1421
Second Level	578
Total Square Ft.	1999

Standard Foundation: Basement

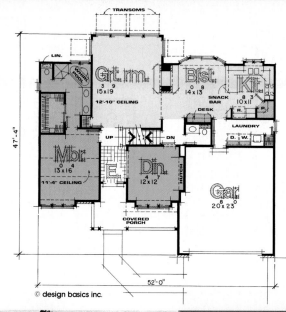

TRANSOMS

LIN.

Grt.rm.
15x19
12'-10" CEILING

Bfst.
14x8

Kit.
10x11

SNACK BAR

DESK

LAUNDRY

D. W.

UP   DN

Mbr.
13x16
11'-4" CEILING

Dn.
12x12

Gar.
20x23

COVERED PORCH

47'-4"

52'-0"

© design basics inc.

Br.
11x11

Br.
11x10

DESK

OPEN TO BELOW

DN

Br.
11x11

OPTIONAL EXPANSION

the Weldon
24136-9JJ
pricecode 20

Main Level	1486
Second Level	519
Total Square Ft.	2005

Standard Foundation: Slab

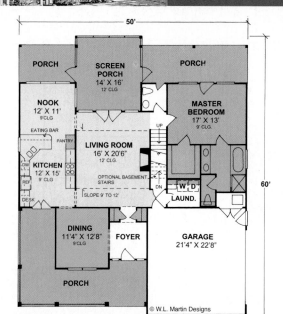

50'

PORCH

SCREEN PORCH
14' X 16'
12' CLG

PORCH

NOOK
12' X 11'
9'CLG

EATING BAR

PANTRY

MASTER BEDROOM
17' X 13'
9' CLG.

UP

LIVING ROOM
16' X 20'6"
12' CLG.

KITCHEN
12' X 15'
9' CLG

DESK

OPTIONAL BASEMENT STAIRS

SLOPE 9' TO 12'

DN

W D

LAUND.

DINING
11'4" X 12'8"
9'CLG

FOYER

GARAGE
21'4" X 22'8"

60'

PORCH

© W.L. Martin Designs

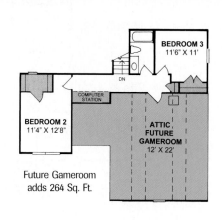

BEDROOM 3
11'6" X 11'

DN

COMPUTER STATION

BEDROOM 2
11'4" X 12'8"

ATTIC FUTURE GAMEROOM
12' X 22'

Future Gameroom adds 264 Sq. Ft.

Livability
at a Glance™

Storing
Entertaining
Flexible Living
De-Stressing

the Jordan Oaks
8035-9JJ
price code 20

Main Level	**1399**
Second Level	**617**
Total Square Ft.	**2016**

Standard Foundation: Basement

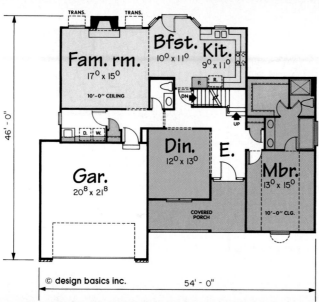

Fam. rm. 17^0 x 15^0
$10'-0''$ CEILING

Bfst. 10^0 x 11^0

Kit. 9^0 x 11^0

Gar. 20^8 x 21^8

Din. 12^0 x 13^0

E.

Mbr. 13^0 x 15^0
$10'-0''$ CLG.

COVERED PORCH

D. W.

TRANS. TRANS.

UP DN P. R.

© design basics inc.

46' - 0"

54' - 0"

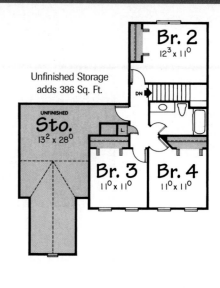

Br. 2 12^3 x 11^0

Unfinished Storage adds 386 Sq. Ft.

UNFINISHED
Sto. 13^2 x 28^0

Br. 3 11^0 x 11^0

Br. 4 11^0 x 11^0

DN

L

---

the Kiran
42000-9JJ
price code 20

Main Level	**1503**
Second Level	**516**
Total Square Ft.	**2019**

Standard Foundation: Basement

Mbr. 13^0 x 16^8
$10'-0''$ CEILING

Great Room 13^8 x 18^0

Eating Area 12^0 x 11^0
$10'-0''$ CEILING

Kit. 11^{10} x 12^0

Dining Room 11^{10} x 11^0
$10'-0''$ CEILING

Garage 23^0 x 23^4

COVERED PORCH

WIC

UP DN

W D

R P.

© dbi

OPTIONAL 3-CAR GARAGE

60'-8"

43'-4"

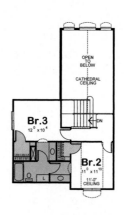

OPEN TO BELOW

CATHEDRAL CEILING

Br.3 12^0 x 10^4

Br.2 11^0 x 11^{10}
$11'-0''$ CEILING

DN

L

Livability
at a Glance™

Storing
Entertaining
Flexible Living
De-Stressing

the Bakerville

24112-9JJ
price code 20

Main Level	1470
Second Level	553
Total Square Ft.	2023

Standard Foundation: Slab

67'

SLOPE 9' TO 12'

MASTER BEDROOM
15'8" X 13'8"
12' CLG.

PORCH

SLOPE TO 18'

KITCHEN
11'8" X 12'
9' CLG.

DW

REF

LIVING ROOM
17'8" X 18'4"
18' CLG.

ISLAND EATING BAR

NOOK
11'8" X 9'8"
9' CLG.

3 CAR GARAGE
20'8" X 29'6"

41'

OPTIONAL BASEMENT STAIRS

UP
OPEN TO ABOVE
18' CLG

DN

LAUND.

W   D

DINING
13'4" X 12'
9' CLG.

PORCH

SEAT

© W.L. Martin Designs

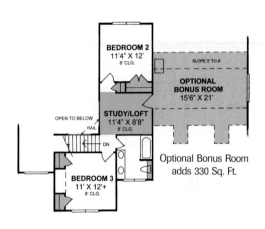

BEDROOM 2
11'4" X 12'
8' CLG.

SLOPE 5' TO 8'

OPTIONAL BONUS ROOM
15'6" X 21'

OPEN TO BELOW

STUDY/LOFT
11'4" X 8'8"
8' CLG.

RAIL

DN

BEDROOM 3
11' X 12'+
8' CLG.

Optional Bonus Room
adds 330 Sq. Ft.

the Hannifan Lane

8065-9JJ
price code 20

Main Level	1411
Second Level	618
Total Square Ft.	2029

Standard Foundation: Basement

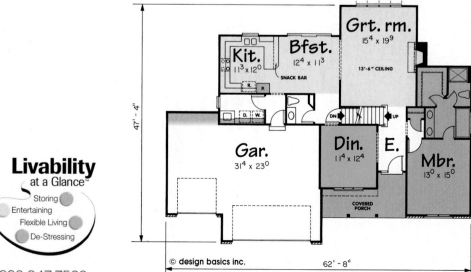

TRANSOMS

Kit.
11³ x 12⁰

Bfst.
12⁴ x 11³

Grt. rm.
15⁴ x 19⁹
13'-6" CEILING

SNACK BAR

R.   R.

D.   W.

DN

UP

Gar.
31⁴ x 23⁰

Din.
11⁴ x 12⁴

E.

Mbr.
13⁰ x 15⁰

COVERED PORCH

47' - 4"

62' - 8"

© design basics inc.

Br. 3
10⁹ x 11³

Br. 4
10⁹ x 11³

OPEN TO BELOW

L.

DN

Bonus
20⁴ x 10⁰

Br. 2
11⁴ x 11⁴

Unfinished Bonus Room
adds 214 Sq. Ft.

Livability
at a Glance™

- Storing
- Entertaining
- Flexible Living
- De-Stressing

the Amanda
3381-9JJ
pricecode 20

Main Level	1426
Second Level	611
Total Square Ft.	2037

Standard Foundation: Basement

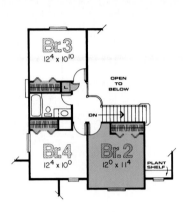

Br. 3
12⁴ x 10¹⁰

OPEN TO BELOW

DN

Br. 4
12⁴ x 10⁰

Br. 2
12⁰ x 11⁴

PLANT SHELF

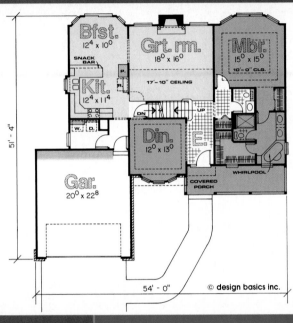

Bfst.
12⁴ x 10⁰

Grt. rm.
18⁰ x 16⁰

Mbr.
15⁰ x 15⁰
10'-0" CLG.

SNACK BAR

Kit.
12⁴ x 11⁴

17'-10" CEILING

51' - 4"

Din.
12⁰ x 13⁰

Gar.
20⁰ x 22⁸

COVERED PORCH

WHIRLPOOL

54' - 0"

© design basics inc.

the Eldridge
3064-9JJ
pricecode 20

Main Level	1414
Second Level	641
Total Square Ft.	2055

Standard Foundation: Basement

Mbr.
14⁰ x 14⁰

WHIRLPOOL

Kit.
13⁸ x 14⁰⁴

Bfst.
11⁰ x 11⁰
10'-0" CLG.

TRANSOMS

SNACK BAR

Grt. rm.
14⁰ x 21⁴

10'-0" CEILING

W. D.

LIN.

50' - 0"

Din.
11⁰ x 14⁴

Gar.
20⁸ x 21⁸

COVERED PORCH

TRANSOMS

UP

© design basics inc.   53' - 4"

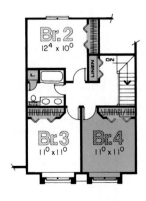

Br. 2
12⁴ x 10⁰

DN

LINEN

Br. 3
11⁰ x 11⁰

Br. 4
11⁰ x 11⁰

Livability
at a Glance
- Storing
- Entertaining
- Flexible Living
- De-Stressing

www.designbasics.com/9JJ

the Buckhead Showcase
9266-9JJ
price code 20

Main Level	**1448**
Second Level	**619**
Total Square Ft.	**2067**

Standard Foundation: Basement

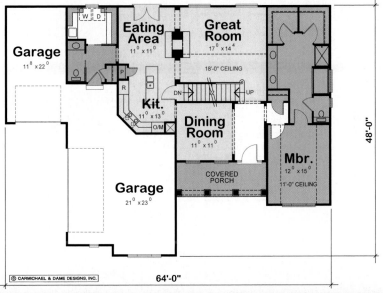

Garage
11⁸ x 22⁰

Eating Area
11⁰ x 11⁰

Great Room
17⁰ x 14⁴
18'-0" CEILING

Kit.
11⁰ x 13⁰

DN   UP

Dining Room
11⁰ x 11⁰

Garage
21⁰ x 23⁰

COVERED PORCH

Mbr.
12⁰ x 15⁰
11'-0" CEILING

48'-0"

64'-0"

© CARMICHAEL & DAME DESIGNS, INC.

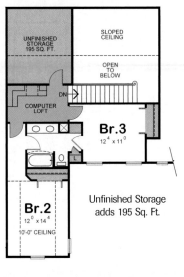

UNFINISHED STORAGE 195 SQ. FT.

SLOPED CEILING

OPEN TO BELOW

COMPUTER LOFT

DN

Br.3
12⁴ x 11⁰

Br.2
12⁰ x 14⁴
10'-0" CEILING

Unfinished Storage adds 195 Sq. Ft.

the Sierra
2745-9JJ
price code 20

Main Level	**1510**
Second Level	**579**
Total Square Ft.	**2089**

Standard Foundation: Basement

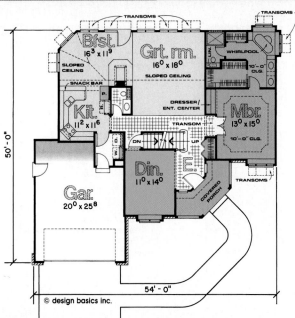

TRANSOMS

Bfst.
16³ x 11⁹

SLOPED CEILING

SNACK BAR

Grt. rm.
16⁰ x 18⁰
SLOPED CEILING

WHIRLPOOL

10'-0" CLG.

Kit.
11² x 11⁶

DRESSER / ENT. CENTER

TRANSOM

Mbr.
13⁰ x 15⁰
10'-0" CLG.

DN   UP

Din.
11⁰ x 14⁰

COVERED PORCH

Gar.
20⁰ x 25⁸

TRANSOMS

50'-0"

54'-0"

© design basics inc.

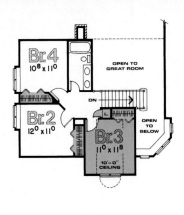

Br 4
10⁸ x 11⁰

OPEN TO GREAT ROOM

Br.2
12⁰ x 11⁰

DN

Br.3
11⁰ x 11⁸
10'-0" CEILING

OPEN TO BELOW

Livability
at a Glance™

- Storing
- Entertaining
- Flexible Living
- De-Stressing

the Newlin
2951-9JJ
price code 21

Main Level	**1406**
Second Level	**703**
Total Square Ft.	**2109**

Standard Foundation: Basement

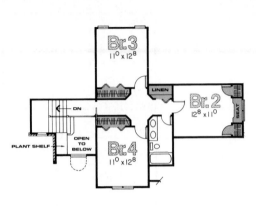

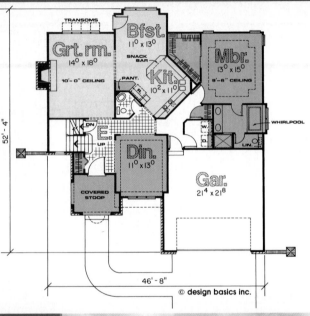

© design basics inc.

the Meredith
2312-9JJ
price code 21

Main Level	**1519**
Second Level	**594**
Total Square Ft.	**2113**

Standard Foundation: Basement

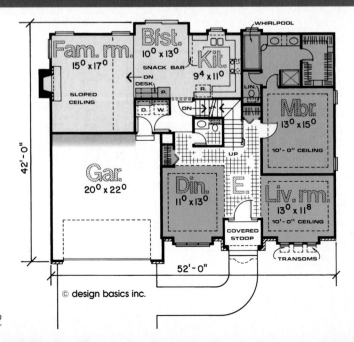

© design basics inc.

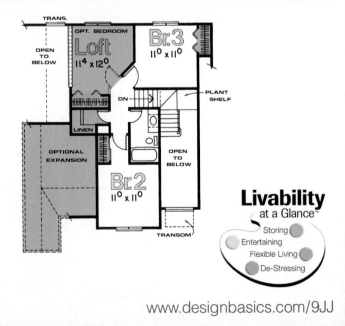

Livability
at a Glance™

Storing
Entertaining
Flexible Living
De-Stressing

the
Kerry Crossing
8054-9JJ
pricecode 21

Main Level	**1505**
Second Level	**610**
Total Square Ft.	**2115**

Standard Foundation: Basement

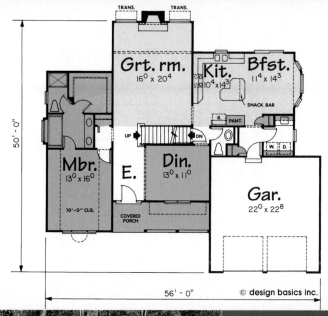

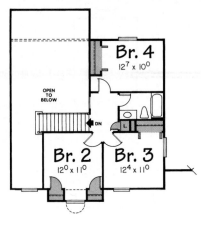

the
Prairie
2285-9JJ
pricecode 21

Main Level	**1505**
Second Level	**610**
Total Square Ft.	**2115**

Standard Foundation: Basement

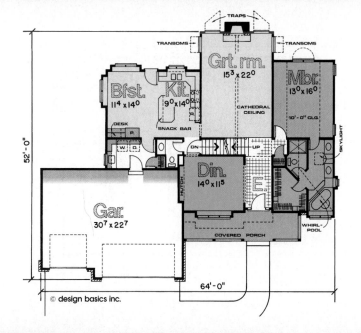

Livability
at a Glance™

- Storing
- Entertaining
- Flexible Living
- De-Stressing

the Gentry
2220-9JJ
pricecode 21

Main Level	1506
Second Level	633
Total Square Ft.	2139

Standard Foundation: Basement

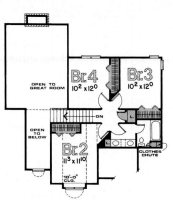

© design basics inc.

---

the Silver Springs
8124-9JJ
pricecode 21

Main Level	1569
Second Level	581
Total Square Ft.	2150

Standard Foundation: Basement

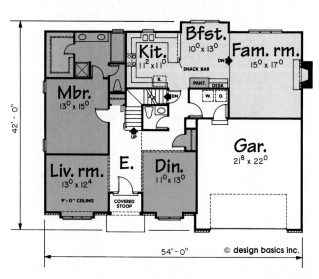

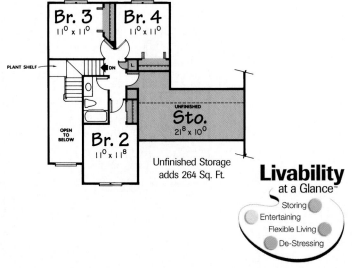

Unfinished Storage adds 264 Sq. Ft.

© design basics inc.

Livability at a Glance™
- Storing
- Entertaining
- Flexible Living
- De-Stressing

www.designbasics.com/9JJ

the Roscoe
8549-9JJ
price code 21

Main Level	**1556**
Second Level	**608**
Total Square Ft.	**2164**

Standard Foundation: Basement

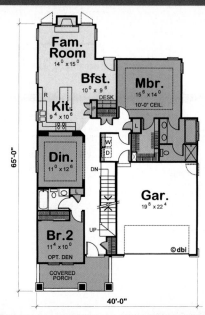

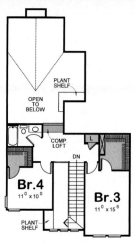

the Pepperwood
24213-9JJ
price code 21

Main Level	**1639**
Second Level	**532**
Total Square Ft.	**2171**

Standard Foundation: Slab

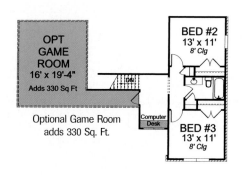

Optional Game Room
adds 330 Sq. Ft.

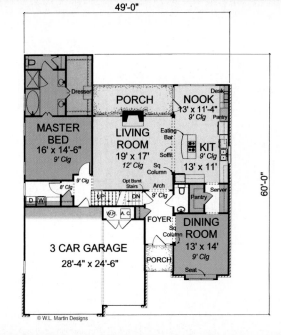

Livability at a Glance™
- Storing
- Entertaining
- Flexible Living
- De-Stressing

© W.L. Martin Designs

the Redbay
24129-9JJ
price code 21

Main Level	**1706**
Second Level	**470**
Total Square Ft.	**2176**

Standard Foundation: Slab

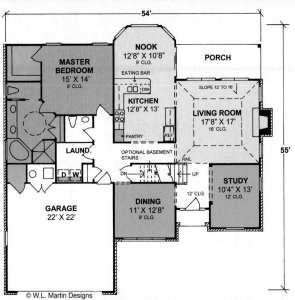

54'

NOOK
12'8" X 10'8"
9' CLG.

EATING BAR

PORCH

MASTER BEDROOM
15' X 14'
9' CLG.

KITCHEN
12'8" X 13'

DW

SLOPE 12' TO 16'

LIVING ROOM
17'8" X 17'
16' CLG.

PANTRY

REF

LAUND.

OPTIONAL BASEMENT STAIRS

D W

GARAGE
22' X 22'

DN

UP

RAIL

12' CLG.

STUDY
10'4" X 13'
12' CLG.

DINING
11' X 12'8"
9' CLG.

55'

© W.L. Martin Designs

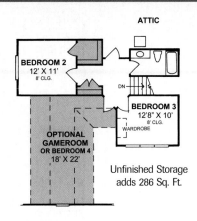

ATTIC

BEDROOM 2
12' X 11'
8' CLG.

DN

BEDROOM 3
12'8" X 10'
8' CLG.

WARDROBE

OPTIONAL GAMEROOM OR BEDROOM 4
18' X 22'

Unfinished Storage
adds 286 Sq. Ft.

the Oak Crest Manor
9180-9JJ
price code 22

Main Level	**1776**
Second Level	**461**
Total Square Ft.	**2237**

Standard Foundation: Slab

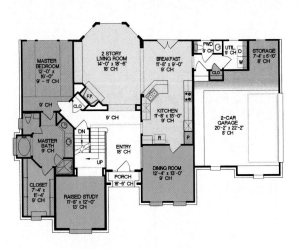

MASTER BEDROOM
12'-0" x 16'-0"
9' - 11' CH

2 STORY LIVING ROOM
14'-0" x 18'-6"
18' CH

BREAKFAST
11'-8" x 9'-0"
9' CH

PWD
9' CH

UTIL
9' CH

D
W

STORAGE
7'-4" x 6'-10"
8' CH

FP.

CLO

9' CH

KITCHEN
11'-8" x 15'-0"
9' CH

2-CAR GARAGE
20'-2" x 22'-2"
8' CH

DN

MASTER BATH
9' CH

ENTRY
18' CH

UP

R.

P

DINING ROOM
12'-4" x 13'-0"
9' CH

CLOSET
7'-4" x 11'-4"
9' CH

RAISED STUDY
11'-8" x 12'-0"
13' CH

PORCH
16'-6" CH

63'-3"

© CARMICHAEL & DAME DESIGNS, INC.

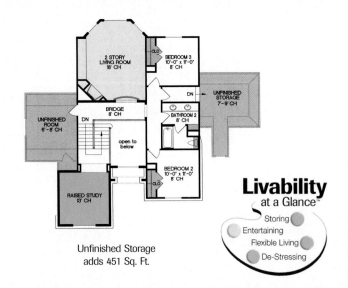

2 STORY LIVING ROOM
18' CH

CLO

BEDROOM 3
10'-0" x 11'-0"
8' CH

DN

UNFINISHED STORAGE
7'-9" CH

UNFINISHED ROOM
6'-8" CH

BRIDGE
8' CH

DN

BATHROOM 2
8' CH

open to below

BEDROOM 2
10'-0" x 11'-0"
8' CH

CLO

RAISED STUDY
13' CH

48'-7 1/2"

Unfinished Storage
adds 451 Sq. Ft.

Livability
at a Glance™

Storing
Entertaining
Flexible Living
De-Stressing

www.designbasics.com/9JJ

the Fillmore
24118-9JJ
pricecode 22

Main Level	1455
Second Level	786
Total Square Ft.	2241

Standard Foundation: Slab

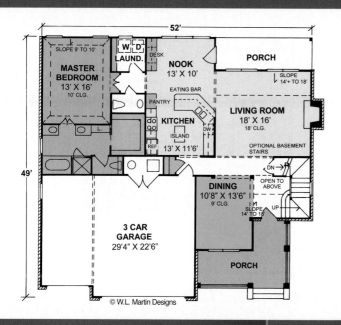

52'

49'

SLOPE 9' TO 10'

W D LAUND.

DESK

NOOK 13' X 10'

PORCH

MASTER BEDROOM 13' X 16' 10' CLG.

SLOPE 14'+ TO 18'

EATING BAR

PANTRY

LIVING ROOM 18' X 16' 18' CLG.

KITCHEN ISLAND 13' X 11'6"

DW

REF

OPTIONAL BASEMENT STAIRS

DN

OPEN TO ABOVE

UP

DINING 10'8" X 13'6" 9' CLG.

SLOPE 14' TO 18'

3 CAR GARAGE 29'4" X 22'6"

PORCH

© W.L. Martin Designs

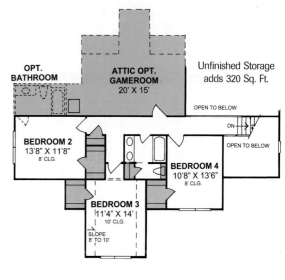

OPT. BATHROOM

ATTIC OPT. GAMEROOM 20' X 15'

Unfinished Storage adds 320 Sq. Ft.

OPEN TO BELOW

BEDROOM 2 13'8" X 11'8" 8' CLG.

DN

OPEN TO BELOW

BEDROOM 4 10'8" X 13'6" 8' CLG.

BEDROOM 3 11'4" X 14' 10' CLG.

SLOPE 8' TO 10'

the Bardel
24004-9JJ
pricecode 22

Main Level	1568
Second Level	680
Total Square Ft.	2248

Standard Foundation: Slab

50'

48'

MASTER SUITE 15'4" X 14'6" 9' CLG.

FAMILY ROOM 15'8" X 18' VOLUME CLG.

VAULT

NOOK 11'4" X 10'8"

EATING BAR

KITCHEN 11'4" X 12'

DESK

LINEN

D W

OPTIONAL BASEMENT STAIRS

RAIL

UP

LIVING ROOM 11'8" X 12'6" 9' CLG.

12' CLG.

BUTLER'S PANTRY

WALK-IN PANTRY

DINING ROOM 11'4" X 12'6" 15' CLG.

GARAGE 19'4" X 21'6"

VAULT

VAULT

© W. L. Martin Designs

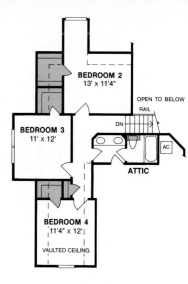

BEDROOM 2 13' x 11'4"

OPEN TO BELOW

RAIL

BEDROOM 3 11' x 12'

DN

AC

ATTIC

BEDROOM 4 11'4" x 12' VAULTED CEILING

Livability at a Glance™

- Storing
- Entertaining
- Flexible Living
- De-Stressing

the Pawnee Point
8012-9JJ
price code 22

Main Level	**1530**
Second Level	**736**
Total Square Ft.	**2266**

Standard Foundation: Basement

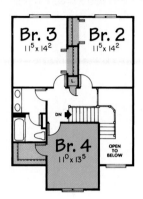

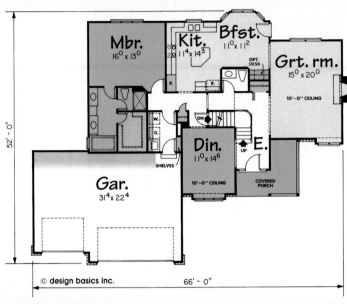

© design basics inc.

the Chandler
1554-9JJ
price code 22

Main Level	**1551**
Second Level	**725**
Total Square Ft.	**2276**

Standard Foundation: Basement

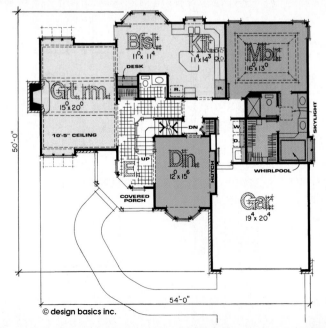

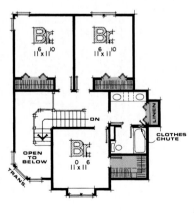

© design basics inc.

Livability
at a Glance™

- Storing
- Entertaining
- Flexible Living
- De-Stressing

www.designbasics.com/9JJ

the Ashville
2811-9JJ
price code 22

Main Level	**1570**
Second Level	**707**
Total Square Ft.	**2277**

Standard Foundation: Basement

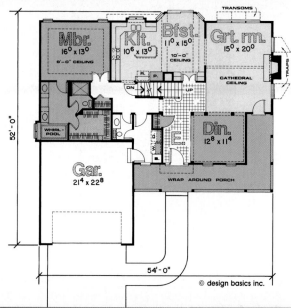

Mbr. 16⁰ x 13⁰ — 8'-0" ceiling
Kit. 10⁶ x 13⁰
Bfst. 11⁰ x 15⁰ — 10'-0" ceiling
Grt. rm. 15⁰ x 20⁰ — CATHEDRAL CEILING
TRANSOMS
Din. 12⁸ x 11⁴
WHIRL-POOL
Gar. 21⁴ x 22⁸
WRAP AROUND PORCH
52'-0"
54'-0"

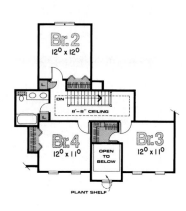

Br. 2 12⁰ x 12⁰
Br. 4 12⁰ x 11⁰
Br. 3 12⁰ x 11⁰
OPEN TO BELOW
8'-8" CEILING
PLANT SHELF

© design basics inc.

the Tanner
3249-9JJ
price code 22

Main Level	**1597**
Second Level	**685**
Total Square Ft.	**2282**

Standard Foundation: Basement

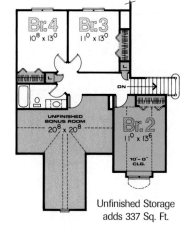

Br. 4 10⁸ x 13⁰
Br. 3 11⁰ x 13⁰
Br. 2 11⁰ x 13⁶ — 10'-0" CLG.
UNFINISHED BONUS ROOM 20⁸ x 20⁸
DN

Unfinished Storage adds 337 Sq. Ft.

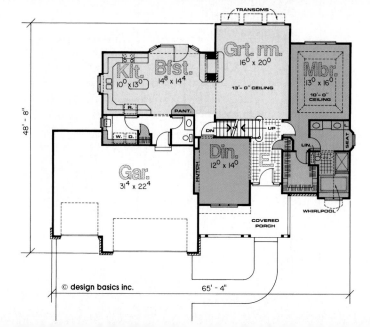

Kit. 10⁰ x 13⁰
Bfst. 14⁸ x 14⁴
Grt. rm. 16⁰ x 20⁰ — 13'-0" CEILING
TRANSOMS
Mbr. 13⁰ x 16⁰ — 10'-0" CEILING
Din. 12⁰ x 14⁰
PANT.
Gar. 31⁴ x 22⁴
COVERED PORCH
WHIRLPOOL
48'-8"
65'-4"

© design basics inc.

Livability
at a Glance™
- Storing
- Entertaining
- Flexible Living
- De-Stressing

the Douglas
3020-9JJ
price code 22

Main Level	1651
Second Level	634
Total Square Ft.	2285

Standard Foundation: Basement

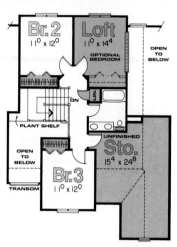

Unfinished Storage
adds 337 Sq. Ft.

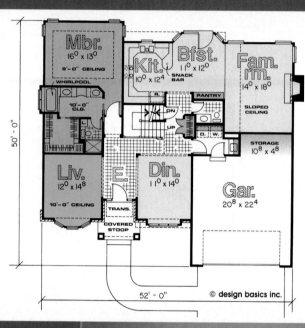

© design basics inc.

---

the Aurora
2836-9JJ
price code 23

Main Level	1654
Second Level	654
Total Square Ft.	2308

Standard Foundation: Basement

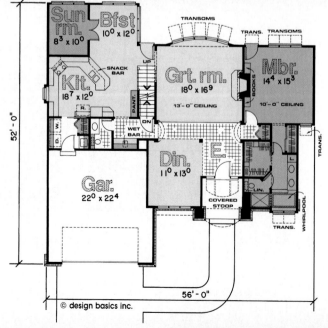

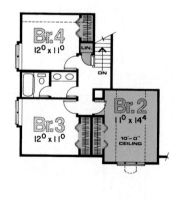

© design basics inc.

Livability
at a Glance™

Storing
Entertaining
Flexible Living
De-Stressing

www.designbasics.com/9JJ

the Autumn Hills
8055-9JJ
price code 23

Main Level	**1620**
Second Level	**702**
Total Square Ft.	**2322**

Standard Foundation: Basement

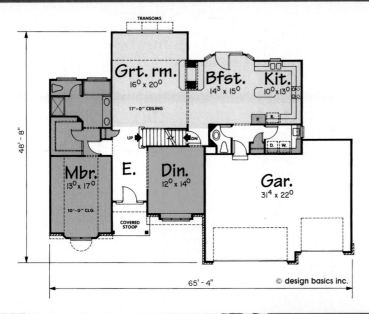

TRANSOMS

Grt. rm. 16⁰ x 20⁰
17'-0" CEILING

Bfst. 14³ x 15⁰

Kit. 10⁰ 13⁰

Mbr. 13⁰ x 17⁰
10'-0" CLG.

E.

Din. 12⁰ x 14⁰

Gar. 31⁴ x 22⁰

UP   DN

COVERED STOOP

48' - 8"

65' - 4"

© design basics inc.

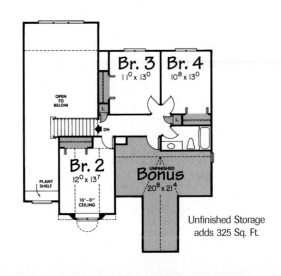

OPEN TO BELOW

Br. 3 11⁰ x 13⁰

Br. 4 10⁸ x 13⁰

DN

Br. 2 12⁰ x 13⁷
10'-0" CEILING

PLANT SHELF

Bonus 20⁸ x 21⁴
UNFINISHED

Unfinished Storage adds 325 Sq. Ft.

the Julian
24204-9JJ
price code 23

Main Level	**1758**
Second Level	**576**
Total Square Ft.	**2334**

Standard Foundation: Slab

68'-0"

BED #1 13'-4" x 18' 9' Clg

PORCH

SCREEN PORCH 18' x 10' 9' Clg

3 CAR GARAGE 21'-4" x 28'

NOOK 10'-8" x 10'-4" 9' Clg

3 Way Gas Fireplace

LIVING ROOM 14' x 20'-4" 11' Clg

Opt Shower For Bed. # 4

W.H.

Seat

Pantry

KIT 10'-8" x 12'

Eating Bar

Opt Bsmt Stairs

UP

DN

W D

9' Clg

54' - 2"

DINING ROOM 12' x 14' 9' Clg

Arch 9' Clg

FOYER

STUDY/ OPT BED #4 12' x 14' 9' Clg

PORCH

© W.L. Martin Designs

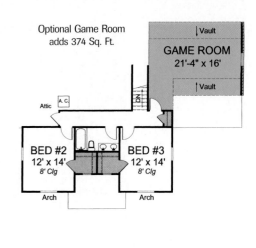

Optional Game Room adds 374 Sq. Ft.

Vault

GAME ROOM 21'-4" x 16'

Vault

Attic

A. C.

DN

BED #2 12' x 14' 8' Clg

BED #3 12' x 14' 8' Clg

Arch

Arch

Livability
at a Glance™
- Storing
- Entertaining
- Flexible Living
- De-Stressing

the Bowden
5148-9JJ
price code 23

Main Level	**1665**
Second Level	**674**
Total Square Ft.	**2339**

Standard Foundation: Basement

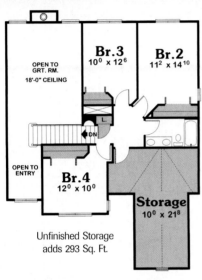

Br.3 $10^0 \times 12^6$

Br.2 $11^2 \times 14^{10}$

OPEN TO GRT. RM. 18'-0" CEILING

OPEN TO ENTRY

Br.4 $12^0 \times 10^0$

Storage $10^0 \times 21^8$

Unfinished Storage adds 293 Sq. Ft.

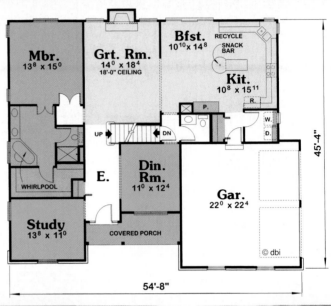

Mbr. $13^8 \times 15^0$

Grt. Rm. $14^0 \times 18^4$ 18'-0" CEILING

Bfst. $10^{10} \times 14^8$

RECYCLE SNACK BAR

Kit. $10^8 \times 15^{11}$

E.

Din. Rm. $11^0 \times 12^4$

Gar. $22^0 \times 22^4$

WHIRLPOOL

Study $13^8 \times 11^0$

COVERED PORCH

© dbi

45'-4"

54'-8"

the Ambrose
2701-9JJ
price code 23

Main Level	**1701**
Second Level	**639**
Total Square Ft.	**2340**

Standard Foundation: Basement

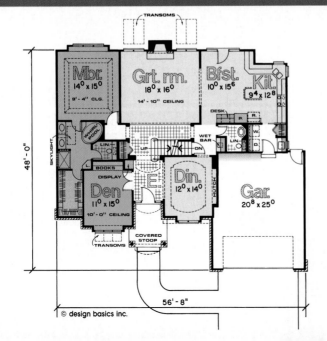

TRANSOMS

Mbr. $14^0 \times 15^0$ 9'-4" CLG.

Grt. rm. $18^0 \times 16^0$ 14'-10" CEILING

Bfst. $10^0 \times 15^6$

Kit. $9^4 \times 12^8$

WHIRLPOOL

BOOKS DISPLAY

Den $11^0 \times 15^0$ 10'-0" CEILING

E

Din. $12^0 \times 14^0$

Gar. $20^8 \times 25^0$

DESK

WET BAR

HUTCH

COVERED STOOP

TRANSOMS

SKYLIGHT

48'-0"

56'-8"

© design basics inc.

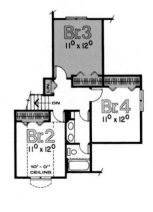

Br.3 $11^0 \times 12^0$

Br.4 $11^0 \times 12^0$

Br.2 $11^0 \times 12^0$ 10'-0" CEILING

Livability at a Glance™

Storing
Entertaining
Flexible Living
De-Stressing

www.designbasics.com/9JJ

the Manchester
1862-9JJ
pricecode 23

Main Level	**1653**
Second Level	**700**
Total Square Ft.	**2353**

Standard Foundation: Basement

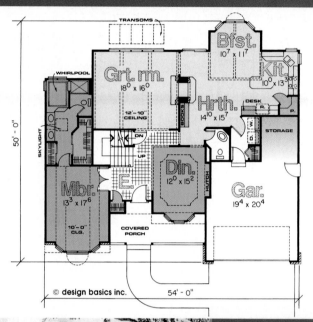

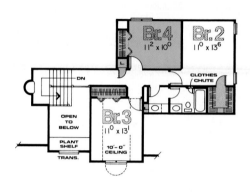

© design basics inc.

the Troon Manor
9166-9JJ
pricecode 23

Main Level	**1649**
Second Level	**712**
Total Square Ft.	**2361**

Standard Foundation: Slab

Livability
at a Glance™

- Storing
- Entertaining
- Flexible Living
- De-Stressing

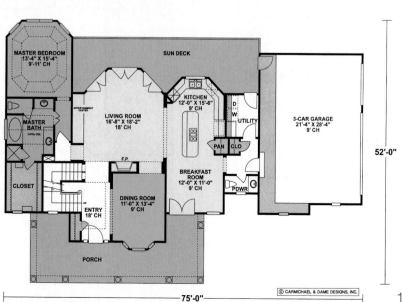

© CARMICHAEL & DAME DESIGNS, INC.

the Butler
24028-9JJ
pricecode 23

Main Level	**1616**
Second Level	**768**
Total Square Ft.	**2384**

Standard Foundation: Slab

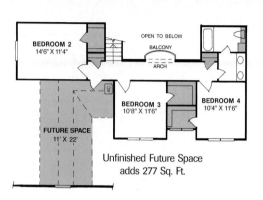

BEDROOM 2
14'6" X 11'4"

OPEN TO BELOW

BALCONY

ARCH

BEDROOM 3
10'8" X 11'6"

BEDROOM 4
10'4" X 11'6"

AC

FUTURE SPACE
11' X 22'

Unfinished Future Space
adds 277 Sq. Ft.

NOOK
11'6" X 10'

PORCH

SITTING
9' X 3'

PANTRY

EATING BAR

UP

LIVING ROOM
16'4" X 17'10"

MASTER BEDROOM
16'4" X 12'
10' CLG.

VAULT

W
D

KITCHEN
11'6" X 12'6"

APPLIANCE
GARAGE

OPEN TO ABOVE

OPTIONAL
BASEMENT
STAIRS

BALCONY ABOVE

STORAGE

AC

DN

OPTIONAL
DOOR

GARAGE
20'4" X 21'6"

DINING
10'4" X 11'6"

STUDY
10'4" X 11'6"

49'

56'

© W. L. Martin Designs

the Ashton
2203-9JJ
pricecode 23

Main Level	**1697**
Second Level	**694**
Total Square Ft.	**2391**

Standard Foundation: Basement

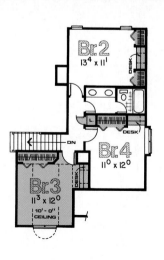

Br. 2
13⁴ x 11¹

DESK

DESK

DN

Br. 4
11⁰ x 12⁰

DESK

Br. 3
11³ x 12⁰
10' - 0"
CEILING

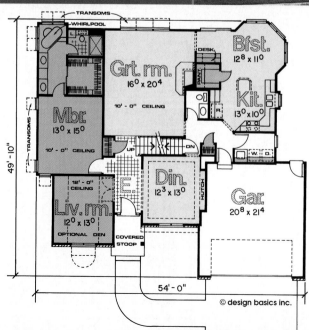

TRANSOMS

WHIRLPOOL

Grt. rm.
16⁰ x 20⁴

DESK

Bfst.
12⁸ x 11⁰

10' - 0" CEILING

PANT.

Kit.
13⁰ x 10⁰

Mbr.
13⁰ x 15⁰

R

10' - 0" CEILING

TRANSOMS

UP

W. D.

DN

Din.
12³ x 13⁰

HUTCH

Gar.
20⁸ x 21⁴

49' - 10"

12' - 0"
CEILING

Liv. rm.
12⁰ x 13⁰

OPTIONAL DEN

COVERED
STOOP

54' - 0"

© design basics inc.

Livability
at a Glance™

Storing
Entertaining
Flexible Living
De-Stressing

www.designbasics.com/9JJ

the Arant
2261-9JJ
pricecode 24

Main Level	**1733**
Second Level	**672**
Total Square Ft.	**2405**

Standard Foundation: Basement

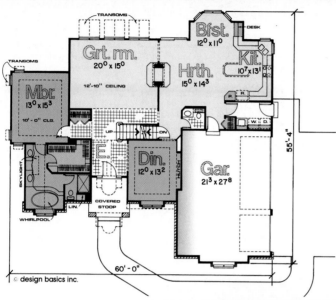

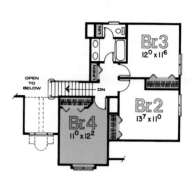

the Magrath
5150-9JJ
pricecode 24

Main Level	**1554**
Second Level	**867**
Total Square Ft.	**2421**

Standard Foundation: Basement

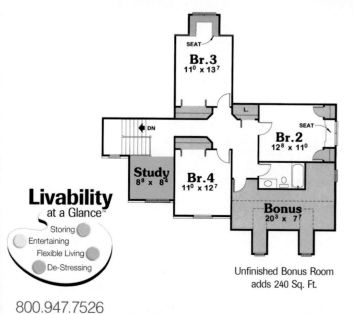

Unfinished Bonus Room adds 240 Sq. Ft.

Livability at a Glance™
- Storing
- Entertaining
- Flexible Living
- De-Stressing

the Pinehurst
2311-9JJ
price code 24

Main Level	**1829**
Second Level	**657**
Total Square Ft.	**2486**

Standard Foundation: Basement

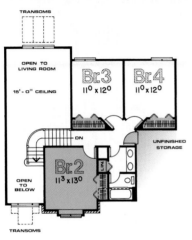

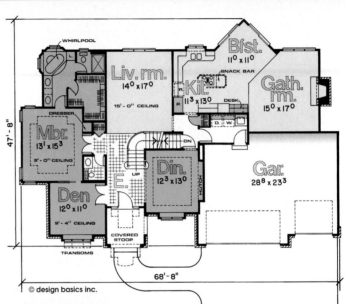

© design basics inc.

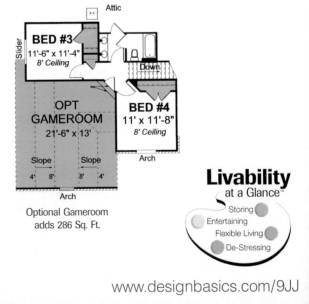

the Delaney
24182-9JJ
price code 24

Main Level	**2019**
Second Level	**468**
Total Square Ft.	**2487**

Standard Foundation: Slab

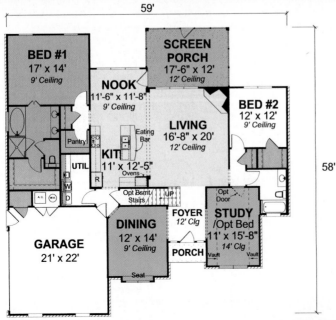

Optional Gameroom
adds 286 Sq. Ft.

Livability
at a Glance™

Storing
Entertaining
Flexible Living
De-Stressing

www.designbasics.com/9JJ

the Pinnacle
3284-9JJ
pricecode 24

Main Level	**1777**
Second Level	**719**
Total Square Ft.	**2496**

Standard Foundation: Basement

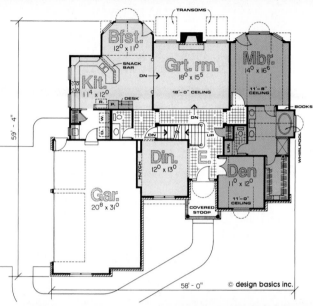

© design basics inc.

the Chasleton Manor
9173-9JJ
pricecode 25

Main Level	**1794**
Second Level	**743**
Total Square Ft.	**2537**

Standard Foundation: Slab

Livability
at a Glance™

- Storing
- Entertaining
- Flexible Living
- De-Stressing

Optional Attic
adds 245 Sq. Ft.

the Farmington
24085-9JJ
price code 25

Main Level	**1762**
Second Level	**784**
Total Square Ft.	**2546**

Standard Foundation: Slab

Optional Bonus Room adds 320 Sq. Ft.

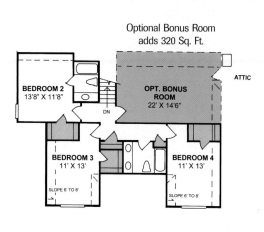

BEDROOM 2
13'8" X 11'8"

OPT. BONUS ROOM
22' X 14'6"

ATTIC

DN

BEDROOM 3
11' X 13'

SLOPE 6' TO 8'

BEDROOM 4
11' X 13'

SLOPE 6' TO 8'

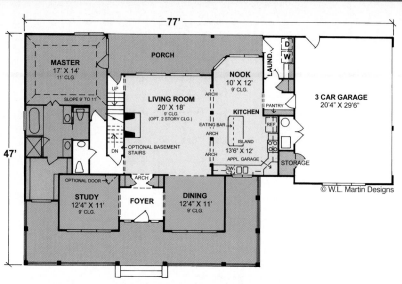

77'

47'

MASTER
17' X 14'
11' CLG.

SLOPE 9' TO 11'

PORCH

UP

LIVING ROOM
20' X 18'
9' CLG.
(OPT. 2 STORY CLG.)

NOOK
10' X 12'
9' CLG.

LAUND.

D / W

3 CAR GARAGE
20'4" X 29'6"

ARCH

EATING BAR

ARCH

KITCHEN
13'6" X 12'

ISLAND

PANTRY

REF

DN

OPTIONAL BASEMENT STAIRS

ARCH

APPL. GARAGE

DW

STORAGE

OPTIONAL DOOR

ARCH

STUDY
12'4" X 11'
9' CLG.

FOYER

DINING
12'4" X 11'
9' CLG.

© W.L. Martin Designs

the Briarwood
2956-9JJ
price code 25

Main Level	**1875**
Second Level	**687**
Total Square Ft.	**2562**

Standard Foundation: Basement

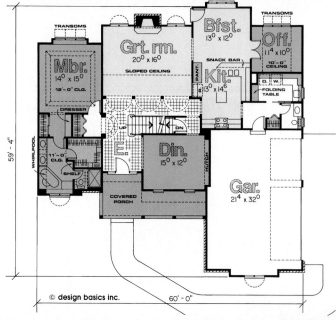

TRANSOMS

Mbr.
14' x 15'
12'-0" CLG.

Grt. rm.
20' x 16'
SLOPED CEILING

Bfst.
13' x 12'

TRANSOMS

Off.
11'4" x 10'0"
10'-0" CEILING

SNACK BAR

Kit.
13' x 14'

PANT.

D. W.

FOLDING TABLE

DRESSER

UP

DN

WHIRLPOOL

11'-0" CLG.

SHELF

E.

Din.
15' x 12'

HUTCH

COVERED PORCH

Gar.
21'4" x 32'0"

59'-4"

60'-0"

© design basics inc.

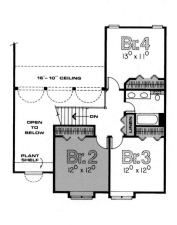

Br. 4
13'0 x 11'0

16'-10" CEILING

DN

OPEN TO BELOW

LINEN

PLANT SHELF

Br. 2
12' x 12'

Br. 3
12' x 12'

Livability at a Glance™
- Storing
- Entertaining
- Flexible Living
- De-Stressing

www.designbasics.com/9JJ

the
Riverbank
24202-9JJ
pricecode 25

Main Level	**1997**
Second Level	**585**
Total Square Ft.	**2562**

Standard Foundation: Slab

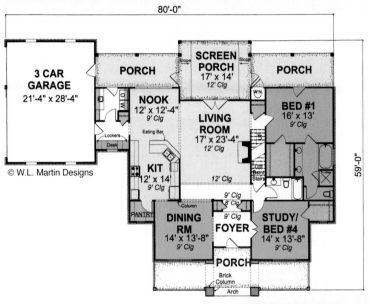

80'-0"

3 CAR
GARAGE
21'-4" x 28'-4"

© W.L. Martin Designs

PORCH

SCREEN
PORCH
17' x 14'
12' Clg

PORCH

NOOK
12' x 12'-4"
9' Clg

LIVING
ROOM
17' x 23'-4"
12' Clg

BED #1
16' x 13'
9' Clg

Lockers

Desk

Eating Bar

KIT
12' x 14'
9' Clg

12' Clg

59'-0"

9' Clg
8' Clg

PANTRY

DINING
RM
14' x 13'-8"
9' Clg

Column

9' Clg

FOYER

STUDY/
BED #4
14' x 13'-8"
9' Clg

PORCH

Brick
Column
Arch

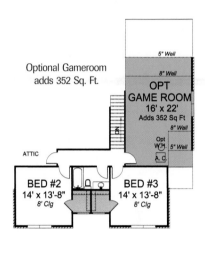

Optional Gameroom
adds 352 Sq. Ft.

5" Wall

8" Wall

OPT
GAME ROOM
16' x 22'
Adds 352 Sq Ft

8" Wall

Opt
W.H.

5" Wall

ATTIC

A. C.

BED #2
14' x 13'-8"
8' Clg

BED #3
14' x 13'-8"
8' Clg

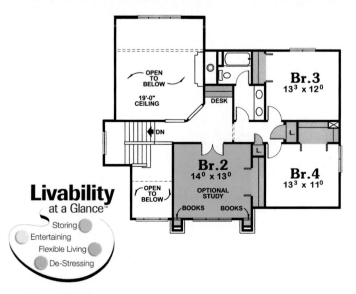

the
Hanna
4081-9JJ
pricecode 25

Main Level	**1735**
Second Level	**841**
Total Square Ft.	**2576**

Standard Foundation: Basement

OPEN
TO
BELOW

19'-0"
CEILING

DESK

DN

Br.3
13³ x 12⁰

Br.2
14⁰ x 13⁰

OPTIONAL
STUDY

BOOKS BOOKS

Br.4
13³ x 11⁰

OPEN
TO
BELOW

Livability
at a Glance™

Storing
Entertaining
Flexible Living
De-Stressing

WHIRLPOOL
TUB

Grt. Rm.
16⁰ x 17¹⁰

19'-0"
CEILING

CATHEDRAL
CEILING

ENTERT.
CENTER

Bfst.
10⁸ x 16⁰

SNACK
BAR

Kit.
11⁰ x 12⁰

DN

UP

Mbr.
14⁰ x 15²

10'-4"
CEILING

BOOKS BOOKS

E.

STOOP

54'-0"

Din.
14⁰ x 13⁰

CURIO CURIO

W. D.

Gar.
22⁰ x 23⁰

58'-8"

© design basics inc.

the Edmonton
2309-9JJ
price code 25

Main Level	**1933**
Second Level	**646**
Total Square Ft.	**2579**

Standard Foundation: Basement

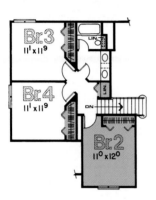

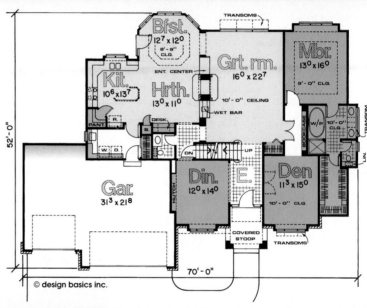

© design basics inc.

the Bayard
24063-9JJ
price code 25

Main Level	**2014**
Second Level	**573**
Total Square Ft.	**2587**

Standard Foundation: Slab

© W.L. Martin Designs

Future Bonus Room
adds 420 Sq. Ft.

Livability
at a Glance™

Storing
Entertaining
Flexible Living
De-Stressing

www.designbasics.com/9JJ

the Addams
3510-9JJ
pricecode 25

Main Level	1878
Second Level	719
Total Square Ft.	2597

Standard Foundation: Basement

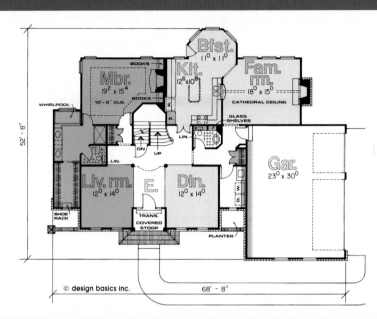

Mbr.
19² x 15⁴
10'-0" CLG.

WHIRLPOOL

BOOKS

Bfst.
11⁰ x 11⁰

Kit.
12⁶ x 10⁸

Fam. rm.
18⁰ x 15⁰
CATHEDRAL CEILING

GLASS SHELVES

BOOKS

Liv. rm.
12⁰ x 14⁰

Din.
12⁰ x 14⁰

Gar.
23⁰ x 30⁰

DN   UP

LIN.

SHOE RACK

TRANS.
COVERED STOOP

PLANTER

52' - 8"

68' - 8"

© design basics inc.

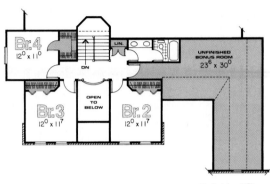

Br.4
12⁰ x 11⁰

Br.3
12⁰ x 11⁷

Br. 2
12⁰ x 11⁷

OPEN TO BELOW

UNFINISHED BONUS ROOM
23⁶ x 30⁰

LIN.

DN

Unfinished Storage
adds 542 Sq. Ft.

the Rollins
2894-9JJ
pricecode 26

Main Level	1800
Second Level	803
Total Square Ft.	2603

Standard Foundation: Basement

TRANSOMS

ENT. CENTER

TRANSOMS

Gath. rm.
15⁴ x 20⁰
10'-0" CEILING

Bfst.
15⁰ x 11⁰

DESK

COVERED DECK

Mbr.
14⁰ x 15⁹

WHIRLPOOL

LIN.

SNACK BAR

Kit.
15⁰ x 11⁰

DN

Din.
15⁰ x 11⁰
18'-0" CEILING

HUTCH

TRANS.

UP

E

Gar.
38⁴ x 23⁴

RECYCLING BINS

COVERED STOOP

Den
12⁰ x 14⁴
10'-0" CLG.

60' - 8"

62' - 0"

© design basics inc.

Br. 2
11⁸ x 12⁰

Br. 4
11⁰ x 13⁰

LOFT

DN

OPEN TO BELOW

PLANT SHELF

Br. 3
11⁰ x 13⁰
11'-0" CEILING

LIN.

Livability
at a Glance™

- Storing
- Entertaining
- Flexible Living
- De-Stressing

the Schuyler
4134-9JJ
pricecode 26

Main Level	**1847**
Second Level	**766**
Total Square Ft.	**2613**

Standard Foundation: Basement

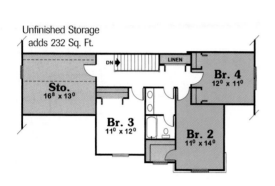

Unfinished Storage adds 232 Sq. Ft.

Sto. 16⁸ x 13⁰
Br. 4 12⁰ x 11⁰
Br. 3 11⁰ x 12⁰
Br. 2 11⁰ x 14⁰
DN LINEN

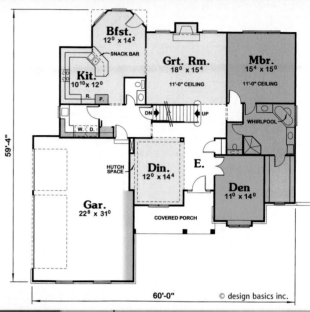

Bfst. 12⁰ x 14²
SNACK BAR
Kit. 10¹⁰ x 12⁰
Grt. Rm. 18⁰ x 15⁴ 11'-0" CEILING
Mbr. 15⁴ x 15⁰ 11'-0" CEILING
WHIRLPOOL
W. D.
DN UP
Gar. 22⁸ x 31⁰
HUTCH SPACE
Din. 12⁰ x 14⁴
E.
Den 11⁰ x 14⁰
COVERED PORCH
59'-4"
60'-0"
© design basics inc.

the Hillcrest
2649-9JJ
pricecode 26

Main Level	**1865**
Second Level	**774**
Total Square Ft.	**2639**

Standard Foundation: Basement

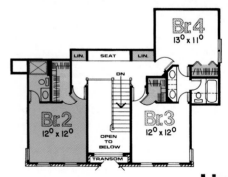

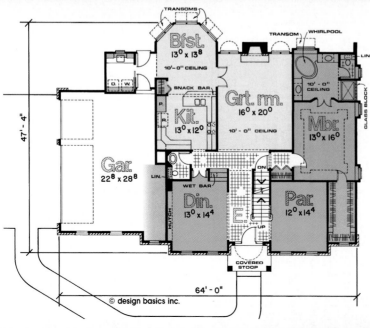

TRANSOMS
Bfst. 13⁰ x 13⁸ 10'-0" CEILING
TRANSOM
WHIRLPOOL
LIN.
SNACK BAR
Grt. rm. 16⁰ x 20⁰ 10'-0" CEILING
Kit. 13⁰ x 12⁰
Mbr. 13⁰ x 16⁰
10'-0" CEILING
GLASS BLOCK
Gar. 22⁸ x 28⁸
WET BAR
Din. 13⁰ x 14⁴
Par. 12⁰ x 14⁴
DN
E.
UP
COVERED STOOP
47'-4"
64'-0"
© design basics inc.

Br 4 13⁰ x 11⁰
LIN. SEAT LIN.
DN
Br 2 12⁰ x 12⁰
Br 3 12⁰ x 12⁰
OPEN TO BELOW
TRANSOM

Livability at a Glance™

Storing
Entertaining
Flexible Living
De-Stressing

152

www.designbasics.com/9JJ

the Wilks Manor
9165-9JJ
price code 26

Main Level	**2087**
Second Level	**552**
Total Square Ft.	**2639**

Standard Foundation: Slab

Future Expansion Space adds 450 Sq. Ft.

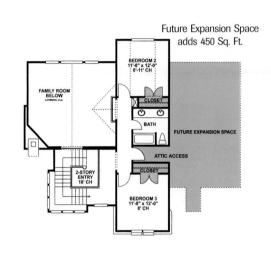

57'-4"

68'-7"

© CARMICHAEL & DAME DESIGNS, INC.

the Nelson
7231-9JJ
price code 26

Main Level	**1910**
Second Level	**732**
Total Square Ft.	**2642**

Standard Foundation: Basement

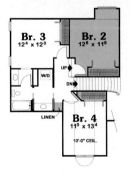

Optional Finished Lower Level adds 1275 Sq. Ft.

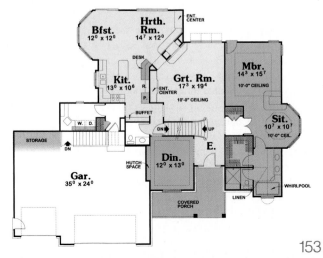

Livability
at a Glance™

- Storing
- Entertaining
- Flexible Living
- De-Stressing

Unfinished Storage adds 500 Sq. Ft.

Planning your New Home?

Don't Wait to Get Started

by Lisa M. Jensen

You're pre-qualified and know what your budget allows. You've scouted out a handful of lots, each potentially ideal. You've chosen a builder you trust and have gradually whittled down a selection of home designs to what appears to be a manageable pile. But now, it's time to take all of this forward. Time to decide exactly what to build, where to build it, and how you want it to look and live – inside and out – when it's finished. It's time to get really serious about one thing – while you still have time.

Your Homework.

"There are thousands of decisions to make when you're building," says Calvin Jen, principal designer and partner at A.M.D.G. Architects, Inc., in Michigan. "Most people don't realize how many decisions there are and they don't allow enough time to plan."

Katherine Slant, author of *The Brand-New House Book*, agrees. She cautions that rushing the process once product selection deadlines kick in may result in a new home that's a lot like your old one – only bigger or smaller.

Looking At Your Lifestyle

"People tend to concentrate on how they want each room to look, but the key to building a home that will really work for you is asking yourself, 'How do I want to live?'" says Harold Spitzer, president of Spitzer & Associates Architects in New York. 'Am I formal or informal? Do I feel most comfortable in spaces that are wide open, or smaller and more intimate?'"

The rooms your family spends the most time in deserve the most attention. Spitzer suggests considering how you spend your time in these rooms. "Do you love to cook? Then invest in a nice range and countertop. Do you love to unwind in front of movies or do you appreciate music? Then make that big screen TV or sound system you've been eyeing a priority. Cut corners in other areas. You don't need to sacrifice these things for a mantle that impresses your guests or extensive built-ins you wouldn't really use."

Study home plans and ask yourself, "How do I want to live? Am I formal or informal? Do I feel most comfortable in spaces that are wide open, or smaller and more intimate?"

Once these primary decisions are made, take a more detailed assessment of needs. What activities will take place in the rooms? How many people will typically occupy each room at a time, along with the largest number? Will you use existing furniture or do you plan to purchase new? What are your storage needs? Do you have family heirlooms or collectibles to exhibit? What is your flooring preference?

If you frequently entertain outside, think about how you can extend living space into "outdoor rooms." Consider where walking paths or gardens might go and whether you'll be able to view these from inside your home.

Making Aesthetic Decisions

Aesthetic preferences can be the most difficult to define and satisfy because of the multitude of directions you can take. For instance, do you prefer formal or casual? Simple or detailed? Open or defined? Structured or whimsical? Rustic or refined? Comfortable or elegant? Airy or cozy? Bright or subdued? Cool or warm?

While you may already have a preconceived notion of what your new home will look like or include, try not to lock in on specifics until after you've investigated all of your options.

"One mistake I often see people make is choosing a certain design element because they admire it in a friend's or neighbor's house," observes Lorene Elzinga Roskamp, ASID, IIDA affiliate and senior interior designer at Design Plus in Michigan. "Just because it may work well in their home doesn't mean it's going to be applicable for your home or lifestyle."

"I'll have clients who say, 'I want a mahogany-paneled living room,' but I'll point out that practically everything they've clipped features light oak," Spitzer says. "They'll tell me that their best friend has mahogany and it's just beautiful. I'll remind them that no matter how beautiful and functional something is in another person's home, it just might not be right for them – and ultimately, they'll wind up unhappy."

Roskamp agrees. "Eighty percent of the people I work with have their mind locked in a certain direction before they begin. They decide they want deep red walls in the family room. But after opening themselves up to all possibilities and working through the design process, they wind up with celery green."

Clip, Clip, Clip

To explore all options, begin by perusing home magazines and catalogs – as many as you can. Clip out photographs that appeal to you instinctively, without trying to analyze why. Stuff these into a folder that you can later organize by room.

Many surprises come out of clipping

images. You may realize you're actually drawn to bolder colors than you'd originally planned to have, or you may see an innovative built-in you wouldn't have considered. You might find that your design style has changed and you're ready to experiment with minimalism or be more eclectic. "You won't know until you look," Spitzer concludes.

Jen also encourages his clients to clip out what they don't like. "That especially helps a designer to focus in on where a client is headed," he notes. "But you're able to keep a more open mind."

Roskamp considers a client's wardrobe. "You can tell a lot about a person by what they choose to wear – whether they are a bolder or more introverted personality – and those traits can be carried over into design choices for the home."

She urges clients to focus on structural and big-ticket items first, elements that will likely remain in the home for years and says window trim and cabinetry style set the tone for a home. "If you're torn between light maple and rich expresso hues, run the two styles side-by-side for a while as you continue to fill up your idea book," she suggests. "Eventually, one style will emerge as working better with the flooring, countertop or furniture you choose."

Consulting a professional designer, even if it's only for a couple of hours to help you sort through your ideas folder, can be very beneficial. Designers draw upon years of experience and can make suggestions regarding lighting, texture and other elements you never would have considered.

"It also helps to solicit opinions from friends and family who know you well and see how your family lives in your current home," Jen comments. "Share your magazine clippings with them. Often they'll raise a point you've completely overlooked. You may be amazed."

left photo courtesy of BloomingPrairie.net

FAR LEFT: If you frequently entertain outside, think about how you can extend living space into "outdoor rooms."

MIDDLE & RIGHT: The rooms where you and your family spend the most time, deserve the most attention. Do you love to cook? Then invest in a nice range and countertop Do you like curling up with a good book? Treat yourself to a cozy spot by the fire.

Shopping Around

Giving yourself more time to shop around means, of course, that you're likely to secure the ideal products – at the best prices. Do your preliminary research on-line, then check out stores and showrooms, armed with a notebook – not a checkbook.

"Your home is the hugest investment you'll ever make," Roskamp says. "You owe it to yourself to see what's out there. If your mindset doesn't allow you to look beyond certain products, you may miss out on something you might have liked even better. Don't be afraid to like something better."

In addition to discovering the latest industry offerings for flooring, plumbing fixtures, lighting, cabinetry and appliances, shopping around also allows you to view the real McCoy up close, early on. Discovering that the cabinetry you've loved on paper for the past six months isn't so perfect

anymore at the store – after the builder has given you two weeks to make your final decision – can result in a rushed selection you aren't crazy about.

Before choosing paint hues, Roskamp encourages clients to walk around each space after it's been dry-walled and to buy a small container of paint and coat a larger-sized sample board, or ask for larger chip sample sheets. "I look at the color on a cloudy day and on a sunny day – to see how natural light changes the color," she says. "Then you can zero in on how intense the color should be."

The myriad of decisions in building a home can be totally overwhelming. Spitzer summarizes the best way to stay in control and ensure an outcome you're happy with for years to come: "Get educated and gather as much information as you can – about yourself and about products."

the
Armburst
2723-9JJ
pricecode 26

Main Level	**1972**
Second Level	**673**
Total Square Ft.	**2645**

Standard Foundation: Basement

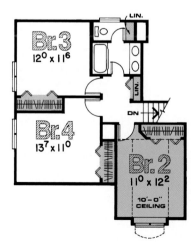

Livability
at a Glance™

- Storing
- Entertaining
- Flexible Living
- De-Stressing

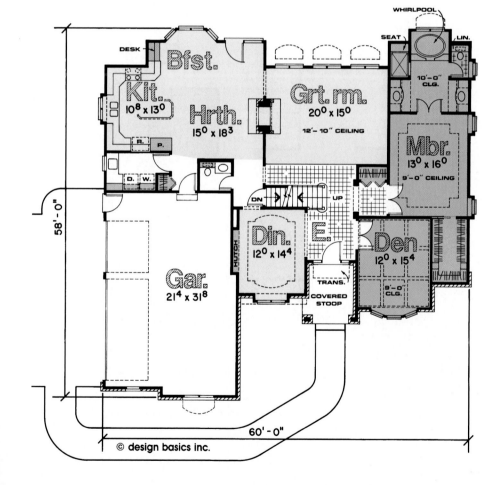

DESK

Bfst.

Kit.
10^8 x 13^0

Hrth.
15^0 x 18^3

Grt. rm.
20^0 x 15^0
12'-10" CEILING

WHIRLPOOL

SEAT

LIN.

$10'-0"$ CLG.

Mbr.
13^0 x 16^0
9'-0" CEILING

R.

P.

D. W.

DN

UP

Din.
12^0 x 14^4

HUTCH

Den
12^0 x 15^4

TRANS.

9'-0" CLG.

Gar.
21^4 x 31^8

COVERED STOOP

58' - 0"

60' - 0"

© design basics inc.

Br. 3
12^0 x 11^6

LIN.

Br. 4
13^7 x 11^0

DN

LIN.

Br. 2
11^0 x 12^2
10'-0" CEILING

the
Clarinda
43020-9JJ
pricecode 26

Main Level	**1904**
Second Level	**747**
Total Square Ft.	**2651**

Standard Foundation: Slab

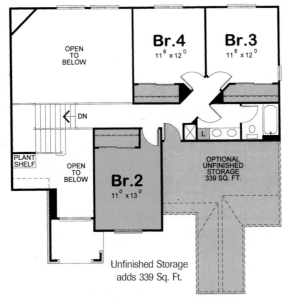

OPEN TO BELOW

Br.4
11⁸ x 12⁰

Br.3
11⁸ x 12⁰

DN

PLANT SHELF

OPEN TO BELOW

Br.2
11⁰ x 13⁰

OPTIONAL UNFINISHED STORAGE 339 SQ. FT.

L

Unfinished Storage adds 339 Sq. Ft.

Optional Master Bath

Livability
at a Glance™

Storing
Entertaining
Flexible Living
De-Stressing

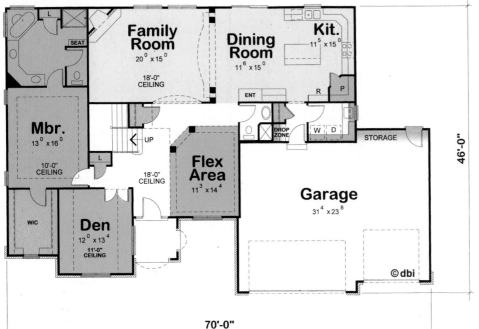

Family Room
20⁰ x 15⁰
18'-0" CEILING

Dining Room
11⁸ x 15⁰

Kit.
11⁵ x 15⁰

ENT

R   P

Mbr.
13⁰ x 16⁰
10'-0" CEILING

SEAT

L

UP

DROP ZONE

W   D

STORAGE

Flex Area
11³ x 14⁴
18'-0" CEILING

Garage
31⁴ x 23⁸

WIC

Den
12⁰ x 13⁴
11'-0" CEILING

©dbi

46'-0"

70'-0"

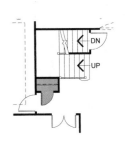

DN

UP

Optional Basement Stair Location

the Plainfield

43019-9JJ

pricecode 26

Main Level	**1904**
Second Level	**747**
Total Square Ft.	**2651**

Standard Foundation: Slab

Livability
at a Glance™

- Storing
- Entertaining
- Flexible Living
- De-Stressing

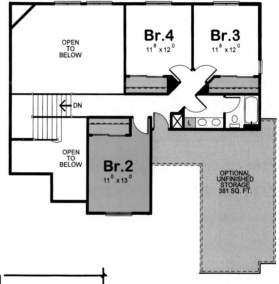

Unfinished Storage
adds 381 Sq. Ft.

Optional Master Bath

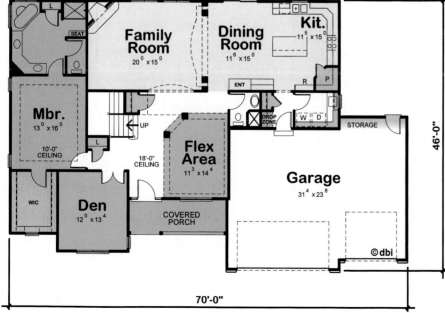

Optional Basement Stair Location

the Woodlands Showcase

9160-9JJ

price code 26

Main Level	**1906**
Second Level	**749**
Total Square Ft.	**2655**

Standard Foundation: Slab

Livability
at a Glance™

- Storing
- Entertaining
- Flexible Living
- De-Stressing

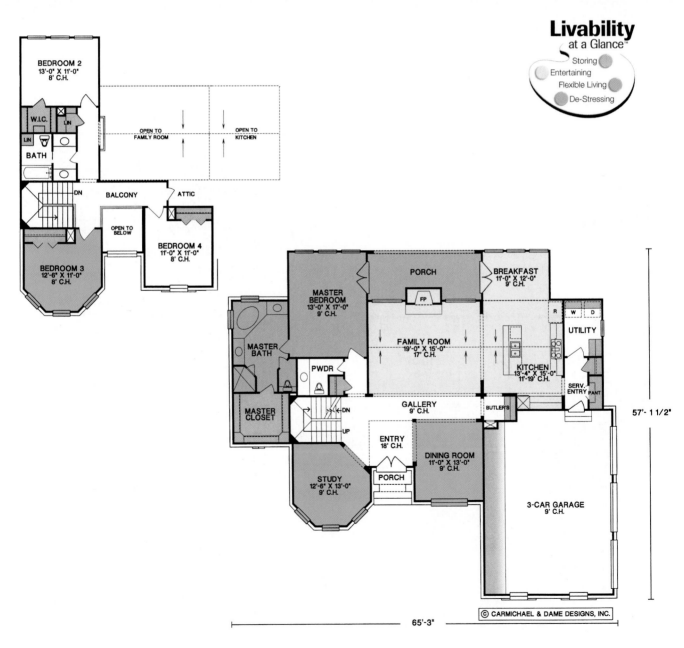

BEDROOM 2 13'-0" X 11'-0" 8' C.H.

W.I.C.

LIN

LIN

BATH

DN

BALCONY

ATTIC

OPEN TO FAMILY ROOM

OPEN TO KITCHEN

OPEN TO BELOW

BEDROOM 4 11'-0" X 11'-0" 8' C.H.

BEDROOM 3 12'-6" X 11'-0" 8' C.H.

PORCH

BREAKFAST 11'-0" X 12'-0" 9' C.H.

MASTER BEDROOM 13'-0" X 17'-0" 9' C.H.

FP

FAMILY ROOM 19'-0" X 15'-0" 17' C.H.

R W D

UTILITY

MASTER BATH

KITCHEN 13'-4" X 15'-0" 11'-19' C.H.

SERV. ENTRY PANT

MASTER CLOSET

PWDR

DN

UP

GALLERY 9' C.H.

BUTLER'S

ENTRY 18' C.H.

STUDY 12'-6" X 13'-0" 9' C.H.

PORCH

DINING ROOM 11'-0" X 13'-0" 9' C.H.

3-CAR GARAGE 9' C.H.

57'- 1 1/2"

© CARMICHAEL & DAME DESIGNS, INC.

65'-3"

the Oliver
24011-9JJ
pricecode 26

Main Level	**1650**
Second Level	**1038**
Total Square Ft.	**2688**

Standard Foundation: Slab

Livability
at a Glance™

- Storing
- Entertaining
- Flexible Living
- De-Stressing

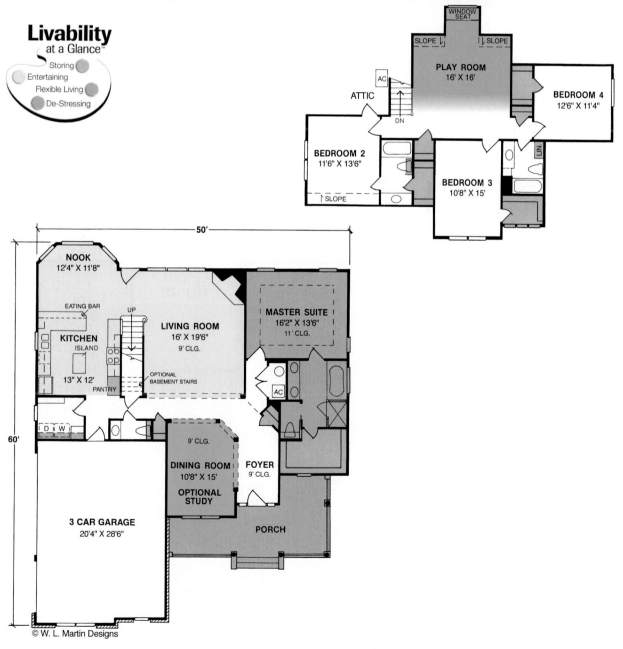

WINDOW SEAT

SLOPE ↓   SLOPE ↓

PLAY ROOM
16' X 16'

AC

ATTIC

DN

BEDROOM 4
12'6" X 11'4"

BEDROOM 2
11'6" X 13'6"

LIN.

BEDROOM 3
10'8" X 15'

SLOPE

NOOK
12'4" X 11'8"

EATING BAR

UP

LIVING ROOM
16' X 19'6"
9' CLG.

MASTER SUITE
16'2" X 13'6"
11' CLG.

KITCHEN
ISLAND

13" X 12'

OPTIONAL
BASEMENT STAIRS

PANTRY

AC

D W

DINING ROOM
10'8" X 15'

9' CLG.

OPTIONAL STUDY

FOYER
9' CLG.

3 CAR GARAGE
20'4" X 28'6"

PORCH

50'

60'

© W. L. Martin Designs

the
Deville
30001-9JJ

pricecode 26

Main Level	**1792**
Second Level	**898**
Total Square Ft.	**2690**

Standard Foundation: Basement

Livability
at a Glance™

- Storing
- Entertaining
- Flexible Living
- De-Stressing

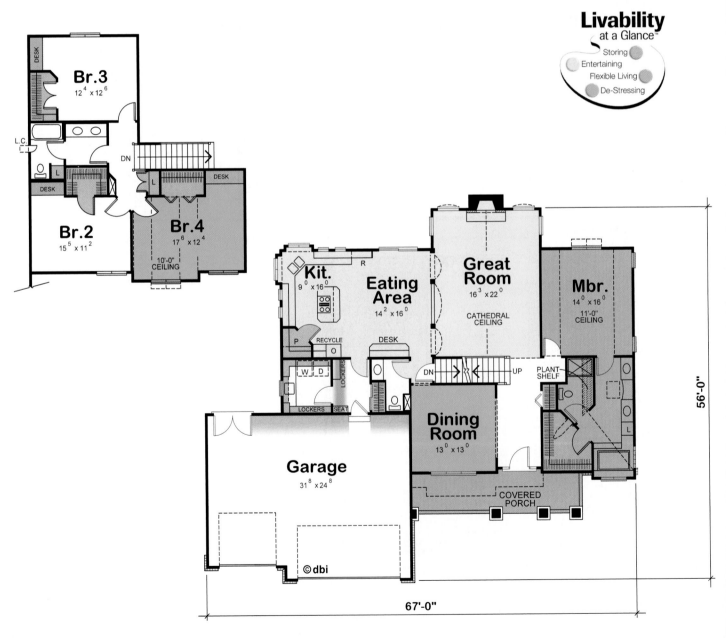

Br.3
12⁴ x 12⁶

Br.2
15⁵ x 11²

Br.4
17⁶ x 12⁴
10'-0" CEILING

L.C.

DESK

DN

Kit.
9⁰ x 16⁰

Eating Area
14² x 16⁰

Great Room
16³ x 22⁰
CATHEDRAL CEILING

Mbr.
14⁰ x 16⁰
11'-0" CEILING

RECYCLE

DESK

P

W D

LOCKERS

LOCKERS   SEAT

DN   UP

PLANT-SHELF

Dining Room
13⁰ x 13⁰

Garage
31⁸ x 24⁸

COVERED PORCH

©dbi

56'-0"

67'-0"

the Bridgeport
2460-9JJ
price code 26

Main Level	**1881**
Second Level	**814**
Total Square Ft.	**2695**

Standard Foundation: Basement

Livability
at a Glance™

Storing
Entertaining
Flexible Living
De-Stressing

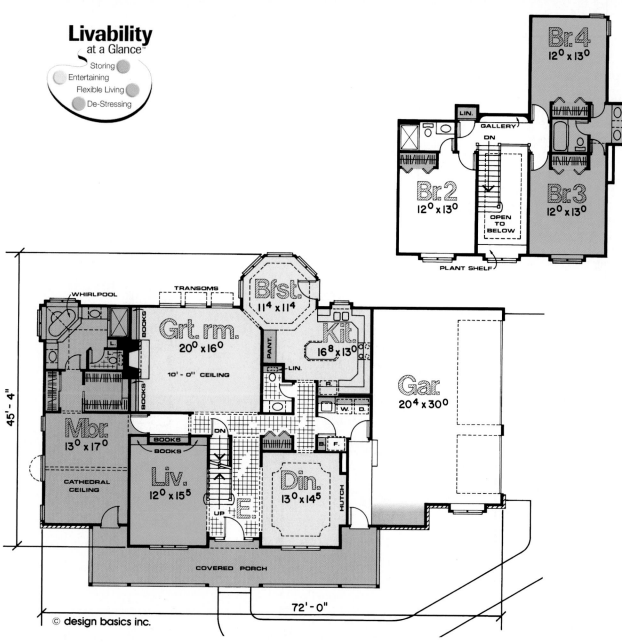

Br.4
12⁰ x 13⁰

LIN.

GALLERY

DN

Br.2
12⁰ x 13⁰

Br.3
12⁰ x 13⁰

OPEN
TO
BELOW

PLANT SHELF

WHIRLPOOL

TRANSOMS

BOOKS

Bfst.
11⁴ x 11⁴

Grt. rm.
20⁰ x 16⁰

10'-0" CEILING

PANT.

LIN.

Kit.
16⁸ x 13⁰

Gar.
20⁴ x 30⁰

45'-4"

BOOKS

Mbr.
13⁰ x 17⁰

CATHEDRAL
CEILING

BOOKS
BOOKS

DN

Liv.
12⁰ x 15⁵

UP

Din.
13⁰ x 14⁵

HUTCH

W. D.

B. F.

COVERED PORCH

72'-0"

© design basics inc.

the
Westfield
42003-9JJ
pricecode 27

Main Level	**1849**
Second Level	**855**
Total Square Ft.	**2704**

Standard Foundation: Basement

Livability
at a Glance™

Storing
Entertaining
Flexible Living
De-Stressing

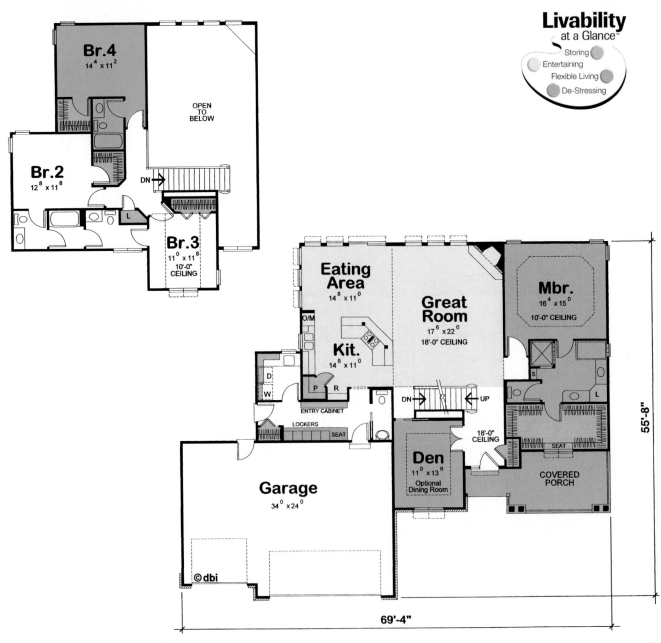

Br. 4
14⁴ x 11²

OPEN TO BELOW

Br. 2
12⁸ x 11⁸

DN

Br. 3
11⁰ x 11⁸
10'-0" CEILING

Eating Area
14⁸ x 11⁰

Great Room
17⁶ x 22⁰
18'-0" CEILING

Mbr.
16⁴ x 15⁰
10'-0" CEILING

Kit.
14⁸ x 11⁰

D
W
P   R

ENTRY CABINET

LOCKERS   SEAT

DN   UP

18'-0" CEILING

Garage
34⁰ x 24⁰

Den
11⁰ x 13⁶
Optional Dining Room

SEAT

COVERED PORCH

©dbi

55'-8"

69'-4"

www.designbasics.com/9JJ

the
Cordeaux
2174-9JJ

pricecode 27

Main Level	**1860**
Second Level	**848**
Total Square Ft.	**2708**

Standard Foundation: Basement

Livability
at a Glance™

- Storing
- Entertaining
- Flexible Living
- De-Stressing

Br. 4
12⁰ x 13⁰

Br. 3
13¹⁰ x 11⁹

LINEN

OPEN TO BELOW

DN

Br. 2
12⁰ x 13¹

L

Mbr.
14⁰ x 15⁰
9' - 0" CEILING

WHIRL POOL

Kit.
9⁷ x 13⁴

9' - 0" CLG.

Bfst.
12⁰ x 14¹

DESK

PANT.

R

TRANSOMS

Fam. rm.
21⁰ x 17⁰

10' - 8" CEILING

ENT. CENTERS

DN

UP

E.

Liv. rm.
12⁰ x 13⁵

10' - 8" CEILING

Gar.
22⁰ x 29⁰

HUTCH

Din.
13⁰ x 14⁶

COVERED STOOP

UP

TRANSOMS

© design basics inc.

59' - 4"

56' - 0"

the
MacCready
3484-9JJ
pricecode 27

Main Level	**2000**
Second Level	**764**
Total Square Ft.	**2764**

Standard Foundation: Basement

Livability
at a Glance™

- Storing
- Entertaining
- Flexible Living
- De-Stressing

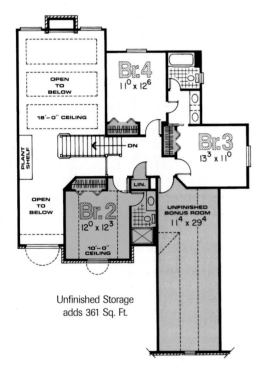

Br. 4
11⁰ x 12⁶

OPEN TO BELOW

18'-0" CEILING

PLANT SHELF

DN

Br. 3
13³ x 11⁰

LIN.

OPEN TO BELOW

Br. 2
12⁰ x 12³

10'-0" CEILING

UNFINISHED BONUS ROOM
11⁴ x 29⁴

Unfinished Storage
adds 361 Sq. Ft.

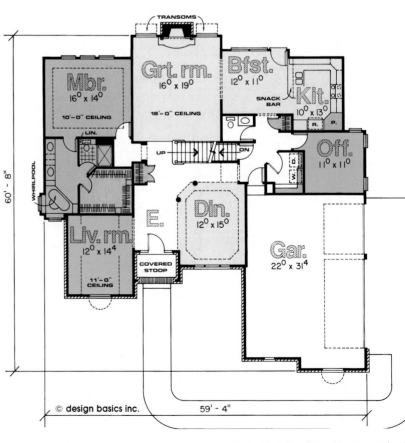

TRANSOMS

Mbr.
16⁰ x 14⁰
10'-0" CEILING

Grt. rm.
16⁰ x 19⁰
18'-0" CEILING

Bfst.
12⁰ x 11⁰

SNACK BAR

Kit.
10⁰ x 13⁰

R.   P.

LIN.

WHIRLPOOL

UP   DN

W. D.

Off.
11⁰ x 11⁰

E.

Din.
12⁰ x 15⁰

Liv. rm.
12⁰ x 14⁴
11'-0" CEILING

COVERED STOOP

Gar.
22⁰ x 31⁴

60' - 8"

59' - 4"

© design basics inc.

166

www.designbasics.com/9JJ

the Brookings
43040-9JJ
price code 27

Main Level	**1855**
Second Level	**910**
Total Square Ft.	**2765**

Standard Foundation: Slab

Livability
at a Glance™

- Storing
- Entertaining
- Flexible Living
- De-Stressing

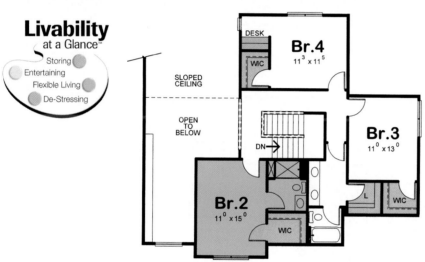

DESK

Br.4
11³ x 11⁵
WIC

SLOPED CEILING

OPEN TO BELOW

DN →

Br.3
11⁰ x 13⁰
L   WIC

Br.2
11⁰ x 15⁰

WIC

DN →

Br.3
11⁰ x 13⁰

L   WIC

WIC

Optional Bath

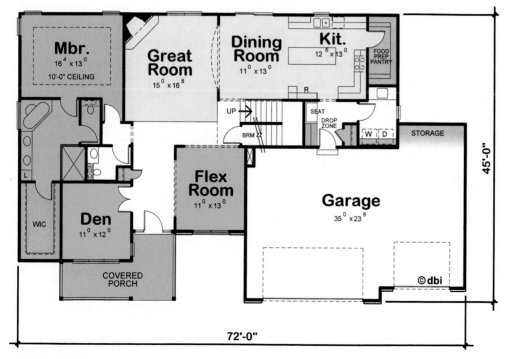

Mbr.
16⁴ x 13⁰
10'-0" CEILING

Great Room
15⁰ x 16⁸

Dining Room
11⁰ x 13⁰

Kit.
12⁸ x 13⁰

FOOD PREP PANTRY

R

UP →

BRM 22

SEAT

DROP ZONE

W D

STORAGE

WIC

Den
11⁰ x 12⁰

Flex Room
11⁰ x 13⁰

Garage
35⁰ x 23⁸

COVERED PORCH

©dbi

45'-0"

72'-0"

DROP ZONE

W D

STORAGE

Optional Laundry
adds 26 Sq. Ft.

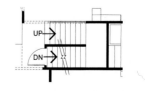

UP →

DN →

Optional Basement Stair Location

the Vermillion
43041-9JJ
price code 27

Main Level	**1862**
Second Level	**910**
Total Square Ft.	**2772**

Standard Foundation: Slab

Optional Bath

Livability at a Glance™
- Storing
- Entertaining
- Flexible Living
- De-Stressing

Br.4
11³ x 11⁵
DESK
WIC

SLOPED CEILING

OPEN TO BELOW

Br.3
11⁰ x 13⁰

DN

Br.2
11⁰ x 15⁰
10'-0" CEILING

Br.3
11⁰ x 13⁰

WIC
L
WIC

Optional Laundry
adds 26 Sq. Ft.

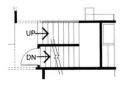

Optional Basement Stair Location

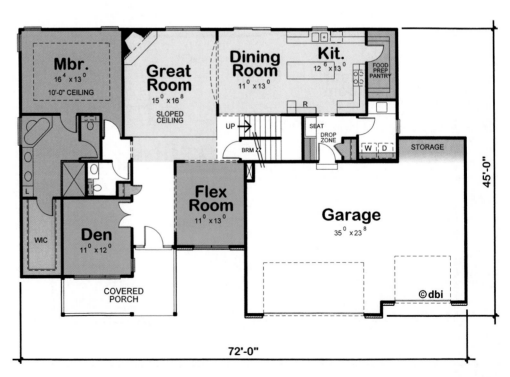

Mbr.
16⁴ x 13⁰
10'-0" CEILING

Great Room
15⁰ x 16⁸
SLOPED CEILING

Dining Room
11⁰ x 13⁰

Kit.
12⁸ x 13⁰

FOOD PREP PANTRY

UP

BRM

SEAT

DROP ZONE

W D

STORAGE

Den
11⁰ x 12⁰

WIC

Flex Room
11⁰ x 13⁰

Garage
35⁰ x 23⁸

COVERED PORCH

©dbi

45'-0"

72'-0"

the
Irwindale
24211-9JJ
price code 28

Main Level	**1884**
Second Level	**925**
Total Square Ft.	**2809**

Standard Foundation: Slab

Livability
at a Glance™

- Storing
- Entertaining
- Flexible Living
- De-Stressing

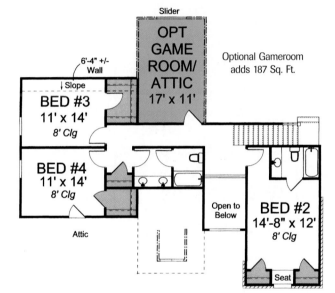

Slider

OPT GAME ROOM/ ATTIC
17' x 11'

Optional Gameroom adds 187 Sq. Ft.

6'-4" +/- Wall

Slope

BED #3
11' x 14'
8' Clg

BED #4
11' x 14'
8' Clg

Attic

Open to Below

BED #2
14'-8" x 12'
8' Clg

Seat

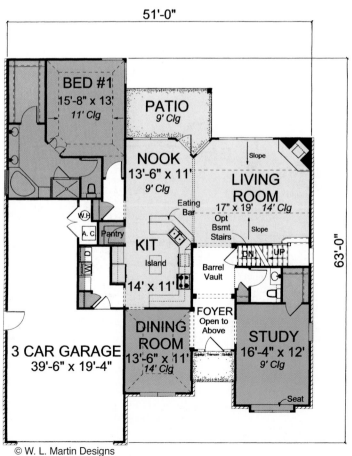

51'-0"

63'-0"

BED #1
15'-8" x 13'
11' Clg

PATIO
9' Clg

NOOK
13'-6" x 11'
9' Clg

LIVING ROOM
17" x 19'   14' Clg

Slope

Eating Bar

Opt Bsmt Stairs

Slope

W.H

A. C.   Pantry

KIT
Island
14' x 11'

Barrel Vault

DN   UP

3 CAR GARAGE
39'-6" x 19'-4"

DINING ROOM
13'-6" x 11'
14' Clg

FOYER
Open to Above

STUDY
16'-4" x 12'
9' Clg

Seat

© W. L. Martin Designs

the Chadsworth

29132-9JJ

price code 28

Main Level	**1936**
Second Level	**907**
Total Square Ft.	**2843**

Standard Foundation: Basement

Livability
at a Glance™

- Storing
- Entertaining
- Flexible Living
- De-Stressing

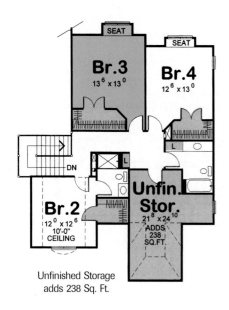

Br.3
13⁶ x 13⁰

Br.4
12⁶ x 13⁰

SEAT

SEAT

DN

Br.2
12⁰ x 12⁶
10'-0"
CEILING

Unfin. Stor.
21⁸ x 24¹⁰
ADDS 238 SQ.FT.

Unfinished Storage
adds 238 Sq. Ft.

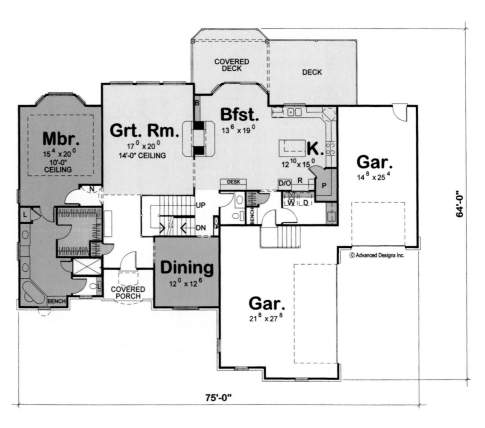

COVERED DECK

DECK

Mbr.
15⁴ x 20⁰
10'-0"
CEILING

Grt. Rm.
17⁰ x 20⁰
14'-0" CEILING

Bfst.
13⁶ x 19⁰

K.
12¹⁰ x 15⁰

Gar.
14⁸ x 25⁴

DESK

D/O R P

UP DN

W D

BENCH

Dining
12⁰ x 12⁶

COVERED PORCH

BENCH

Gar.
21⁸ x 27⁸

© Advanced Designs Inc.

64'-0"

75'-0"

the
Thornhill
3494-9JJ
pricecode 28

Main Level	**2041**
Second Level	**809**
Total Square Ft.	**2850**

Standard Foundation: Basement

Livability
at a Glance™

Storing
Entertaining
Flexible Living
De-Stressing

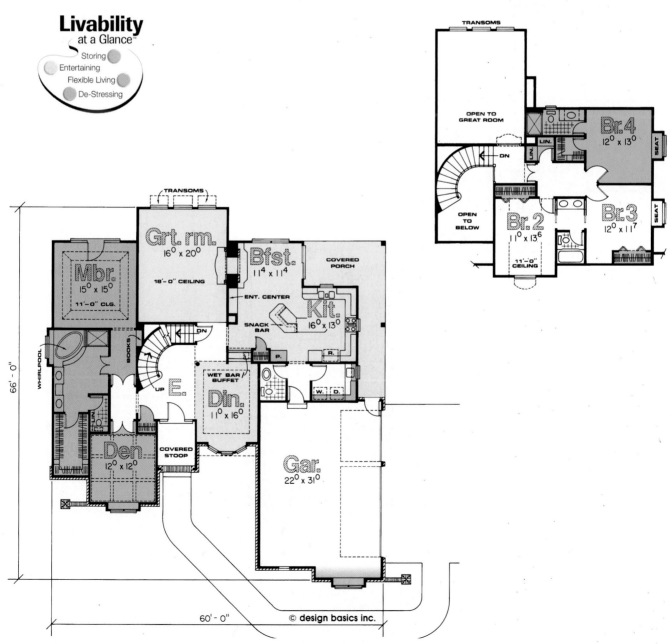

the Remington
1486-9JJ
pricecode 28

Main Level	1972
Second Level	893
Total Square Ft.	2865

Standard Foundation: Basement

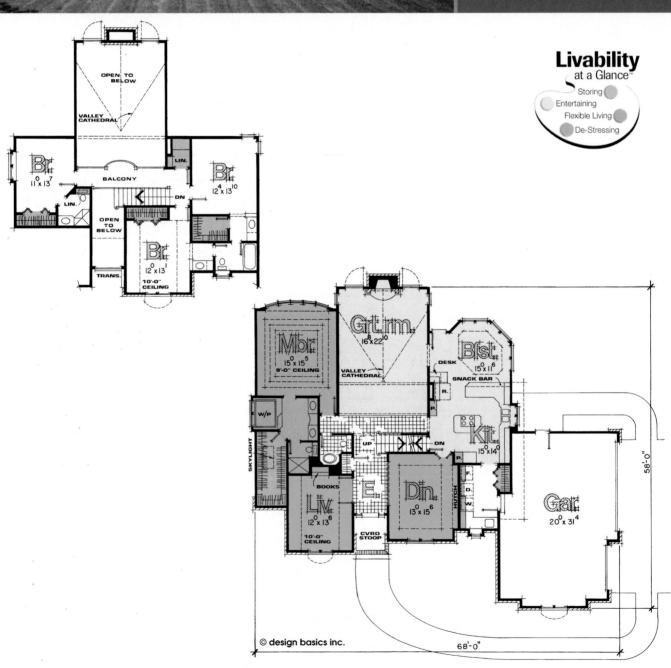

Livability at a Glance™
- Storing
- Entertaining
- Flexible Living
- De-Stressing

© design basics inc.

68'-0"
58'-0"

the
Dundee
2476-9JJ
pricecode 28

Main Level	**2183**
Second Level	**701**
Total Square Ft.	**2884**

Standard Foundation: Basement

Livability
at a Glance™

Storing
Entertaining
Flexible Living
De-Stressing

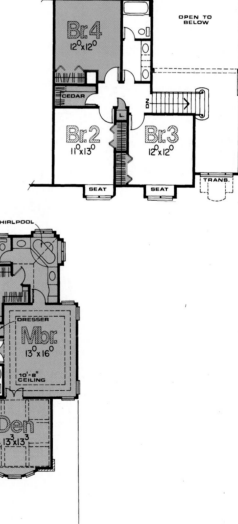

Br.4
12⁰x12⁰

OPEN TO BELOW

CEDAR

Br.2
11⁰x13⁰

DN

Br.3
12⁰x12⁰

SEAT   SEAT   TRANS.

TRANSOMS

WHIRLPOOL

Bfst.
12⁰x12⁰

Kit.
12⁶x17⁰

Grt. rm.
16⁰x19⁰
13'-3" CEILING

SNACK BAR

Gath. rm.
17⁶x16⁰

BOOKS

ENT. CENTER

DESK

DRESSER

Mbr.
13⁰x16⁰
10'-8" CEILING

Gar.
21³x30³

Din.
12⁰x16⁰

Den
13³x13³
9'-4" CLG.

COVERED STOOP

PLANTER

59'-4"

67'-4"

© design basics inc.

the
Hartford
2458-9JJ

pricecode 29

Main Level	**2084**
Second Level	**848**
Total Square Ft.	**2932**

Standard Foundation: Basement

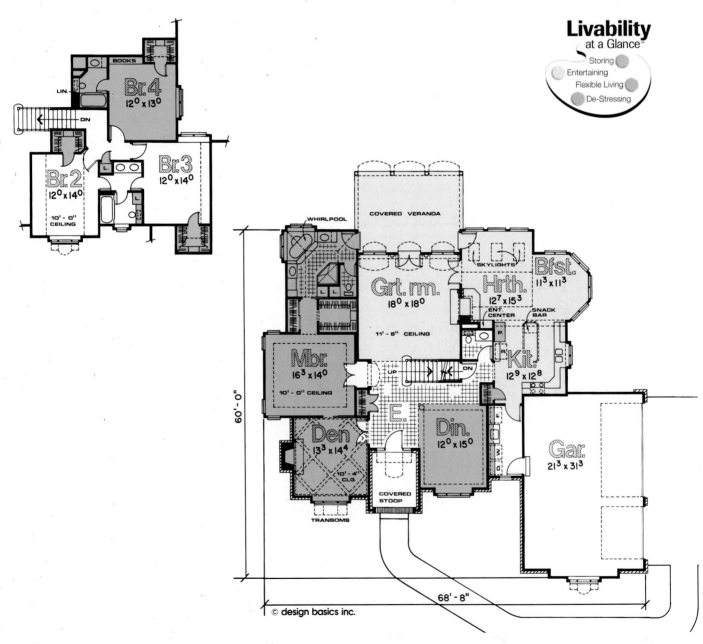

Livability
at a Glance™

Storing
Entertaining
Flexible Living
De-Stressing

BOOKS

Br.4
12⁰ x 13⁰

LIN.

DN

Br.2
12⁰ x 14⁰

10' - 0"
CEILING

Br.3
12⁰ x 14⁰

WHIRLPOOL

COVERED VERANDA

Grt. rm.
18⁰ x 18⁰

11' - 8" CEILING

SKYLIGHTS

Hrth.
12⁷ x 15³

Bfst.
11³ x 11³

ENT. CENTER

SNACK BAR

Mbr.
16³ x 14⁰

10' - 0" CEILING

UP

DN

Kit.
12⁹ x 12⁸

E.

Den
13³ x 14⁴

10' - 4" CLG.

Din.
12⁰ x 15⁰

Gar.
21³ x 31³

COVERED STOOP

TRANSOMS

60' - 0"

68' - 8"

© design basics inc.

the Pembrook
24007-9JJ
pricecode 29

Main Level	**2101**
Second Level	**877**
Total Square Ft.	**2978**

Standard Foundation: Slab

Livability
at a Glance™

- Storing
- Entertaining
- Flexible Living
- De-Stressing

BEDROOM 3
11'4" X 12'6"

OPEN TO BELOW

RAIL

WALKWAY

STUDY
12'6" X 10'10"

DN

RAIL

PLAY ROOM
13'8" X 11'6"

OPEN TO BELOW

BEDROOM 4
11'4" X 12'8"

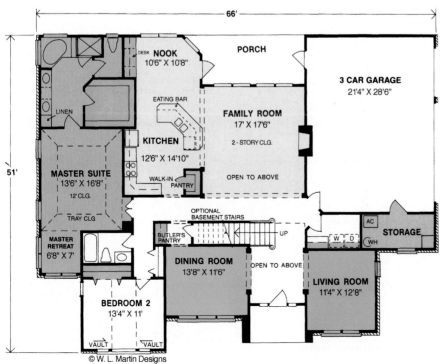

66'

51'

DESK NOOK
10'6" X 10'8"

PORCH

3 CAR GARAGE
21'4" X 28'6"

EATING BAR

FAMILY ROOM
17' X 17'6"
2 - STORY CLG.

KITCHEN
12'6" X 14'10"

LINEN

MASTER SUITE
13'6" X 16'8"
12' CLG.

WALK-IN PANTRY

OPEN TO ABOVE

TRAY CLG.

MASTER RETREAT
6'8" X 7'

OPTIONAL BASEMENT STAIRS

BUTLER'S PANTRY

UP

AC

STORAGE

W D WH

DINING ROOM
13'8" X 11'6"

OPEN TO ABOVE

LIVING ROOM
11'4" X 12'8"

BEDROOM 2
13'4" X 11'

VAULT   VAULT

© W. L. Martin Designs

the
Appleton
2800-9JJ

pricecode 29

Main Level	**2158**
Second Level	**821**
Total Square Ft.	**2979**

Standard Foundation: Basement

Livability
at a Glance™

- Storing
- Entertaining
- Flexible Living
- De-Stressing

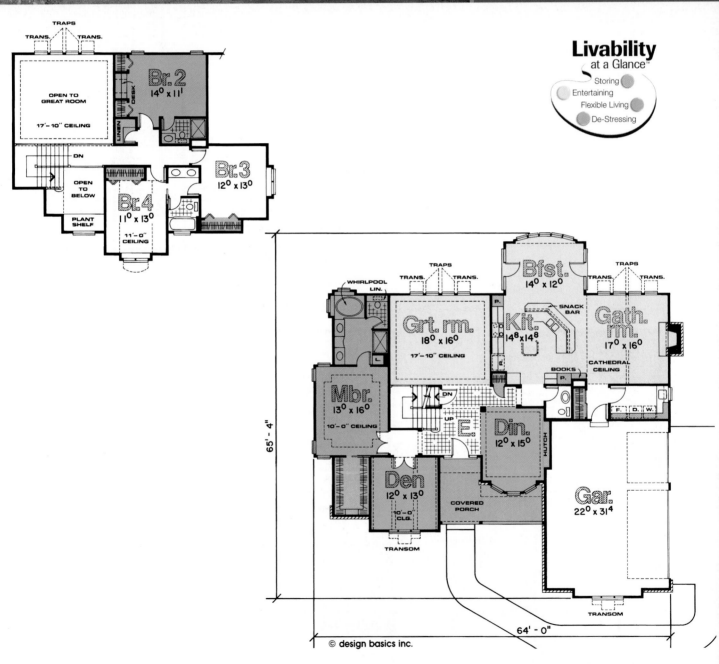

© design basics inc.

the
Korbyn
29500-9JJ
*price**code** 29*

Main Level	**1872**
Second Level	**1127**
Total Square Ft.	**2999**

Standard Foundation: Slab

Livability
at a Glance™

- Storing
- Entertaining
- Flexible Living
- De-Stressing

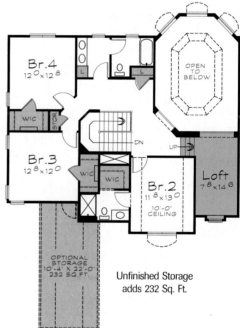

Unfinished Storage
adds 232 Sq. Ft.

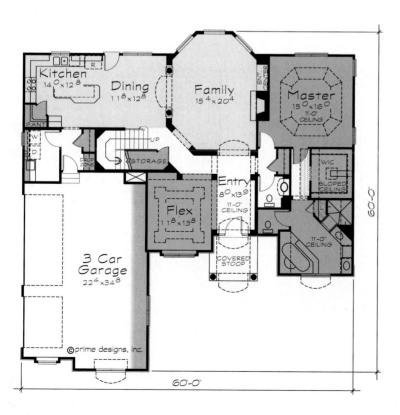

Kitchen 14⁰×12⁸
Dining 11⁸×12⁸
Family 15⁴×20⁴
Master 15⁰×16⁰ 11'-0" CEILING
PANT
W/D
DROP ZONE
STORAGE
UP
Entry 8⁰×13⁹ 11'-0" CEILING
Flex 11⁸×13⁸
WIC
SLOPED CEILING
11'-0" CEILING
11'-0" CEILING
COVERED STOOP
3 Car Garage 22⁴×34⁸
© prime designs, inc.
60'-0"
60'-0"

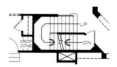

Optional Basement Stair Location

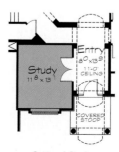

Optional Study

Study 11⁸×13
Entry 8⁰×13⁹ 11'-0" CEILING
COVERED STOOP

the Oakdale
3326-9JJ
pricecode 30

Main Level	**2179**
Second Level	**838**
Total Square Ft.	**3017**

Standard Foundation: Basement

Livability at a Glance™

- Storing
- Entertaining
- Flexible Living
- De-Stressing

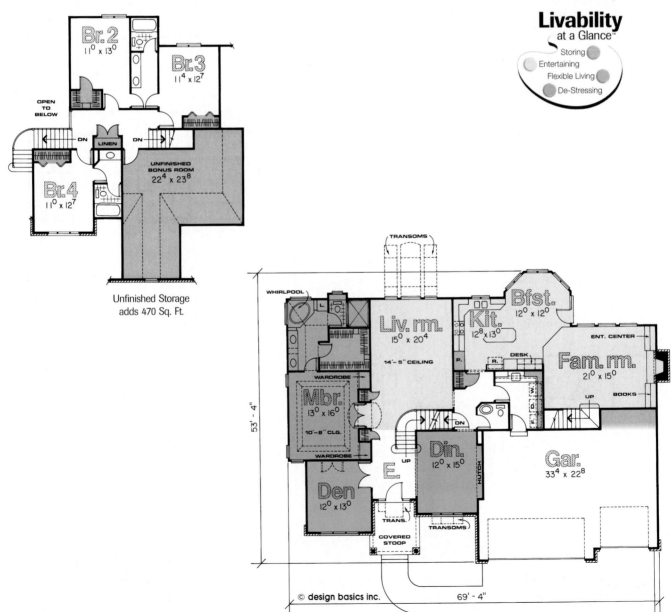

Unfinished Storage
adds 470 Sq. Ft.

© design basics inc.

www.designbasics.com/9JJ

the
Durand
2671-9JJ
pricecode 30

Main Level	**1923**
Second Level	**1106**
Total Square Ft.	**3029**

Standard Foundation: Basement

Livability
at a Glance™

- Storing
- Entertaining
- Flexible Living
- De-Stressing

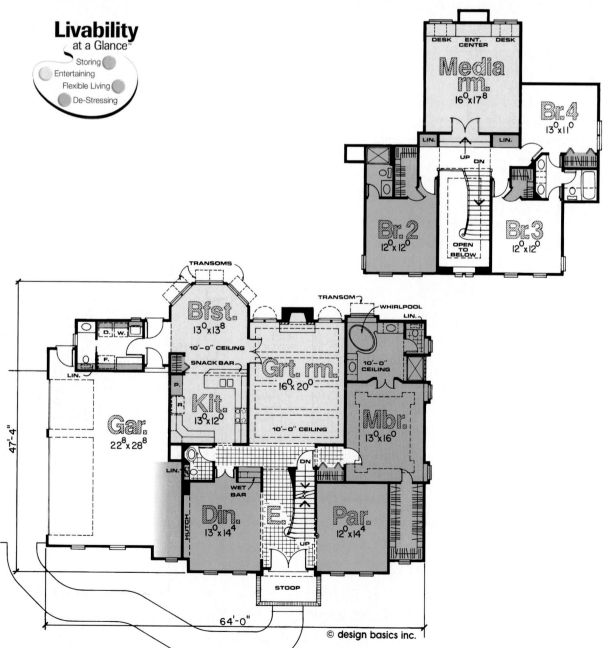

Media rm.
16⁰x17⁸

Br. 4
13⁰x11⁰

Br. 2
12⁰x12⁰

Br. 3
12⁰x12⁰

DESK   ENT. CENTER   DESK

LIN.   UP DN   LIN.

OPEN TO BELOW

TRANSOMS

Bfst.
13⁰x13⁸
10'-0" CEILING

SNACK BAR

TRANSOM

WHIRLPOOL   LIN.

Grt. rm.
16⁰x20⁰
10'-0" CEILING

10'-0" CEILING

Gar.
22⁸x28⁸

Kit.
13⁰x12⁰

Mbr.
13⁰x16⁰

WET BAR

Din.
13⁰x14⁴

Par.
12⁰x14⁴

STOOP

47'-4"

64'-0"

© design basics inc.

the
Marlow
4144-9JJ
pricecode 30

Main Level	**2215**
Second Level	**825**
Total Square Ft.	**3040**

Standard Foundation: Basement

Livability
at a Glance™

- Storing
- Entertaining
- Flexible Living
- De-Stressing

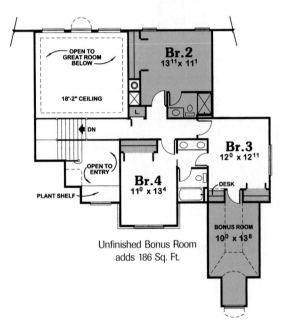

OPEN TO GREAT ROOM BELOW

18'-2" CEILING

Br.2
13¹¹x 11¹

DN

Br.3
12⁰ x 12¹¹

OPEN TO ENTRY

DESK

Br.4
11⁰ x 13⁴

PLANT SHELF

BONUS ROOM
10⁰ x 13⁸

Unfinished Bonus Room
adds 186 Sq. Ft.

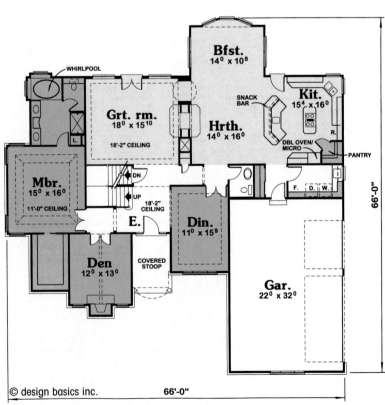

WHIRLPOOL

Bfst.
14⁰ x 10⁸

SNACK BAR

Kit.
15⁴ x 16⁰

Grt. rm.
18⁰ x 15¹⁰

18'-2" CEILING

Hrth.
14⁰ x 16⁰

DBL OVEN/ MICRO

R.

PANTRY

Mbr.
15⁰ x 16⁰

11'-0" CEILING

DN

UP

18'-2" CEILING

F. D. W.

Din.
11⁰ x 15⁹

E.

COVERED STOOP

Den
12⁰ x 13⁰

Gar.
22⁰ x 32⁰

66'-0"

© design basics inc.   66'-0"

the
Northland
2322-9JJ
pricecode 30

Main Level	**2169**
Second Level	**898**
Total Square Ft.	**3067**

Standard Foundation: Basement

Livability
at a Glance™

- Storing
- Entertaining
- Flexible Living
- De-Stressing

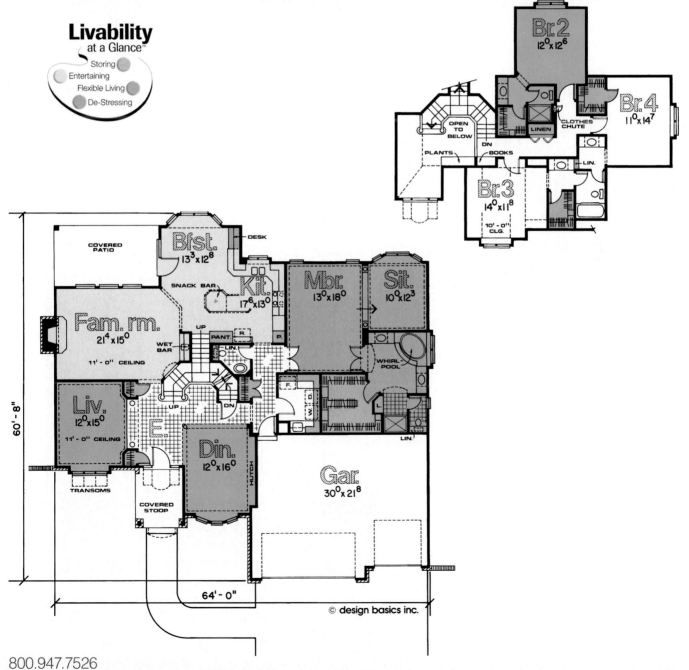

the
Tealwood
Estate
9162-9JJ

price code 30

Main Level	**2116**
Second Level	**956**
Total Square Ft.	**3072**

Standard Foundation: Slab

Livability
at a Glance™

- Storing
- Entertaining
- Flexible Living
- De-Stressing

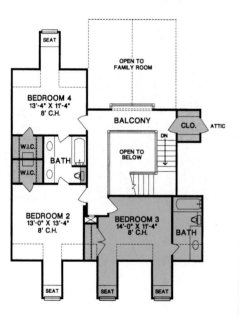

SEAT

OPEN TO
FAMILY ROOM

BEDROOM 4
13'-4" X 11'-4"
8' C.H.

BALCONY

CLO.   ATTIC

W.I.C.

BATH   DN

OPEN TO
BELOW

W.I.C.

BEDROOM 2
13'-0" X 13'-4"
8' C.H.

BEDROOM 3
14'-0" X 11'-4"
8' C.H.

BATH

SEAT   SEAT   SEAT

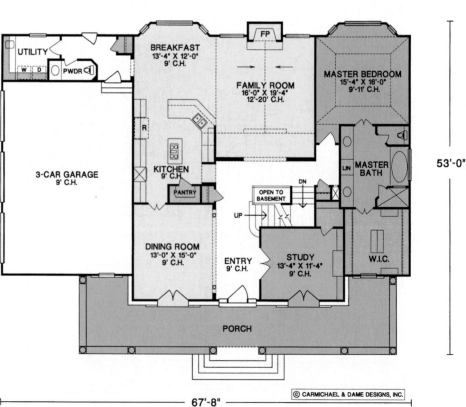

UTILITY

W D   PWDR

BREAKFAST
13'-4" X 12'-0"
9' C.H.

FP

FAMILY ROOM
16'-0" X 19'-4"
12'-20' C.H.

MASTER BEDROOM
15'-4" X 16'-0"
9'-11' C.H.

R

3-CAR GARAGE
9' C.H.

KITCHEN
9' C.H.

PANTRY

LIN   MASTER
BATH

DN

OPEN TO
BASEMENT

UP

DINING ROOM
13'-0" X 15'-0"
9' C.H.

ENTRY
9' C.H.

STUDY
13'-4" X 11'-4"
9' C.H.

W.I.C.

PORCH

53'-0"

67'-8"

© CARMICHAEL & DAME DESIGNS, INC.

the
Channing
42005-9JJ
price code 30

Main Level	**2059**
Second Level	**1021**
Total Square Ft.	**3080**

Standard Foundation: Basement

Livability
at a Glance™

- Storing
- Entertaining
- Flexible Living
- De-Stressing

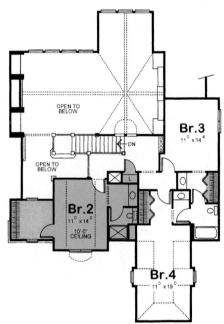

Br.3
11⁰ x 14⁴

OPEN TO BELOW

OPEN TO BELOW

DN

BOOKS

Br.2
11⁰ x 14⁰
10'-0" CEILING

L

Br.4
11⁰ x 19⁰

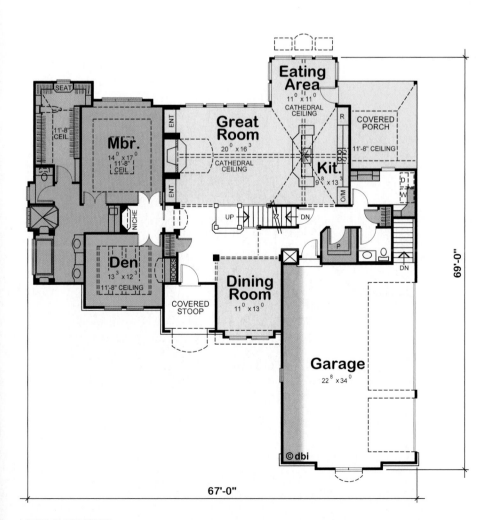

SEAT

11'-8" CEIL

Mbr.
14⁰ x 17⁰
11'-8" CEIL

ENT

Eating Area
11⁰ x 11⁰
CATHEDRAL CEILING

Great Room
20⁰ x 16³
CATHEDRAL CEILING

R

COVERED PORCH
11'-8" CEILING

Kit.
9³ x 13³

O/M

ENT

NICHE

UP

DN

DN

P

D W

Den
13³ x 12³
11'-8" CEILING

BOOKS

COVERED STOOP

Dining Room
11⁰ x 13⁰

Garage
22⁸ x 34⁰

©dbi

69'-0"

67'-0"

the
Kempton
Court
9169-9JJ

pricecode 30

Main Level	2112
Second Level	982
Total Square Ft.	3094

Standard Foundation: Slab

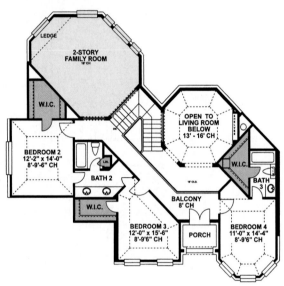

LEDGE

2-STORY FAMILY ROOM 18' CH

W.I.C.

BEDROOM 2 12'-2" x 14'-0" 8'-9'-6" CH

BATH 2

W.I.C.

OPEN TO LIVING ROOM BELOW 13' - 16' CH

18' CLG.

W.I.C.

BATH 3

BALCONY 8' CH

PORCH

BEDROOM 3 12'-0" x 15'-6" 8'-9'6" CH

BEDROOM 4 11'-0" x 14'-4" 8'-9'6" CH

Livability
at a Glance™
- Storing
- Entertaining
- Flexible Living
- De-Stressing

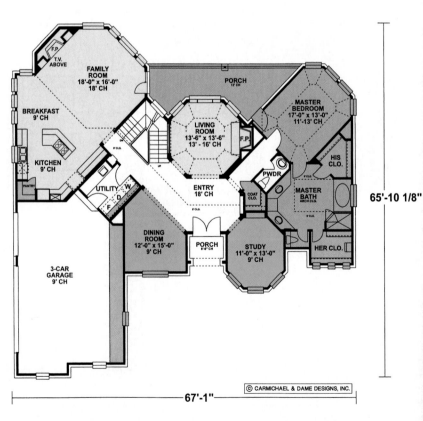

F.P.
T.V. ABOVE

FAMILY ROOM 18'-0" x 16'-0" 18' CH

PORCH 12' CH

MASTER BEDROOM 17'-0" x 13'-0" 11'-13' CH

BREAKFAST 9' CH

LIVING ROOM 13'-6" x 13'-6" 13' - 16' CH

F.P.

HIS CLO.

KITCHEN 9' CH

PANTRY

UTILITY W D F

ENTRY 18' CH

PWDR

COAT CLO.

MASTER BATH ARCH CLO.

3-CAR GARAGE 9' CH

DINING ROOM 12'-0" x 15'-0" 9' CH

PORCH 8'4" CH

STUDY 11'-0" x 13'-0" 9' CH

HER CLO.

65'-10 1/8"

67'-1"

© CARMICHAEL & DAME DESIGNS, INC.

the Dyson
29098-9JJ
pricecode 31

Main Level	**1988**
Second Level	**1136**
Total Square Ft.	**3124**

Standard Foundation: Slab

Livability
at a Glance™

- Storing
- Entertaining
- Flexible Living
- De-Stressing

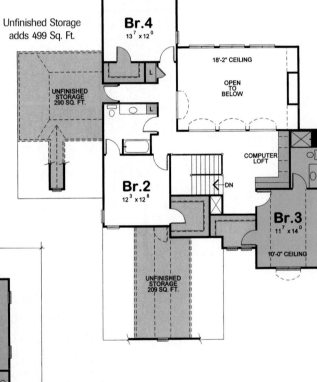

Unfinished Storage
adds 499 Sq. Ft.

Br.4
13⁷ x 12⁰

18'-2" CEILING

OPEN TO BELOW

UNFINISHED STORAGE 290 SQ. FT.

COMPUTER LOFT

Br.2
12³ x 12⁸

DN

Br.3
11⁷ x 14⁰

10'-0" CEILING

UNFINISHED STORAGE 209 SQ. FT.

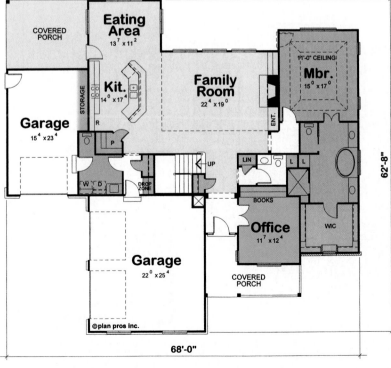

COVERED PORCH

Eating Area
13⁷ x 11²

Kit.
14⁰ x 17⁴

STORAGE

Garage
15⁴ x 23⁴

R

P

W D

DROP ZONE

UP

Family Room
22⁴ x 19⁰

ENT.

11'-0" CEILING

Mbr.
15⁰ x 17⁰

LIN

L L L

BOOKS

Garage
22⁰ x 25⁴

COVERED PORCH

Office
11⁷ x 12⁴

WIC

62'-8"

©plan pros inc.

68'-0"

UP

DROP ZONE

DN

Optional Basement
Stair Location

the
Normandy
2249-9JJ
pricecode 31

Main Level	**2252**
Second Level	**920**
Total Square Ft.	**3172**

Standard Foundation: Basement

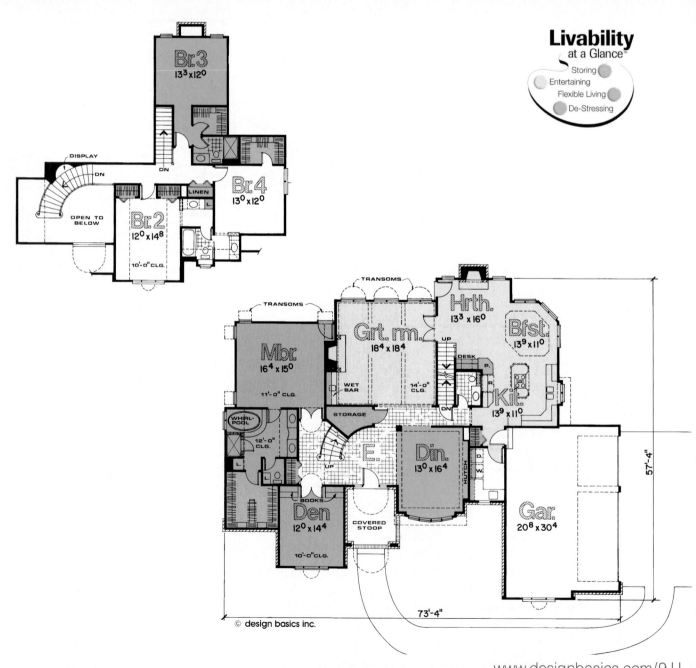

Livability
at a Glance

Storing
Entertaining
Flexible Living
De-Stressing

Br. 3
13³ x 12⁰

DISPLAY

DN

DN

OPEN TO BELOW

Br. 2
12⁰ x 14⁸
10'-0" CLG.

LINEN
L.

Br. 4
13⁰ x 12⁰

TRANSOMS

Hrth.
13³ x 16⁰

Grt. rm.
18⁴ x 18⁴

Bfst.
13⁹ x 11⁰

Mbr.
16⁴ x 15⁰
11'-0" CLG.

UP

DESK
P.
R.

WET BAR

14'-0" CLG.

DN

Kit.
13⁹ x 11⁰

WHIRL-POOL

12'-0" CLG.

STORAGE

E.

UP

Din.
13⁰ x 16⁴

HUTCH
D.
W.

Gar.
20⁸ x 30⁴

BOOKS

Den
12⁰ x 14⁴
10'-0" CLG.

COVERED STOOP

57'-4"

73'-4"

© design basics inc.

www.designbasics.com/9JJ

the
Olsen
30000-9JJ
price**code** 32

Main Level	**2351**
Second Level	**899**
Total Square Ft.	**3250**

Standard Foundation: Basement

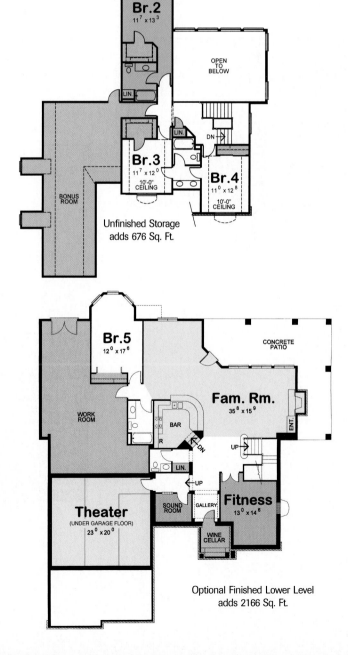

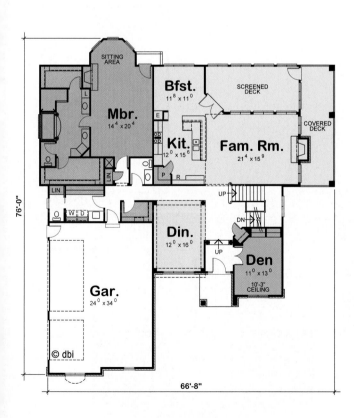

Livability
at a Glance™

- Storing
- Entertaining
- Flexible Living
- De-Stressing

Main Level

SITTING AREA

Bfst.
$11^8 \times 11^0$

SCREENED DECK

Mbr.
$14^4 \times 20^4$

Kit.
$12^0 \times 15^6$

Fam. Rm.
$21^4 \times 15^9$

COVERED DECK

E

LIN.

LIN.

W D

UP

Din.
$12^0 \times 16^0$

DN.

UP

Den
$11^0 \times 13^0$
10'-3" CEILING

Gar.
$24^0 \times 34^0$

© dbi

66'-8"

76'-0"

Second Level

Br.2
$11^7 \times 13^3$

OPEN TO BELOW

LIN.

LIN.

DN

Br.3
$11^7 \times 12^0$
10'-0" CEILING

Br.4
$11^0 \times 12^8$
10'-0" CEILING

BONUS ROOM

Unfinished Storage
adds 676 Sq. Ft.

Lower Level

Br.5
$12^0 \times 17^6$

CONCRETE PATIO

WORK ROOM

BAR

R

Fam. Rm.
$35^8 \times 15^9$

ENT.

DN

UP

LIN.

UP

Theater
(UNDER GARAGE FLOOR)
$23^0 \times 20^0$

SOUND ROOM

GALLERY

WINE CELLAR

Fitness
$13^0 \times 14^8$

Optional Finished Lower Level
adds 2166 Sq. Ft.

the
Valleyford
24084-9JJ
pricecode 32

Main Level	2090
Second Level	1180
Total Square Ft.	3270

Standard Foundation: Slab

Livability
at a Glance

- Storing
- Entertaining
- Flexible Living
- De-Stressing

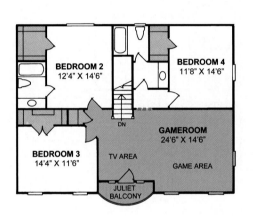

BEDROOM 2
12'4" X 14'6"

BEDROOM 4
11'8" X 14'6"

DN

BEDROOM 3
14'4" X 11'6"

TV AREA

GAMEROOM
24'6" X 14'6"

GAME AREA

JULIET BALCONY

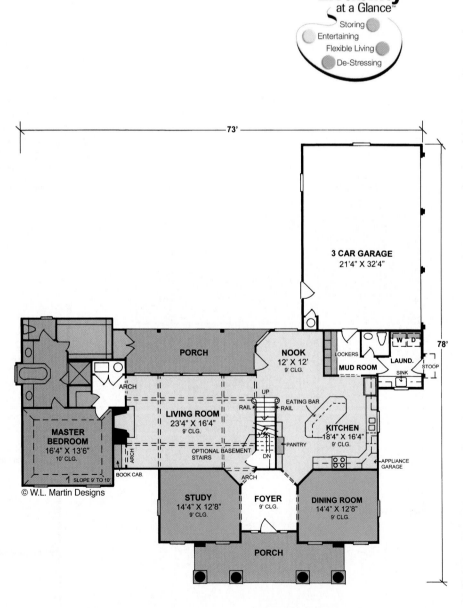

73'

78'

3 CAR GARAGE
21'4" X 32'4"

PORCH

NOOK
12' X 12'
9' CLG.

LOCKERS

W D

LAUND.

MUD ROOM

SINK

STOOP

ARCH

EATING BAR

UP
RAIL   RAIL

LIVING ROOM
23'4" X 16'4"
9' CLG.

KITCHEN
18'4" X 16'4"
9' CLG.

MASTER BEDROOM
16'4" X 13'6"
10' CLG.

ARCH

OPTIONAL BASEMENT STAIRS

DN

PANTRY

APPLIANCE GARAGE

SLOPE 9' TO 10'

BOOK CAB.

© W.L. Martin Designs

STUDY
14'4" X 12'8"
9' CLG.

ARCH

FOYER
9' CLG.

DINING ROOM
14'4" X 12'8"
9' CLG.

PORCH

the
Pomona
24209-9JJ
price code 33

Main Level	**2321**
Second Level	**1060**
Total Square Ft.	**3381**

Standard Foundation: Slab

Livability
at a Glance™

- Storing
- Entertaining
- Flexible Living
- De-Stressing

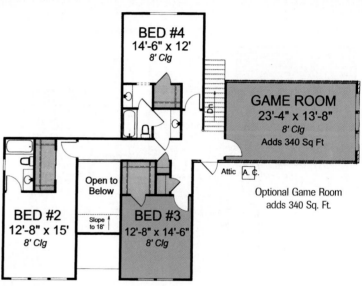

BED #4
14'-6" x 12'
8' Clg

GAME ROOM
23'-4" x 13'-8"
8' Clg
Adds 340 Sq Ft

Attic   A. C.

Optional Game Room
adds 340 Sq. Ft.

BED #2
12'-8" x 15'
8' Clg

Open to
Below

Slope
to 18'

BED #3
12'-8" x 14'-6"
8' Clg

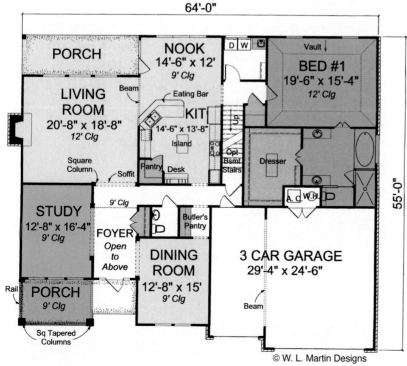

64'-0"

PORCH

NOOK
14'-6" x 12'
9' Clg

D W

Vault ↓

BED #1
19'-6" x 15'-4"
12' Clg

LIVING
ROOM
20'-8" x 18'-8"
12' Clg

Beam

Eating Bar

KIT
14'-6" x 13'-8"

Island

Up

Opt
Bsmt
Stairs

Dresser

Square
Column

Soffit

Pantry   Desk

A. C. W. D.

STUDY
12'-8" x 16'-4"
9' Clg

9' Clg

FOYER
Open to Above

Butler's
Pantry

DINING
ROOM
12'-8" x 15'
9' Clg

3 CAR GARAGE
29'-4" x 24'-6"

Rail

PORCH
9' Clg

Sq Tapered
Columns

Beam

55'-0"

© W. L. Martin Designs

the Drakewood Manor

9138-9JJ

pricecode 33

Main Level	**2144**
Second Level	**1253**
Total Square Ft.	**3397**

Standard Foundation: Slab

Livability at a Glance™

- Storing
- Entertaining
- Flexible Living
- De-Stressing

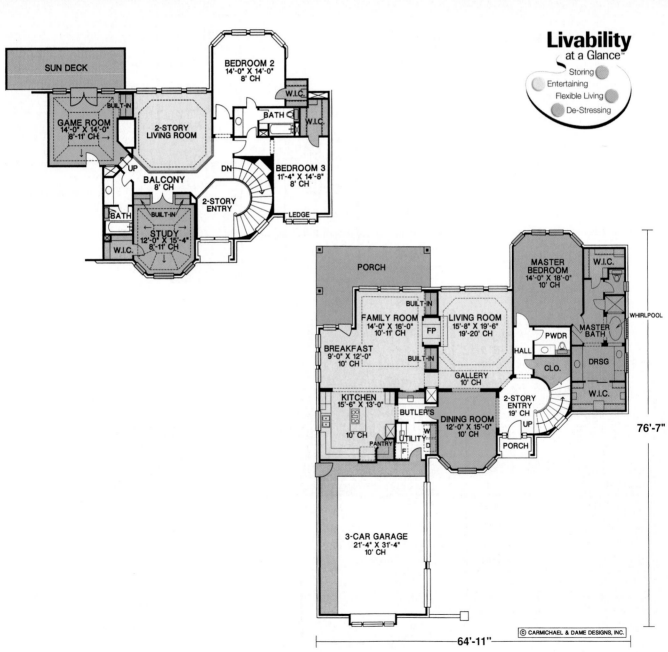

SUN DECK

GAME ROOM
14'-0" X 14'-0"
8'-11' CH →

BUILT-IN

2-STORY
LIVING ROOM

BEDROOM 2
14'-0" X 14'-0"
8' CH

W.I.C.

BATH

W.I.C.

UP

BALCONY
8' CH

DN

2-STORY
ENTRY

BEDROOM 3
11'-4" X 14'-8"
8' CH

LEDGE

BATH

BUILT-IN

STUDY
12'-0" X 15'-4"
8'-11" CH

W.I.C.

PORCH

FAMILY ROOM
14'-0" X 16'-0"
10'-11' CH

BUILT-IN

FP

BUILT-IN

LIVING ROOM
15'-8" X 19'-6"
19'-20' CH

MASTER
BEDROOM
14'-0" X 18'-0"
10' CH

W.I.C.

WHIRLPOOL

BREAKFAST
9'-0" X 12'-0"
10' CH

PWDR

HALL

MASTER
BATH

CLO.

DRSG

KITCHEN
15'-6" X 13'-0"

GALLERY
10' CH

W.I.C.

10' CH

BUTLER'S

DINING ROOM
12'-0" X 15'-0"
10' CH

2-STORY
ENTRY
19' CH

PANTRY

UTILITY

W
D

F

UP

PORCH

3-CAR GARAGE
21'-4" X 31'-4"
10' CH

76'-7"

64'-11"

© CARMICHAEL & DAME DESIGNS, INC.

www.designbasics.com/9JJ

the Humphrey
24187-9JJ

price code 34

Main Level	**2304**
Second Level	**1147**
Total Square Ft.	**3451**

Standard Foundation: Slab

Livability
at a Glance™

- Storing
- Entertaining
- Flexible Living
- De-Stressing

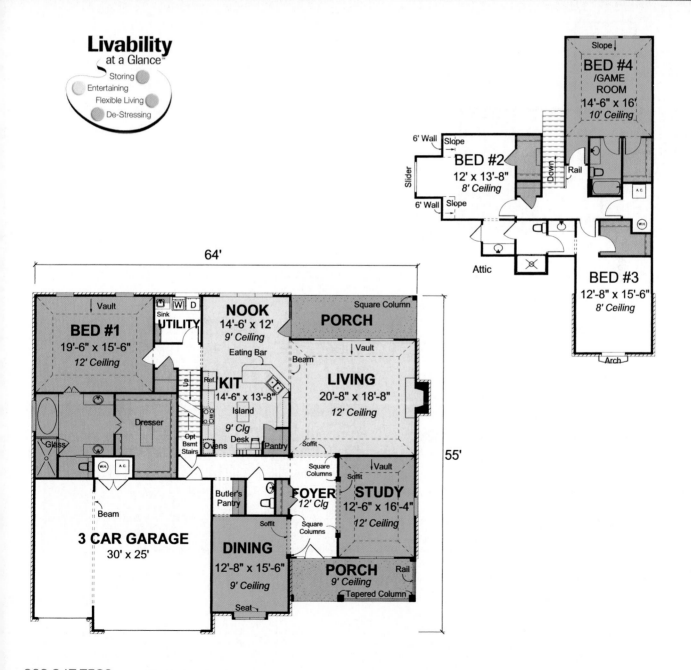

BED #4 /GAME ROOM
14'-6" x 16'
10' Ceiling
Slope

6' Wall | Slope
BED #2
12' x 13'-8"
8' Ceiling
6' Wall | Slope
Slider

Down
Rail

A.C.

W.H.

Attic

BED #3
12'-8" x 15'-6"
8' Ceiling
Arch

64'

55'

Vault
BED #1
19'-6" x 15'-6"
12' Ceiling

Sink
W | D
UTILITY

NOOK
14'-6" x 12'
9' Ceiling

Square Column
PORCH

Eating Bar
Beam
Vault

Ref.
KIT
14'-6" x 13'-8"
Island
9' Clg

LIVING
20'-8" x 18'-8"
12' Ceiling

Dresser

Opt Bsmt Stairs
Ovens
Desk
Pantry
Soffit

Glass
W.H. | A.C.

Square Columns
Vault
Soffit

Beam

Butler's Pantry

FOYER
12' Clg

STUDY
12'-6" x 16'-4"
12' Ceiling

3 CAR GARAGE
30' x 25'

Soffit
Square Columns

DINING
12'-8" x 15'-6"
9' Ceiling

PORCH
9' Ceiling
Rail

Seat
Tapered Column

Main Level	2500
Second Level	973
Total Square Ft.	3473

Standard Foundation: Basement

Br
11x14²

CLOTHES
CHUTE IN LIN.

DN   DN

Br
14⁰x13⁶

OPEN TO
BELOW

Br
14⁰x13¹

TRANSOMS

Livability
at a Glance™

Storing
Entertaining
Flexible Living
De-Stressing

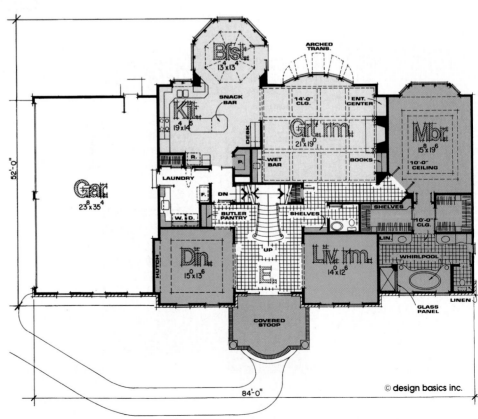

Bfst
13⁴x13⁴

ARCHED
TRANS.

Kit
19x14

SNACK
BAR

14'-0"
CLG.

ENT.
CENTER

Grt rm
21⁶x19⁰

Mbr
15⁶x19⁶

10'-0"
CEILING

DESK

Gar
23⁸x35⁴

WET
BAR

BOOKS

P.

R.

LAUNDRY

F.

DN

SHELVES

10'-0"
CLG.

52'-0"

W. D.

BUTLER
PANTRY

SHELVES

LIN

HUTCH

Dn
15⁰x13⁶

UP

Liv rm
14⁰x12⁶

WHIRLPOOL

GLASS
PANEL

LINEN

COVERED
STOOP

© design basics inc.

84'-0"

the Stallworth

29141-9JJ
price code 35

Main Level	**2135**
Second Level	**1410**
Total Square Ft.	**3545**

Standard Foundation: Basement

Livability
at a Glance™

- Storing
- Entertaining
- Flexible Living
- De-Stressing

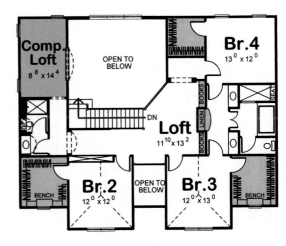

Comp. Loft 8⁸ x 14⁴

OPEN TO BELOW

Br.4 13⁰ x 12⁰

DN

Loft 11¹⁰ x 13²

Br.2 12⁰ x 12⁰

OPEN TO BELOW

Br.3 12⁰ x 13⁰

BENCH

BENCH

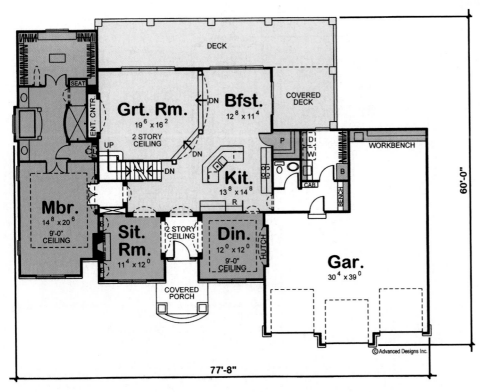

DECK

Grt. Rm. 19⁶ x 16² 2 STORY CEILING

Bfst. 12⁸ x 11⁴

COVERED DECK

WORKBENCH

Kit. 13⁸ x 14⁸

UP

Mbr. 14⁸ x 20⁶ 9'-0" CEILING

Sit. Rm. 11⁴ x 12⁰

2 STORY CEILING

Din. 12⁰ x 12⁰ 9'-0" CEILING

Gar. 30⁴ x 39⁰

COVERED PORCH

60'-0"

77'-8"

© Advanced Designs Inc.

the
Winchester
2475-9JJ
price code 35

Main Level	2555
Second Level	1001
Total Square Ft.	3556

Standard Foundation: Basement

Br.3
13⁰ x 14⁰
9' - 0" CLG.

LINEN

DN
9' - 0"
CLG.
DN

OPEN
TO
BELOW

Br.4
13⁵ x 13⁰
9' - 0" CLG.

SEAT

Br.2
13⁰ x 14⁰
9' - 0" CEILING

Livability
at a Glance™

Storing
Entertaining
Flexible Living
De-Stressing

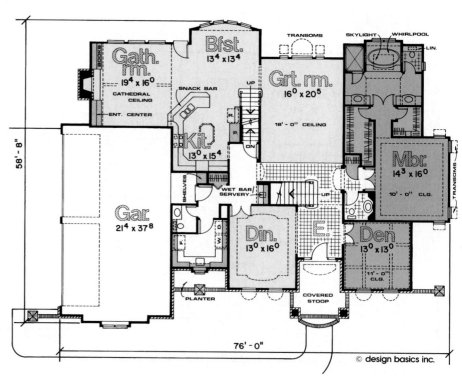

Gath.
rm.
19⁴ x 16⁰

CATHEDRAL
CEILING

ENT. CENTER

BOOKS

Bfst.
13⁴ x 13⁴

SNACK BAR

TRANSOMS

SKYLIGHT   WHIRLPOOL

Grt. rm.
16⁰ x 20⁵

18' - 0" CEILING

UP

Kit.
13⁰ x 15⁴

58' - 8"

SHELVES

WET BAR/
SERVERY

Gar.
21⁴ x 37⁸

W D

F.

PLANTER

Din.
13⁰ x 16⁰

UP

E.

COVERED
STOOP

LIN.

Mbr.
14³ x 16⁰

10' - 0" CLG.

TRANSOMS

Den
13⁰ x 13⁰

11' - 0"
CLG.

76' - 0"

© design basics inc.

the Canterbury

2411-9JJ

price code 36

Main Level	**2603**
Second Level	**1020**
Total Square Ft.	**3623**

Standard Foundation: Basement

Livability
at a Glance™

- Storing
- Entertaining
- Flexible Living
- De-Stressing

© design basics inc.

the
Le Grand
2218-9JJ
price code 36

Main Level	**2617**
Second Level	**1072**
Total Square Ft.	**3689**

Standard Foundation: Basement

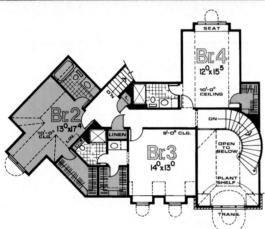

Livability
at a Glance™

Storing
Entertaining
Flexible Living
De-Stressing

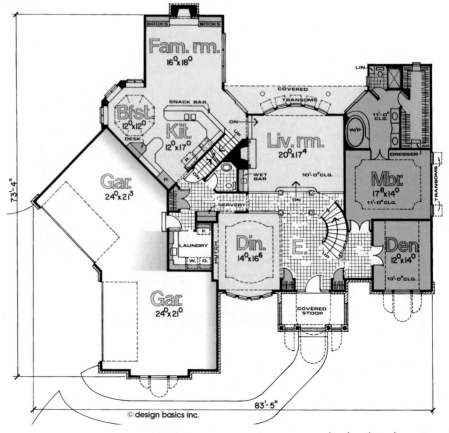

© design basics inc.

the
Oak Grove
Estate
9143-9JJ

price code 37

Main Level	**2274**
Second Level	**1476**
Total Square Ft.	**3750**

Standard Foundation: Slab

Livability
at a Glance™

- Storing
- Entertaining
- Flexible Living
- De-Stressing

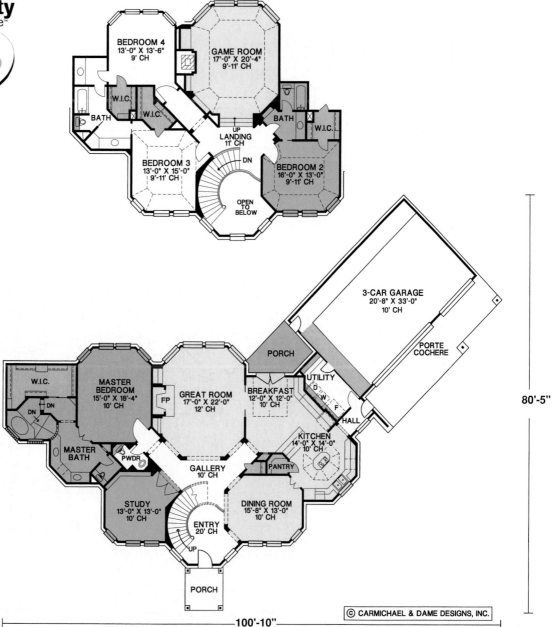

Second Level

BEDROOM 4
13'-0" X 13'-6"
9' CH

GAME ROOM
17'-0" X 20'-4"
9'-11" CH

W.I.C.

BATH

W.I.C.

BATH

W.I.C.

UP
LANDING
11' CH

BEDROOM 3
13'-0" X 15'-0"
9'-11" CH

DN

BEDROOM 2
16'-0" X 13'-0"
9'-11' CH

OPEN
TO
BELOW

Main Level

3-CAR GARAGE
20'-8" X 33'-0"
10' CH

PORCH

PORTE
COCHERE

W.I.C.

MASTER
BEDROOM
15'-0" X 18'-4"
10' CH

FP

GREAT ROOM
17'-0" X 22'-0"
12' CH

BREAKFAST
12'-0" X 12'-0"
10' CH

UTILITY

D W

F

HALL

DN

DN

MASTER
BATH

PWDR

GALLERY
10' CH

PANTRY

KITCHEN
14'-0" X 14'-0"
10' CH

STUDY
13'-0" X 13'-0"
10' CH

ENTRY
20' CH

DINING ROOM
15'-8" X 13'-0"
10' CH

UP

PORCH

80'-5"

100'-10"

the
Fairchild
2733-9JJ
pricecode 39

Main Level	**2813**
Second Level	**1091**
Total Square Ft.	**3904**

Standard Foundation: Basement

Livability
at a Glance™

- Storing
- Entertaining
- Flexible Living
- De-Stressing

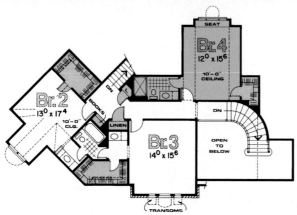

Br. 2 13⁰ x 17⁴ — 10'-0" CLG.

Br. 4 12⁰ x 15⁶ — 10'-0" CEILING — SEAT

BOOKS — DN — LINEN

Br. 3 14⁰ x 15⁶

OPEN TO BELOW — DN

TRANSOMS

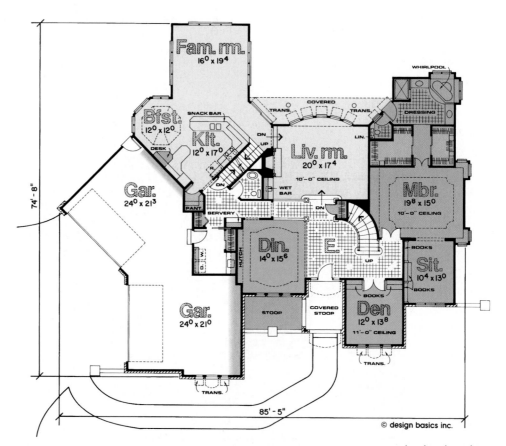

Fam. rm. 16⁰ x 19⁴

Bfst. 12⁰ x 12⁰ — DESK

Kit. 12⁰ x 17⁰ — SNACK BAR

COVERED — TRANS. — TRANS.

WHIRLPOOL — DRESSING

Liv. rm. 20⁰ x 17⁴ — 10'-0" CEILING — LIN.

Gar. 24⁰ x 21³

WET BAR — BEVERVY — PANT

Mbr. 19⁸ x 15⁰ — 10'-0" CEILING — BOOKS

Din. 14⁰ x 15⁶ — HUTCH

E.

Sit. 10⁴ x 13⁰ — BOOKS — BOOKS

Gar. 24⁰ x 21⁰

STOOP — COVERED STOOP

Den 12⁰ x 13⁸ — 11'-0" CEILING — BOOKS

TRANS.

74'- 8"

85'- 5"

TRANS.

© design basics inc.

the Meadowview Manor

9114-9JJ

price code 41

Main Level	**2489**
Second Level	**1650**
Total Square Ft.	**4139**

Standard Foundation: Slab

Livability
at a Glance™

- Storing
- Entertaining
- Flexible Living
- De-Stressing

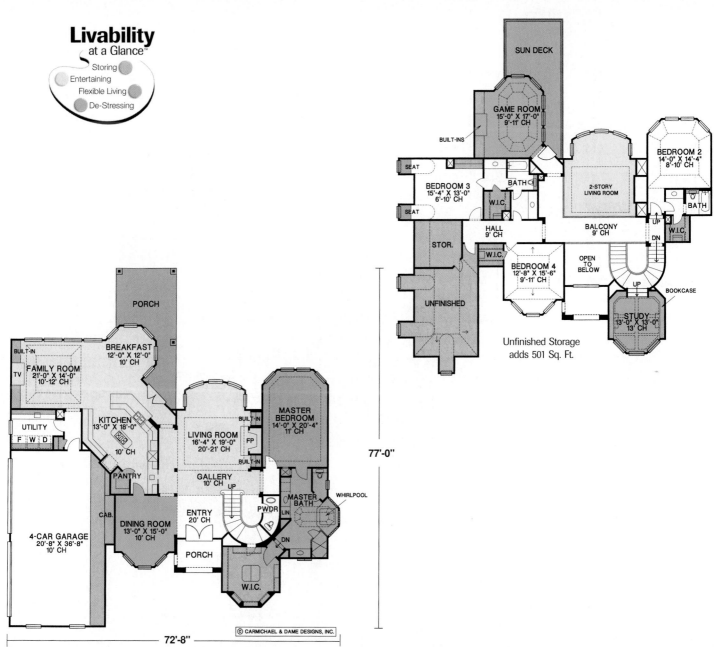

SUN DECK

GAME ROOM
15'-0" X 17'-0"
9'-11" CH

BUILT-INS

SEAT

BEDROOM 3
15'-4" X 13'-0"
6'-10" CH

BATH

W.I.C.

BEDROOM 2
14'-0" X 14'-4"
8'-10" CH

BATH

W.I.C.

SEAT

2-STORY
LIVING ROOM

UP

DN

HALL
9' CH

W.I.C.

STOR.

W.I.C.

BALCONY
9' CH

BEDROOM 4
12'-8" X 15'-6"
9'-11" CH

OPEN
TO
BELOW

UP

BOOKCASE

UNFINISHED

STUDY
13'-0" X 13'-0"
13' CH

Unfinished Storage
adds 501 Sq. Ft.

PORCH

BREAKFAST
12'-0" X 12'-0"
10' CH

BUILT-IN

TV

FAMILY ROOM
21'-0" X 14'-0"
10'-12' CH

KITCHEN
13'-0" X 18'-0"
10' CH

BUILT-IN

LIVING ROOM
16'-4" X 19'-0"
20'-21' CH

FP

MASTER
BEDROOM
14'-0" X 20'-4"
11' CH

BUILT-IN

UTILITY

F W D

PANTRY

GALLERY
10' CH

UP

MASTER
BATH

WHIRLPOOL

CAB.

4-CAR GARAGE
20'-8" X 36'-8"
10' CH

DINING ROOM
13'-0" X 15'-0"
10' CH

ENTRY
20' CH

PWDR

LIN

LIN

DN

PORCH

W.I.C.

77'-0"

72'-8"

© CARMICHAEL & DAME DESIGNS, INC.

the Ashwood Manor
9254-9JJ
price code 42

Main Level	**3337**
Second Level	**1292**
Total Square Ft.	**4629**

Standard Foundation: Slab

Unfinished Storage
adds 191 Sq. Ft.

Livability
at a Glance™

Storing
Entertaining
Flexible Living
De-Stressing

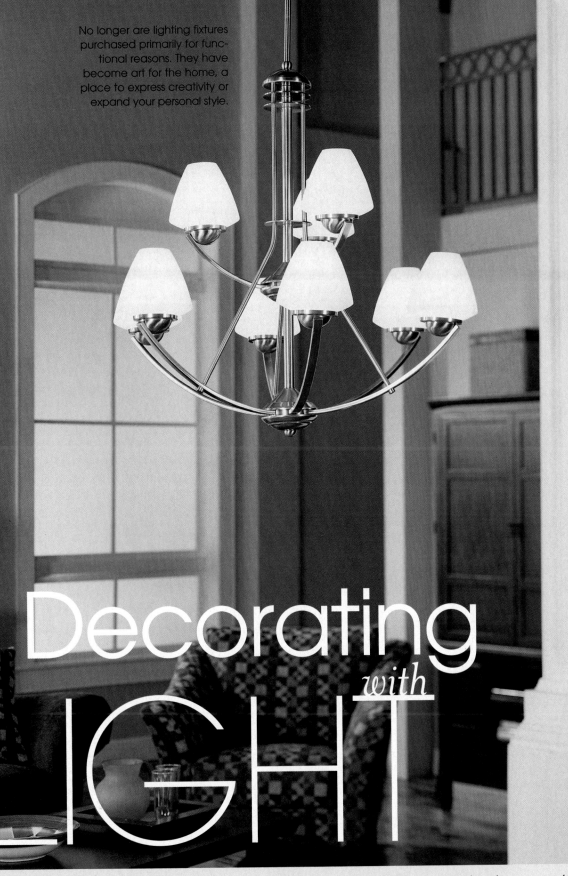

No longer are lighting fixtures purchased primarily for functional reasons. They have become art for the home, a place to express creativity or expand your personal style.

Decorating *with* LIGHT

Before you build or redecorate, note that planning your lighting will make a tremendous difference in the total look and functional convenience of your home. Lighting is an integral part of your environment. It affects the mood, the color, the safety, the convenience and the decorative quality of your home.

Lighting can help you relax and can also keep you awake. Too much or too little illumination in a room can make you feel tired and fatigued. So it is very important to plan the lighting in your rooms according to their function, balanced by the look you are attempting to achieve.

Proper lighting is also critical from a safety and security standpoint. Whether it's viewing the perimeter of your home, working around the house or moving through it, lighting plays a major role in your safety. (It's helpful to remember we require more light to assist us in daily tasks as our eyes age.)

Lighting styles can be selected to complement and enhance most decorative themes. The combined effects of direct and ambient lighting can achieve spectacular decorating results and add drama to wall coverings, art objects and floral arrangements.

CHOOSING YOUR LIGHT FIXTURES. There are no strict rules to follow when choosing fixtures, but it's wise to establish a pleasing visual flow throughout the home – especially in adjoining rooms where you are able to view one room from another. One way to do this is by carrying a single design element throughout the rooms – perhaps the same type or color of glass, metal finish or design detail (such as carved leaves). Another thing to consider is the size of the fixtures – to ensure that they provide the desired illumination and that their size blends with the scale of other furnishings. Different areas of the home require unique considerations.

FOYER LIGHTING. Your foyer's lighting reflects your sense of style and pride in your home and establishes the decorative theme for the rest of the interior. It should provide ample illumination for a welcome greeting by casting a soft, congenial light. The fixture can be ceiling mounted or chain hung. If the foyer is large enough, you may choose a chandelier. The height and location must allow ample clearance for the door.

FAMILY ROOMS. The family room, which is usually multi-faceted, needs various lighting sources, such as recessed downlighting and portable lamps. You'll need to avoid placing fixtures where they will produce glare on television or computer monitors. Note too, that many plasma, flat screen and large screen televisions require low-level illumination so the image will not appear to be washed out.

LIVING ROOMS. Most living rooms benefit from a combination of general and accent lighting. A quiet comfortable mood, ideal for relaxed conversation and reading, can be accomplished with wall brackets, directed accent lighting (such as lights in a display cabinet) and table or floor lamps.

BEDROOMS. Today's bedrooms are used for reading, studying and video watching – as well as sleeping and dressing. Some people prefer subdued lighting in the bedroom, achieved by lamps on night stands or rope lighting hidden in a boxed ceiling. Children's and older adults' (50+) bedrooms will require more light. For children's study areas, a hanging light or a desk lamp should be used approximately 15" - 18" from the front of the desk and off to one side.

BATH/DRESSING ROOM AREAS. Larger rooms will require a combination of ambient, accent and task lighting. Wall sconces at eye level on either side of the vanity mirror will help prevent the dark shadows common with overhead lighting. This lighting should not be directed onto the mirror surface, but instead, illuminate the face. A partitioned bath or shower will require a minimum of a 75-watt light. Recessed ceiling lights and hanging lights are popular in larger baths. Rope lighting hidden in ceiling details or in the toe space of cabinetry can provide a pleasing effect at night.

KITCHENS. Because of the multiple tasks performed in the kitchen, the primary objective in choosing lighting should be function, followed by decorative appeal. Bright, well-diffused, evenly spaced lighting sources from the ceiling are a dependable way to ensure all open spaces are free of annoying shadows or glare. Ceiling lights (either pendant or recessed) should also illuminate the counters and the inside of the kitchen cabinets. Work areas – counters, sinks and ranges – may need task lighting provided by under-cabinet lighting. Decorative pendant lights are often used above snack bars, islands or dining areas.

ABOVE: When choosing lighting for the home, keep in mind your surroundings. Light colors and reflective surfaces will require less wattage while dark or porous surfaces will require more. The reflection of the light source in the mirror will enhance the light output which is so critical in the bathroom.

RIGHT: Many fixtures today feature elaborate, hand-painted finishes. This complexity can either enhance existing complementary finishes in the interior, or can act as a focal point by contrasting with the surrounding surfaces. Both directions can be equally rewarding.

1

2

3

4

1 Interiors today benefit from the texture and warmth provided by the growing emergence of specialty glass. Color, surface design and a vast array of glass finishing techniques offer unique ways to bring dimension and interest to home lighting.

2 Time and time again the kitchen table has proven itself the primary gathering space in the home. A fixture with light shining down can provide the necessary illumination for homework, reading the paper and, of course, dining.

3 If strengthening a current interior design direction is your goal, consider existing architectural elements, color schemes, and furniture details. The simple and clean lines of these fixtures further define the already present Mission Style.

4 The hand-forged leaves and textured scavo glass of this pendant embody all that is rustic in this country kitchen.

DINING ROOMS. The most frequently asked question regarding chandeliers in dining rooms is "How high should they be hung?" The general answer is 30" - 36" above the table. While there should be a minimum of 150 total watts in the fixture, you may want to use a dimmer to vary the illumination to match your preferred dining atmosphere. This will allow you to choose a bright, cheerful light for family dinners and a softer light for formal dinners.

Other lighting possibilities in the dining room include wall sconces on either side of a mirror or above a sideboard or serving table, recessed lighting in the corners of the room (which will visually expand the room) and accent lights inside a display cabinet. ■

Lighting Tips

Plan for all the functional and decorative lighting you require, so the wiring can be installed at the correct time during the construction period. This is especially critical for recessed lighting.

Plan your switch locations so that you can walk from one lighted area to the next lighted area without having to go back and turn off a light.

Make sure you have plenty of outlets throughout the home, including the halls and foyer, where you might need additional lamps (and plug-ins for the vacuum cleaner).

Don't forget the aesthetic and energy saving potential of dimmers and other lighting control systems.

Plan your outdoor light controls in easily accessible locations. For added security, you may want to include an outdoor light controlled by a photocell.

Include all the areas where you may need additional lighting – such as the shower, closets, stairways and under kitchen cabinets.

For more information about decorating your home with light, contact Thomas Lighting at 800-825-5844 or visit ThomasLighting.com.

the
Alenhurst
5470-9JJ
pricecode 15

Main Level	**842**
Second Level	**722**
Total Square Ft.	**1564**

Standard Foundation: Basement

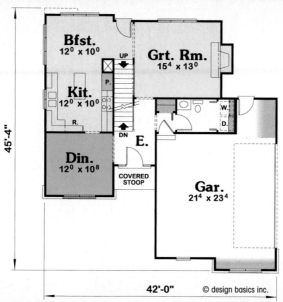

Bfst. 12⁰ x 10⁰

Grt. Rm. 15⁴ x 13⁰

UP

Kit. 12⁰ x 10⁰

P.

R.

DN

E.

Din. 12⁰ x 10⁸

COVERED STOOP

W.
D.

Gar. 21⁴ x 23⁴

45'-4"

42'-0"   © design basics inc.

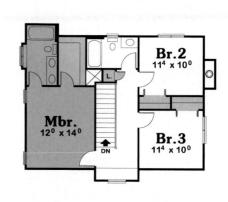

Br. 2 11⁴ x 10⁰

L.

Mbr. 12⁰ x 14⁰

DN

Br. 3 11⁴ x 10⁰

---

the
Bartels
2579-9JJ
pricecode 15

Main Level	**869**
Second Level	**725**
Total Square Ft.	**1594**

Standard Foundation: Basement

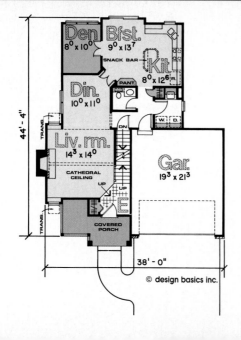

Den 8⁰ x 10⁰

Bfst. 9⁰ x 13⁷

SNACK BAR

Kit 8⁰ x 12⁶

R.

PANT.

Din. 10⁰ x 11⁰

TRANS.

W. D.

DN

Liv. rm. 14³ x 14⁰

CATHEDRAL CEILING

UP UP

E.

Gar. 19³ x 21³

TRANS.

COVERED PORCH

44'-4"

38'-0"

© design basics inc.

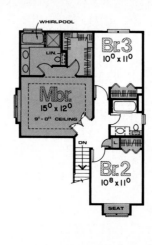

WHIRLPOOL

LIN.

Br. 3 10⁰ x 11⁰

Mbr. 15⁰ x 12⁰
9'-0" CEILING

L.

DN

Br. 2 10⁸ x 11⁰

SEAT

Livability at a Glance™

Storing
Entertaining
Flexible Living
De-Stressing

www.designbasics.com/9JJ

the Arbor
2526-9JJ
price code 16

Main Level	**845**
Second Level	**760**
Total Square Ft.	**1605**

Standard Foundation: Basement

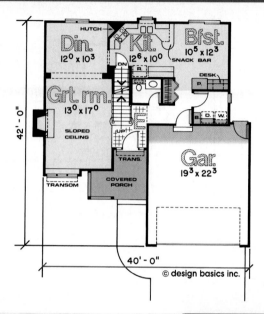

Din. 12⁰ x 10³
HUTCH
Kit. 12⁶ x 10⁰
Bfst. 10⁵ x 12³
SNACK BAR
DESK
P.
Grt. rm. 13⁰ x 17⁰
SLOPED CEILING
DN
UP
TRANS.
D W
Gar. 19³ x 22³
COVERED PORCH
TRANSOM

42'- 0"
40'- 0"

© design basics inc.

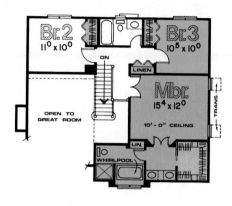

Br. 2 11⁰ x 10⁰
Br. 3 10⁵ x 10⁰
LINEN
DN
Mbr. 15⁴ x 12⁰
10'- 0" CEILING
TRANS.
OPEN TO GREAT ROOM
WHIRLPOOL
LIN.

the Wendell
43028-9JJ
price code 16

Main Level	**807**
Second Level	**842**
Total Square Ft.	**1649**

Standard Foundation: Slab

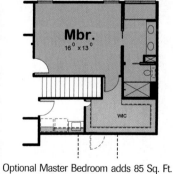

Mbr. 16⁰ x 13⁰
WIC

Optional Master Bedroom adds 85 Sq. Ft.

Livability
at a Glance™

Storing
Entertaining
Flexible Living
De-Stressing

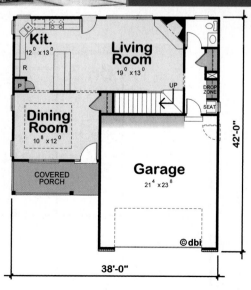

Kit. 12⁰ x 13⁰
Living Room 19⁰ x 13⁰
R
P
Dining Room 10⁸ x 12⁰
DROP ZONE
SEAT
UP
Garage 21⁴ x 23⁸
COVERED PORCH

© dbi

42'-0"
38'-0"

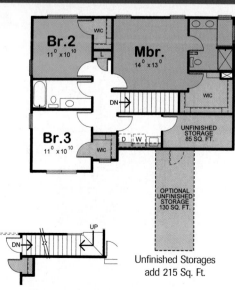

Br. 2 11⁰ x 10¹⁰
WIC
L
Mbr. 14⁰ x 13⁰
WIC
DN
Br. 3 11⁰ x 10¹⁰
WIC
D W
UNFINISHED STORAGE 85 SQ. FT.
OPTIONAL UNFINISHED STORAGE 130 SQ. FT.

DN
UP
Optional Basement Stair Location adds 8 Sq. Ft.

Unfinished Storages add 215 Sq. Ft.

800.947.7526

207

the
Laverton
2248-9JJ
pricecode 16

Main Level	**891**
Second Level	**759**
Total Square Ft.	**1650**

Standard Foundation: Basement

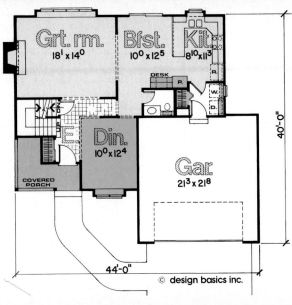

Grt. rm. 18¹ x 14⁰
Bfst. 10⁰ x 12⁵
Kit. 8¹⁰ x 11³
DESK
P.
R.
W.
D.
UP DN
Din. 10⁰ x 12⁴
Gar. 21³ x 21⁸
COVERED PORCH
40'-0"
44'-0"
© design basics inc.

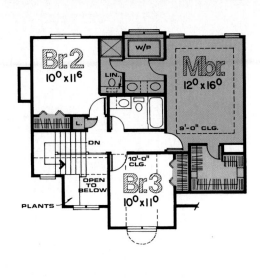

Br. 2 10⁰ x 11⁶
w/p
LIN.
Mbr. 12⁰ x 16⁰
9'-0" CLG.
L.
DN
10'-0" CLG.
OPEN TO BELOW
Br. 3 10⁰ x 11⁰
PLANTS

the
Harbor Lane
8139-9JJ
pricecode 16

Main Level	**866**
Second Level	**788**
Total Square Ft.	**1654**

Standard Foundation: Basement

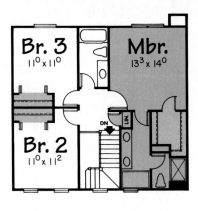

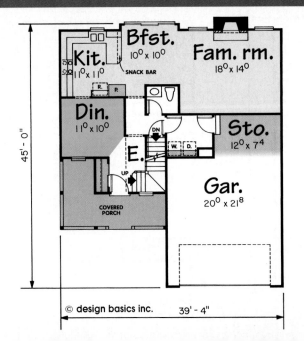

Kit. 11⁰ x 11⁰
Bfst. 10⁰ x 10⁰
Fam. rm. 18⁰ x 14⁰
SNACK BAR
R. R.
Din. 11⁰ x 10⁰
DN
E.
W. D.
Sto. 12⁰ x 7⁴
UP
COVERED PORCH
Gar. 20⁰ x 21⁸
45'-0"
39'-4"
© design basics inc.

Br. 3 11⁰ x 11⁰
Mbr. 13³ x 14⁰
DN
LIN.
Br. 2 11⁰ x 11²

Livability
at a Glance™

Storing
Entertaining
Flexible Living
De-Stressing

www.designbasics.com/9JJ

the Menlo
43029-9JJ
pricecode 16

Main Level	**807**
Second Level	**853**
Total Square Ft.	**1660**

Standard Foundation: Slab

Mbr.
16⁰ x 13⁰

WIC

Optional Master Bedroom
adds 85 Sq. Ft.

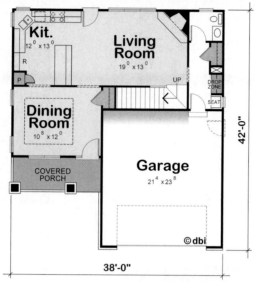

Kit.
12⁰ x 13⁰

Living Room
19⁰ x 13⁰

UP

DROP ZONE

SEAT

Dining Room
10⁸ x 12⁰

COVERED PORCH

Garage
21⁴ x 23⁸

© dbi

38'-0"

42'-0"

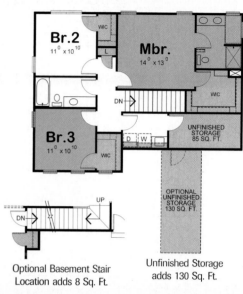

Br.2
11⁰ x 10¹⁰

WIC

Mbr.
14⁰ x 13⁰

DN

WIC

Br.3
11⁰ x 10¹⁰

WIC

D W

UNFINISHED STORAGE 85 SQ. FT.

OPTIONAL UNFINISHED STORAGE 130 SQ. FT.

DN UP

Optional Basement Stair
Location adds 8 Sq. Ft.

Unfinished Storage
adds 130 Sq. Ft.

the Adams Creek
8105-9JJ
pricecode 16

Main Level	**910**
Second Level	**775**
Total Square Ft.	**1685**

Standard Foundation: Basement

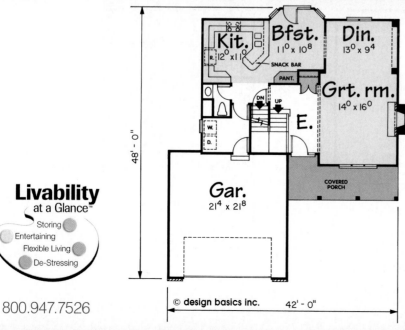

Kit.
R. 12⁰ x 11⁰

Bfst.
11⁰ x 10⁸

Din.
13⁰ x 9⁴

SNACK BAR

PANT.

DN UP

E.

Grt. rm.
14⁰ x 16⁰

W.

D.

Gar.
21⁴ x 21⁸

COVERED PORCH

48'-0"

42'-0"

© design basics inc.

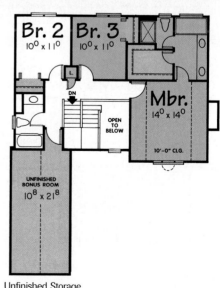

Br. 2
10⁰ x 11⁰

Br. 3
10⁰ x 11⁰

L

DN

OPEN TO BELOW

Mbr.
14⁰ x 14⁰

10'-0" CLG.

UNFINISHED BONUS ROOM
10⁸ x 21⁸

Unfinished Storage
adds 262 Sq. Ft.

Livability
at a Glance™

Storing
Entertaining
Flexible Living
De-Stressing

the
Ashworth
3103-9JJ
pricecode 17

Main Level	**904**
Second Level	**796**
Total Square Ft.	**1700**

Standard Foundation: Basement

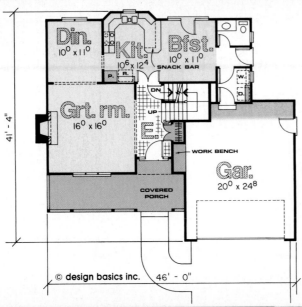

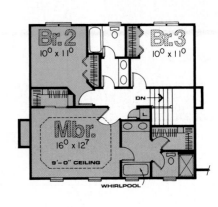

© design basics inc.

the
Englewood
5469-9JJ
pricecode 17

Main Level	**948**
Second Level	**758**
Total Square Ft.	**1706**

Standard Foundation: Basement

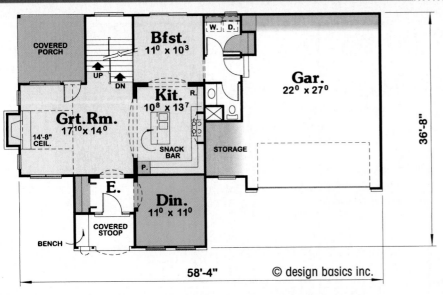

© design basics inc.

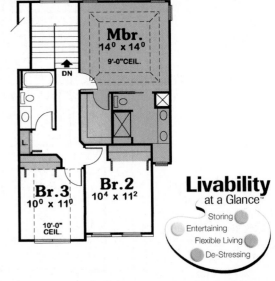

Livability
at a Glance™

Storing
Entertaining
Flexible Living
De-Stressing

www.designbasics.com/9JJ

the Deming
2545-9JJ
price code 17

Main Level	**845**
Second Level	**883**
Total Square Ft.	**1728**

Standard Foundation: Basement

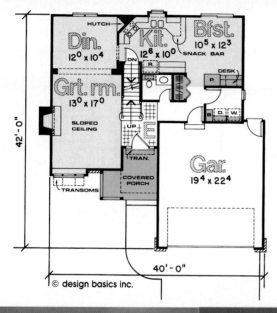

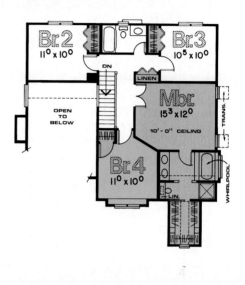

© design basics inc.

the Jefferson
2890-9JJ
price code 17

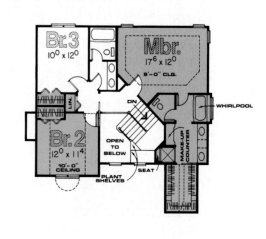

Main Level	**884**
Second Level	**848**
Total Square Ft.	**1732**

Standard Foundation: Basement

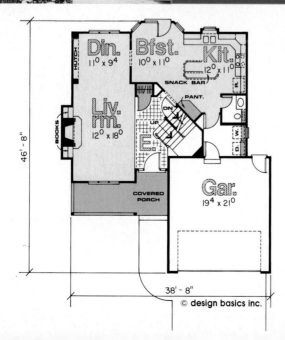

© design basics inc.

Livability
at a Glance

Storing
Entertaining
Flexible Living
De-Stressing

the Linden Acres
8029-9JJ
pricecode 17

Main Level	860
Second Level	893
Total Square Ft.	1753

Standard Foundation: Basement

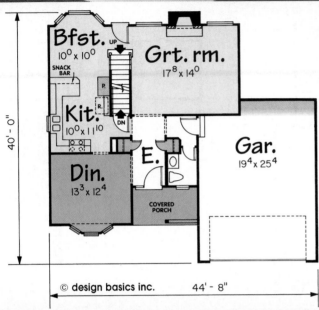

Bfst.
$10^0 \times 10^0$

SNACK BAR

Grt. rm.
$17^8 \times 14^0$

UP

P.

R.

DN

Kit.
$10^0 \times 11^{10}$

Din.
$13^3 \times 12^4$

E.

Gar.
$19^4 \times 25^4$

COVERED PORCH

40' - 0"

© design basics inc.   44' - 8"

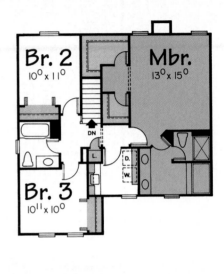

Br. 2
$10^0 \times 11^0$

Mbr.
$13^0 \times 15^0$

DN

L.

D.

W.

Br. 3
$10^{11} \times 10^0$

---

the Torrey
3096-9JJ
pricecode 17

Main Level	905
Second Level	863
Total Square Ft.	1768

Standard Foundation: Basement

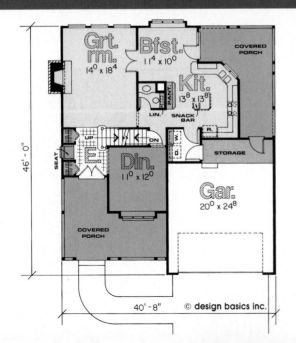

Grt. rm.
$14^0 \times 18^4$

Bfst.
$11^4 \times 10^0$

COVERED PORCH

Kit.
$13^8 \times 13^8$

PANT.

LIN.

SNACK BAR

UP

DN

D.

W.

R.

STORAGE

E.

SEAT

Din.
$11^0 \times 12^0$

Gar.
$20^0 \times 24^8$

COVERED PORCH

46' - 0"

40' - 8"   © design basics inc.

WHIRLPOOL

SEAT

Mbr.
$13^0 \times 14^4$

CATHEDRAL CEILING

SKYLIGHT

LIN.

DN

Br. 2
$10^0 \times 12^0$

Br. 3
$11^0 \times 10^0$

10'-0" CLG.

SEAT

Livability at a Glance™

Storing

Entertaining

Flexible Living

De-Stressing

www.designbasics.com/9JJ

the Paige
3581-9JJ
price code 17

Main Level	866
Second Level	905
Total Square Ft.	1771

Standard Foundation: Basement

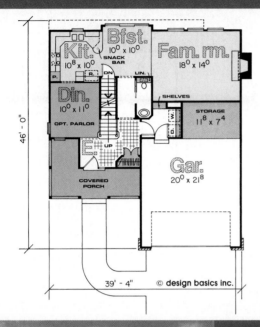

Kit. 10⁸ x 10⁰
Bfst. 10⁰ x 10⁰
Fam. rm. 18⁰ x 14⁰
SNACK BAR
Din. 10⁰ x 11⁰
OPT. PARLOR
LIN.
SHELVES
STORAGE 11⁸ x 7⁴
Gar. 20⁰ x 21⁸
COVERED PORCH
46' - 0"
39' - 4"
© design basics inc.

Br. 4 10⁰ x 10⁶
Mbr. 13⁰ x 16⁰
Br. 3 10⁰ x 10⁰
Br. 2 10⁰ x 10⁸
WHIRL-POOL
OPTIONAL TOY CLOSET
PLANT SHELF
OPEN TO BELOW
SEAT

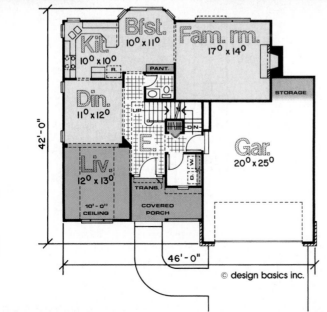

the Juniper
2308-9JJ
price code 17

Main Level	1032
Second Level	743
Total Square Ft.	1775

Standard Foundation: Basement

Kit. 10⁰ x 10⁰
Bfst. 10⁰ x 11⁰
Fam. rm. 17⁰ x 14⁰
PANT.
STORAGE
Din. 11⁰ x 12⁰
Gar. 20⁰ x 25⁰
Liv. 12⁰ x 13⁰
10' - 0" CEILING
TRANS.
COVERED PORCH
42' - 0"
46' - 0"
© design basics inc.

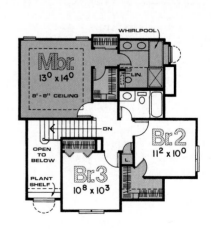

Mbr. 13⁰ x 14⁰
8' - 8" CEILING
WHIRLPOOL
LIN.
Br. 2 11² x 10⁰
Br. 3 10⁸ x 10³
OPEN TO BELOW
PLANT SHELF

Livability at a Glance
- Storing
- Entertaining
- Flexible Living
- De-Stressing

the
Francis
2952-9JJ
pricecode 17

Main Level	**976**
Second Level	**823**
Total Square Ft.	**1799**

Standard Foundation: Basement

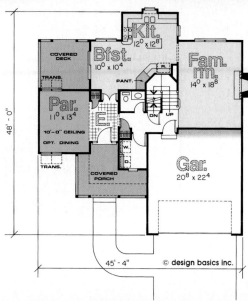

COVERED DECK

TRANS.

Par.
11⁰ x 13⁴
10'-0" CEILING
OPT. DINING

TRANS.

Bfst.
10⁰ x 10⁴

PANT.

Kit.
12⁰ x 12⁸

Fam. rm.
14⁰ x 18⁸

E.

W.

D.

DN UP

R.

Gar.
20⁸ x 22⁴

COVERED PORCH

48' - 0"

45' - 4"

© design basics inc.

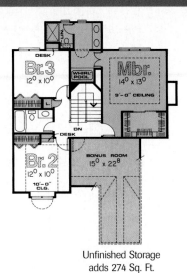

DESK

Br. 3
12⁰ x 10⁰

WHIRL-POOL

Mbr.
14⁰ x 13⁰
9'-0" CEILING

L.

DN

DESK

Br. 2
12⁰ x 10⁰
10'-0" CLG.

BONUS ROOM
15⁰ x 22⁸

Unfinished Storage
adds 274 Sq. Ft.

---

the
Evandale
5478-9JJ
pricecode 18

Main Level	**927**
Second Level	**880**
Total Square Ft.	**1807**

Standard Foundation: Basement

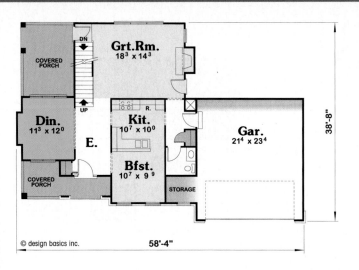

COVERED PORCH

DN

Grt. Rm.
18³ x 14³

UP

Din.
11³ x 12⁰

E.

Kit.
10⁷ x 10⁰

R.

Bfst.
10⁷ x 9⁹

STORAGE

Gar.
21⁴ x 23⁴

COVERED PORCH

38'-8"

58'-4"

© design basics inc.

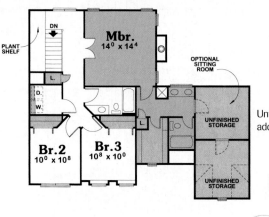

DN

PLANT SHELF

L.

Mbr.
14⁰ x 14⁴

OPTIONAL SITTING ROOM

D.

W.

L.

Br. 2
10⁰ x 10⁸

Br. 3
10⁸ x 10⁰

UNFINISHED STORAGE

UNFINISHED STORAGE

Unfinished Storages
add 244 Sq. Ft.

Livability
at a Glance™

Storing
Entertaining
Flexible Living
De-Stressing

the Creswell
5458-9JJ
pricecode 18

Main Level	837
Second Level	977
Total Square Ft.	1814

Standard Foundation: Basement

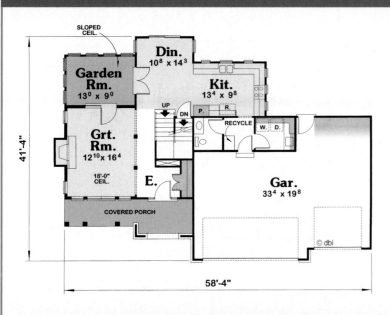

SLOPED CEIL.

Garden Rm. 13⁰ x 9⁰

Din. 10⁸ x 14³

Kit. 13⁴ x 9⁸

UP
DN
P.
R.
RECYCLE
W. D.

Grt. Rm. 12¹⁰ x 16⁴
18'-0" CEIL.

E.

Gar. 33⁴ x 19⁸

COVERED PORCH

41'-4"

58'-4"

© dbi

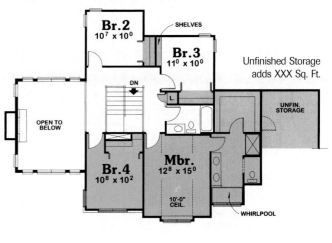

Br.2 10⁷ x 10⁰

SHELVES

Br.3 11⁰ x 10⁰

Unfinished Storage adds XXX Sq. Ft.

DN
L.

OPEN TO BELOW

UNFIN. STORAGE

Br.4 10⁸ x 10²

Mbr. 12⁸ x 15⁰
10'-0" CEIL.

WHIRLPOOL

the Lancaster
1752-9JJ
pricecode 18

Main Level	919
Second Level	927
Total Square Ft.	1846

Standard Foundation: Basement

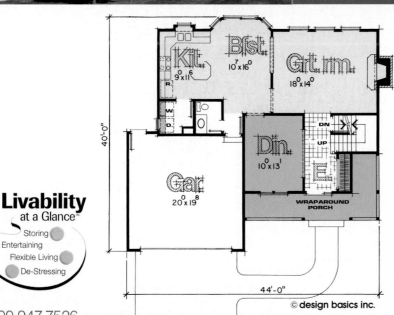

Kit. 9⁷ x 11⁰

Bfst. 10⁰ x 16⁰

Grt. rm. 18⁰ x 14⁰

W. D.

DN
UP
E.

Din. 10⁰ x 13¹

Gar. 20⁰ x 19⁸

WRAPAROUND PORCH

40'-0"

44'-0"

© design basics inc.

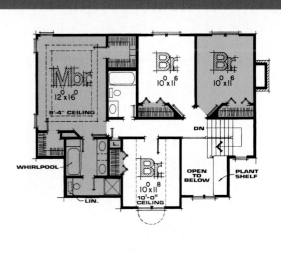

Mbr. 12⁰ x 16⁰
9'-4" CEILING

Br. 10⁰ x 11⁶

Br. 10⁰ x 11⁶

DN

WHIRLPOOL
L.
LIN.

Br. 10⁰ x 11⁸
10'-0" CEILING

OPEN TO BELOW

PLANT SHELF

Livability at a Glance™
- Storing
- Entertaining
- Flexible Living
- De-Stressing

the Sherman Oaks
8098-9JJ
pricecode 18

Main Level	**852**
Second Level	**1029**
Total Square Ft.	**1881**

Standard Foundation: Basement

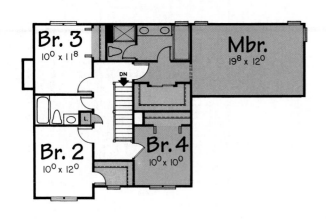

Br. 3
10⁰ x 11⁸

Mbr.
19⁸ x 12⁰

DN

Br. 2
10⁰ x 12⁰

Br. 4
10⁰ x 10⁰

L.

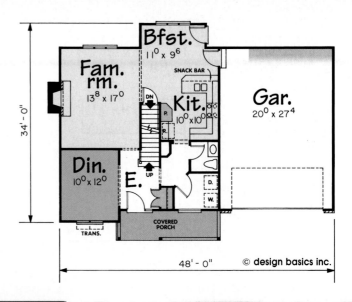

Bfst.
11⁰ x 9⁶

Fam. rm.
13⁸ x 17⁰

SNACK BAR

DN

Kit.
10⁰ x 10⁰

P.
R.

Gar.
20⁰ x 27⁴

34' - 0"

Din.
10⁰ x 12⁰

UP

E.

D.
W.

COVERED PORCH

TRANS.

48' - 0"

© design basics inc.

the Branford
5085-9JJ
pricecode 19

Main Level	**1002**
Second Level	**926**
Total Square Ft.	**1928**

Standard Foundation: Basement

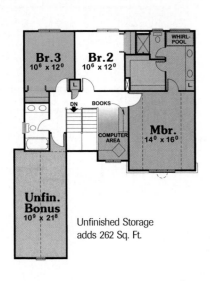

WHIRL-POOL

Br. 3
10⁶ x 12⁰

Br. 2
10⁶ x 12⁰

L.

L.

DN

BOOKS

COMPUTER AREA

Mbr.
14⁰ x 16⁰

Unfin. Bonus
10⁹ x 21⁸

Unfinished Storage
adds 262 Sq. Ft.

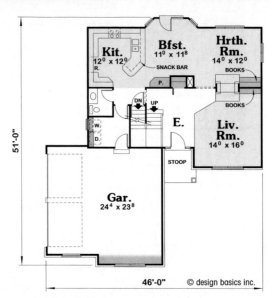

Kit.
12⁰ x 12⁰
R.

Bfst.
11⁰ x 11⁸

SNACK BAR

Hrth. Rm.
14⁰ x 12⁰

BOOKS

P.

DN UP

E.

W.
D.

BOOKS

Liv. Rm.
14⁰ x 16⁰

51'-0"

Gar.
24⁴ x 23⁸

STOOP

46'-0"

© design basics inc.

Livability at a Glance™

Storing
Entertaining
Flexible Living
De-Stressing

the
Columbus
2963-9JJ
price code 19

Main Level	**941**
Second Level	**992**
Total Square Ft.	**1933**

Standard Foundation: Basement

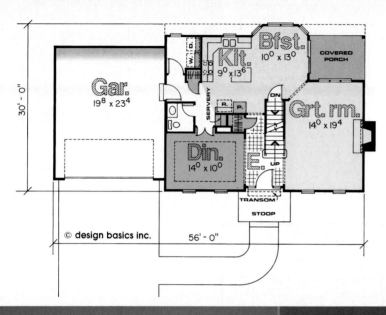

Gar.
19⁸ x 23⁴

Kit.
9⁰ x 13⁶

Bfst.
10⁰ x 13⁰

COVERED PORCH

W. D.

SERVERY

R. P.

Din.
14⁰ x 10⁰

DN

Grt. rm.
14⁰ x 19⁴

UP

E.

TRANSOM

STOOP

30' - 0"

56' - 0"

© design basics inc.

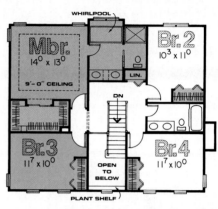

WHIRLPOOL

Mbr.
14⁰ x 13⁰
9'-0" CEILING

Br. 2
10³ x 11⁰

LIN.

DN

Br. 3
11⁷ x 10⁰

Br. 4
11⁷ x 10⁰

OPEN TO BELOW

PLANT SHELF

the
Cyprus
2648-9JJ
price code 19

Main Level	**1082**
Second Level	**869**
Total Square Ft.	**1951**

Standard Foundation: Basement

Fam. rm.
18⁰ x 14⁰

Bfst.
10⁰ x 14⁰

Kit.
9⁰ x 11⁰

BOOK

DESK

P.

R.

W. D.

E.

UP

Par.
11⁰ x 12⁰
10'-0" CLG.

Din.
11⁰ x 12²

Gar.
20⁰ x 24⁰

COVERED STOOP

TRANS.

40' - 0"

50' - 0"

© design basics inc.

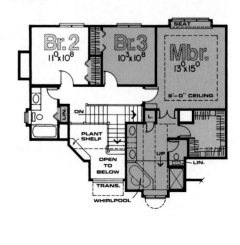

Br. 2
11⁰ x 10⁸

Br. 3
10³ x 10⁸

SEAT

Mbr.
13⁰ x 15⁰
9'-0" CEILING

LIN.

DN

PLANT SHELF

OPEN TO BELOW

TRANS.

UP

LIN.

WHIRLPOOL

Livability
at a Glance™

Storing
Entertaining
Flexible Living
De-Stressing

the
Bentley Woods
8082-9JJ

price code 19

Main Level	**945**
Second Level	**1007**
Total Square Ft.	**1952**

Standard Foundation: Basement

Livability
at a Glance™

- Storing
- Entertaining
- Flexible Living
- De-Stressing

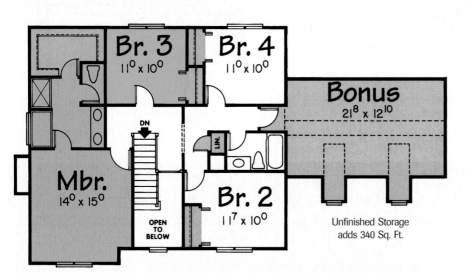

Br. 3
11⁰ x 10⁰

Br. 4
11⁰ x 10⁰

Bonus
21⁸ x 12¹⁰

DN

Mbr.
14⁰ x 15⁰

LIN.

Br. 2
11⁷ x 10⁰

OPEN TO BELOW

Unfinished Storage
adds 340 Sq. Ft.

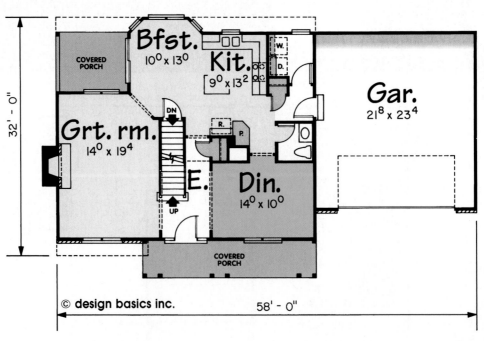

Bfst.
10⁰ x 13⁰

Kit.
9⁰ x 13²

W. D.

Gar.
21⁸ x 23⁴

COVERED PORCH

DN

R.

P.

Grt. rm.
14⁰ x 19⁴

E.

Din.
14⁰ x 10⁰

UP

32' - 0"

COVERED PORCH

© design basics inc.

58' - 0"

the
Harrisburg
2315-9JJ
pricecode 19

Main Level	**1000**
Second Level	**993**
Total Square Ft.	**1993**

Standard Foundation: Basement

Livability
at a Glance™

- Storing
- Entertaining
- Flexible Living
- De-Stressing

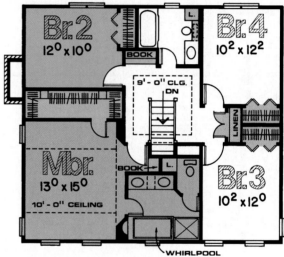

Br. 2
12⁰ x 10⁰

BOOK

Br. 4
10² x 12²

9'-0" CLG.
DN

LINEN

Mbr.
13⁰ x 15⁰
10'-0" CEILING

BOOK→

Br. 3
10² x 12⁰

WHIRLPOOL

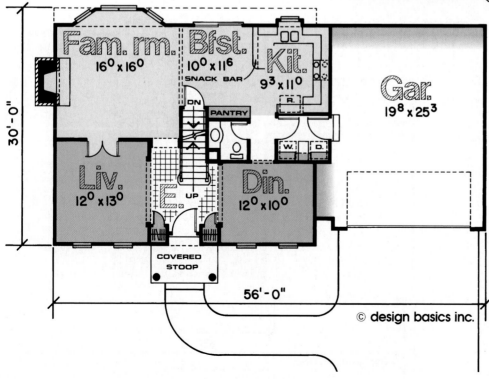

Fam. rm.
16⁰ x 16⁰

Bfst.
10⁰ x 11⁶
SNACK BAR

Kit.
9³ x 11⁰

Gar.
19⁸ x 25³

DN

PANTRY

R.

W.   D.

30'-0"

Liv.
12⁰ x 13⁰

UP

Din.
12⁰ x 10⁰

COVERED
STOOP

56'-0"

© design basics inc.

the Oakbrook
2619-9JJ
pricecode 19

Main Level	**1093**
Second Level	**905**
Total Square Ft.	**1998**

Standard Foundation: Basement

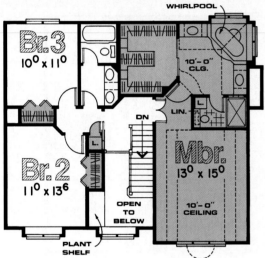

Livability at a Glance™

Storing
Entertaining
Flexible Living
De-Stressing

Br.3 10⁰ x 11⁰

WHIRLPOOL

10'- 0" CLG.

Br.2 11⁰ x 13⁶

DN

LIN.

L.

Mbr. 13⁰ x 15⁰

OPEN TO BELOW

10'- 0" CEILING

PLANT SHELF

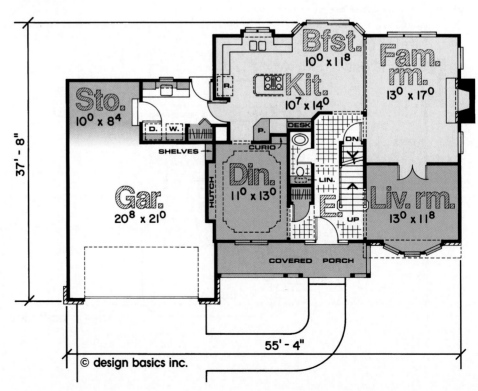

Sto. 10⁰ x 8⁴

Bfst. 10⁰ x 11⁸

Fam. rm. 13⁰ x 17⁰

Kit. 10⁷ x 14⁰

DESK

P.

CURIO

SHELVES

Gar. 20⁸ x 21⁰

Din. 11⁰ x 13⁰

HUTCH

LIN.

DN

UP

Liv. rm. 13⁰ x 11⁸

D.   W.

37' - 8"

COVERED   PORCH

55' - 4"

© design basics inc.

the
Ballobin
3552-9JJ
pricecode 20

Main Level	**989**
Second Level	**1039**
Total Square Ft.	**2028**

Standard Foundation: Basement

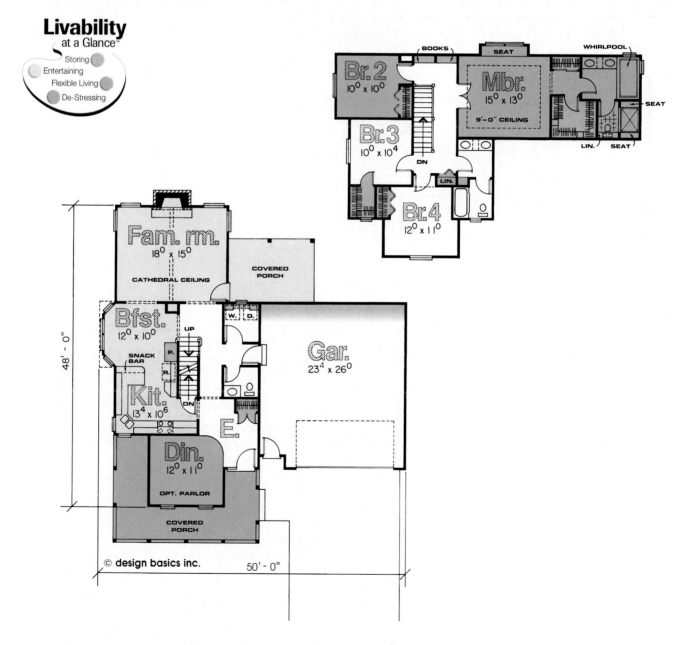

Livability
at a Glance™

- Storing
- Entertaining
- Flexible Living
- De-Stressing

BOOKS

SEAT

WHIRLPOOL

Br. 2
10^0 x 10^0

Mbr.
15^0 x 13^0

Br. 3
10^0 x 10^4

9'-0" CEILING

SEAT

DN

LIN.

SEAT

LIN.

Br. 4
12^0 x 11^0

Fam. rm.
18^0 x 15^0

CATHEDRAL CEILING

COVERED PORCH

Bfst.
12^0 x 10^0

UP

W. D.

SNACK BAR

P.

Gar.
23^4 x 26^0

R.

Kit.
13^4 x 10^6

DN

Din.
12^0 x 11^0

OPT. PARLOR

COVERED PORCH

48' - 0"

50' - 0"

© design basics inc.

the
Robins Lane
8031-9JJ
price code 20

Main Level	**1046**
Second Level	**983**
Total Square Ft.	**2029**

Standard Foundation: Basement

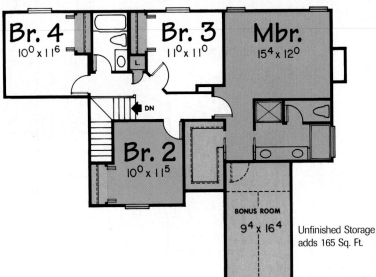

Br. 4
10⁰ x 11⁶

Br. 3
11⁰ x 11⁰

Mbr.
15⁴ x 12⁰

DN

Br. 2
10⁰ x 11⁵

BONUS ROOM
9⁴ x 16⁴

Unfinished Storage
adds 165 Sq. Ft.

Livability
at a Glance™

Storing
Entertaining
Flexible Living
De-Stressing

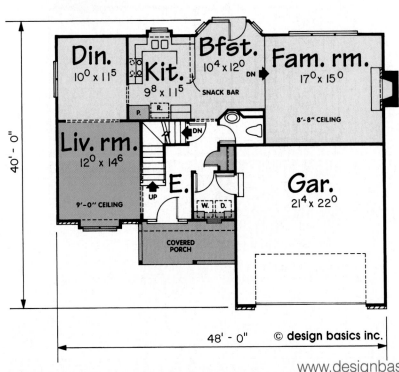

Din.
10⁰ x 11⁵

Kit.
9⁸ x 11⁵

Bfst.
10⁴ x 12⁰

DN

Fam. rm.
17⁰ x 15⁰

SNACK BAR

8'-8" CEILING

Liv. rm.
12⁰ x 14⁶

9'-0" CEILING

P.   R.

DN

E.

W. D.

UP

Gar.
21⁴ x 22⁰

40' - 0"

COVERED PORCH

48' - 0"

© **design basics inc.**

www.designbasics.com/9JJ

the
Curtiss
2401-9JJ
pricecode 20

Main Level	**1020**
Second Level	**1038**
Total Square Ft.	**2058**

Standard Foundation: Basement

Livability
at a Glance™

Storing
Entertaining
Flexible Living
De-Stressing

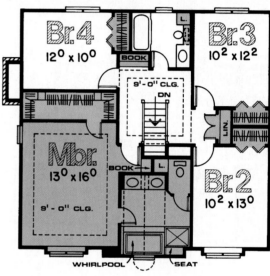

Br.4
12⁰ x 10⁰

BOOK

Br.3
10² x 12²

9'-0" CLG.

DN

LIN.

Mbr.
13⁰ x 16⁰

9'-0" CLG.

BOOK

Br.2
10² x 13⁰

WHIRLPOOL   SEAT

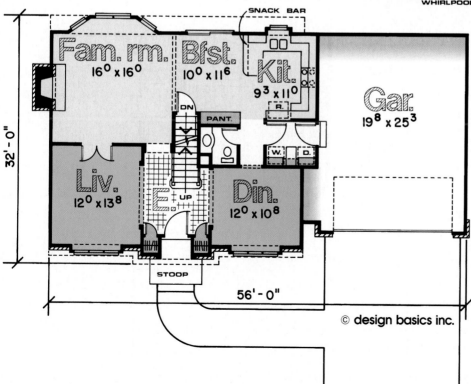

SNACK BAR

Fam. rm.
16⁰ x 16⁰

Bfst.
10⁰ x 11⁶

Kit.
9³ x 11⁰

Gar.
19⁸ x 25³

DN

PANT.

R.

W.   D.

Liv.
12⁰ x 13⁸

UP

Din.
12⁰ x 10⁸

32' - 0"

STOOP

56' - 0"

© design basics inc.

the
Bristol
1870-9JJ
price code 20

Main Level	**1113**
Second Level	**965**
Total Square Ft.	**2078**

Standard Foundation: Basement

Livability at a Glance™

- Storing
- Entertaining
- Flexible Living
- De-Stressing

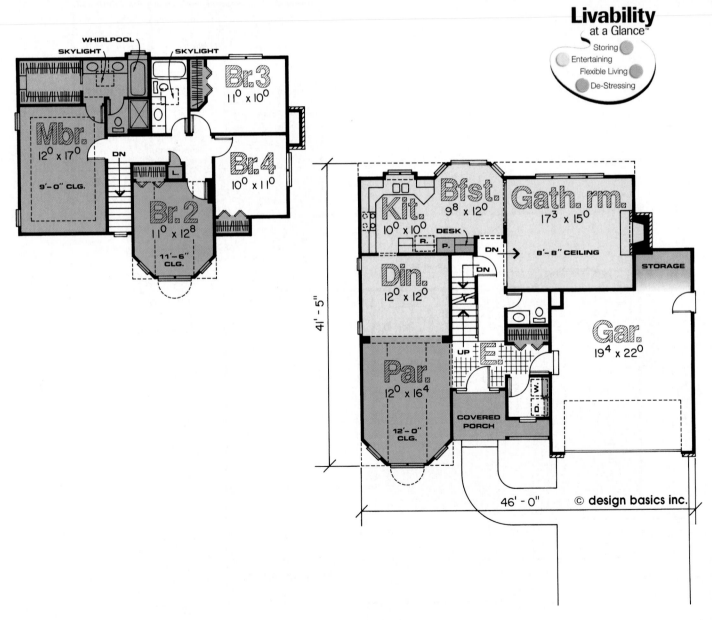

WHIRLPOOL
SKYLIGHT
SKYLIGHT

Br. 3
11⁰ x 10⁰

Mbr.
12⁰ x 17⁰
9'-0" CLG.

DN

Br. 4
10⁰ x 11⁰

L.

Br. 2
11⁰ x 12⁸
11'-6" CLG.

Kit.
10⁰ x 10⁰

Bfst.
9⁸ x 12⁰

Gath. rm.
17³ x 15⁰
8'-8" CEILING

DESK
R.
P.
DN

STORAGE

Din.
12⁰ x 12⁰

DN

Gar.
19⁴ x 22⁰

41' - 5"

Par.
12⁰ x 16⁴
12'-0" CLG.

UP

D. W.

COVERED PORCH

46' - 0"

© design basics inc.

the Yorke

2217-9JJ

pricecode 20

Main Level	**1062**
Second Level	**1023**
Total Square Ft.	**2085**

Standard Foundation: Basement

Livability
at a Glance™

- Storing
- Entertaining
- Flexible Living
- De-Stressing

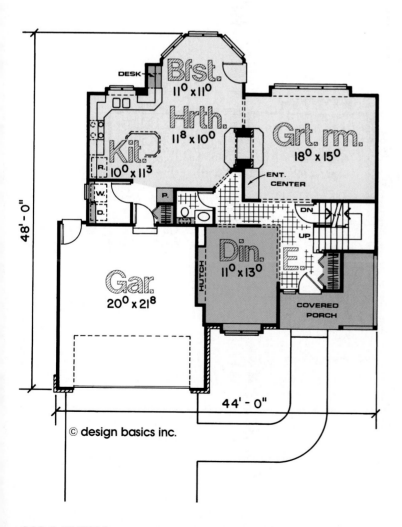

Bfst.
11⁰ x 11⁰

DESK

Hrth.
11⁸ x 10⁰

Kit.
10⁰ x 11³

Grt. rm.
18⁰ x 15⁰

ENT. CENTER

W.
D.
P.

DN
UP

Din.
11⁰ x 13⁰

HUTCH

Gar.
20⁰ x 21⁸

COVERED PORCH

48' - 0"

44' - 0"

© design basics inc.

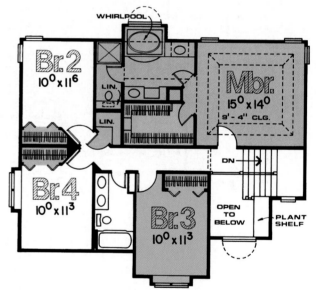

WHIRLPOOL

Br. 2
10⁰ x 11⁶

LIN.
LIN.

Mbr.
15⁰ x 14⁰
9' - 4" CLG.

Br. 4
10⁰ x 11³

DN

Br. 3
10⁰ x 11³

OPEN TO BELOW

PLANT SHELF

the
Linden
2638-9JJ
price**code** 21

Main Level **1082**

Second Level **1021**

Total Square Ft. **2103**

Standard Foundation: Basement

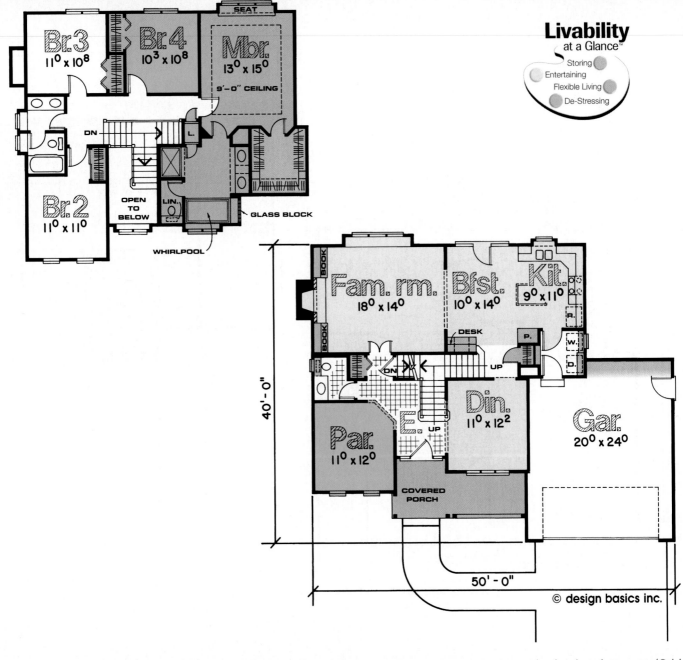

Livability
at a Glance™

Storing

Entertaining

Flexible Living

De-Stressing

Br. 3
11⁰ x 10⁸

Br. 4
10³ x 10⁸

Mbr.
13⁰ x 15⁰

9'–0" CEILING

SEAT

DN

L.

Br. 2
11⁰ x 11⁰

OPEN
TO
BELOW

LIN.

GLASS BLOCK

WHIRLPOOL

Fam. rm.
18⁰ x 14⁰

Bfst.
10⁰ x 14⁰

Kit.
9⁰ x 11⁰

BOOK

BOOK

DESK

R.

P.

W.

D.

DN

UP

Par.
11⁰ x 12⁰

Din.
11⁰ x 12²

Gar.
20⁰ x 24⁰

E.

UP

COVERED
PORCH

40'-0"

50'-0"

© design basics inc.

the
Paisley
2618-9JJ
pricecode 21

Main Level **1093**

Second Level **1038**

Total Square Ft. **2131**

Standard Foundation: Basement

Livability
at a Glance™

- Storing
- Entertaining
- Flexible Living
- De-Stressing

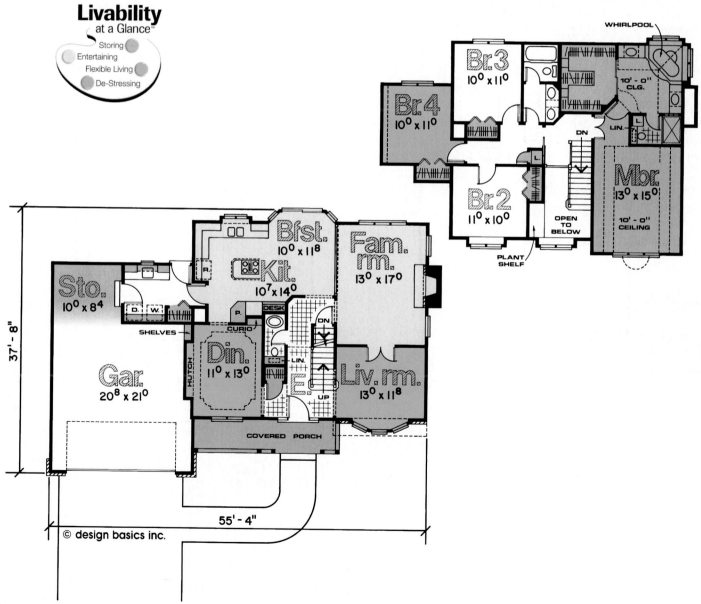

Br.3 10⁰ x 11⁰

Br.4 10⁰ x 11⁰

Br.2 11⁰ x 10⁰

WHIRLPOOL

10' - 0" CLG.

DN

LIN.

OPEN TO BELOW

PLANT SHELF

Mbr. 13⁰ x 15⁰

10' - 0" CEILING

Sto. 10⁰ x 8⁴

Gar. 20⁸ x 21⁰

SHELVES

Bfst. 10⁰ x 11⁸

Kit. 10⁷ x 14⁰

Fam. rm. 13⁰ x 17⁰

DESK

CURIO

Din. 11⁰ x 13⁰

HUTCH

LIN.

DN

UP

Liv. rm. 13⁰ x 11⁸

COVERED PORCH

37' - 8"

55' - 4"

© design basics inc.

the
Caldera
4952-9JJ
pricecode 21

Main Level	**1008**
Second Level	**1136**
Total Square Ft.	**2144**

Standard Foundation: Basement

Livability
at a Glance™

Storing
Entertaining
Flexible Living
De-Stressing

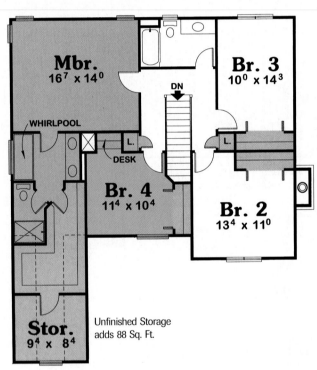

Mbr.
16⁷ x 14⁰

WHIRLPOOL

DN

Br. 3
10⁰ x 14³

L.

DESK

L.

Br. 4
11⁴ x 10⁴

Br. 2
13⁴ x 11⁰

Stor.
9⁴ x 8⁴

Unfinished Storage
adds 88 Sq. Ft.

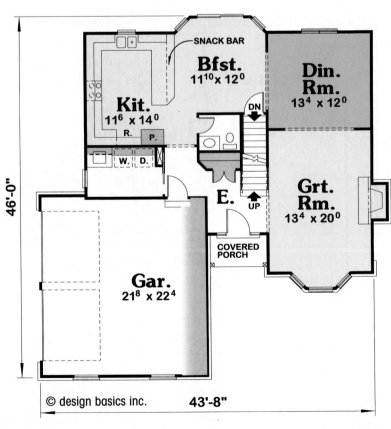

SNACK BAR

Bfst.
11¹⁰ x 12⁰

Din. Rm.
13⁴ x 12⁰

Kit.
11⁶ x 14⁰

R.

P.

DN

W. D.

E.

UP

Grt. Rm.
13⁴ x 20⁰

46'-0"

Gar.
21⁸ x 22⁴

COVERED PORCH

© design basics inc.   43'-8"

the
Burlington
43023-9JJ
price code 21

Main Level	**1075**
Second Level	**1080**
Total Square Ft.	**2155**

Standard Foundation: Slab

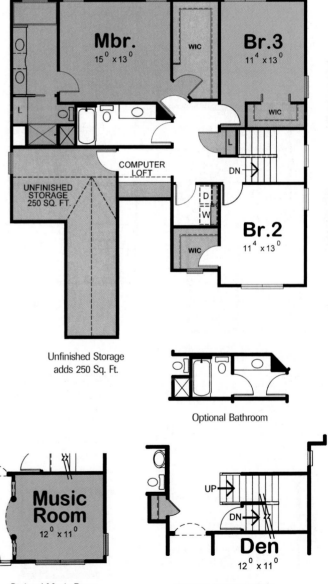

Unfinished Storage adds 250 Sq. Ft.

Optional Bathroom

Livability
at a Glance™

- Storing
- Entertaining
- Flexible Living
- De-Stressing

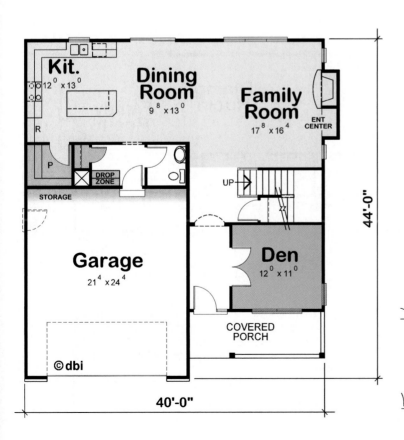

Music Room 12⁰ x 11⁰

Optional Music Room

Den 12⁰ x 11⁰

Optional Basement Stair Location adds 8 Sq. Ft.

the
Monona
43022-9JJ
pricecode 21

Main Level	**1075**
Second Level	**1093**
Total Square Ft.	**2168**

Standard Foundation: Slab

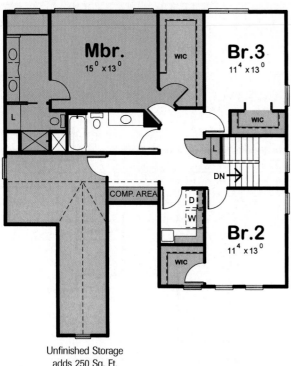

Unfinished Storage
adds 250 Sq. Ft.

Mbr.
15⁰ x 13⁰

WIC

Br.3
11⁴ x 13⁰

WIC

L

DN →

COMP. AREA

D
W

Br.2
11⁴ x 13⁰

WIC

Livability
at a Glance™

Storing
Entertaining
Flexible Living
De-Stressing

Optional Bathroom

UP →

DN →

Den
12⁰ x 11⁰

Optional Basement Stair
Location adds 8 Sq. Ft.

**Music
Room**
12⁰ x 11⁰

Optional Music Room

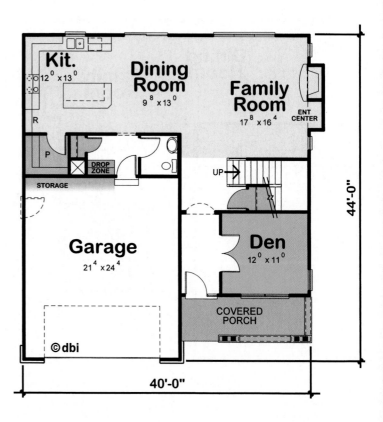

Kit.
12⁰ x 13⁰

**Dining
Room**
9⁸ x 13⁰

**Family
Room**
17⁸ x 16⁴

ENT
CENTER

R

P

DROP
ZONE

STORAGE

UP →

Garage
21⁴ x 24⁴

Den
12⁰ x 11⁰

COVERED
PORCH

©dbi

44'-0"

40'-0"

the
Collier
2216-9JJ
price code 21

Main Level **1224**

Second Level **950**

Total Square Ft. **2174**

Standard Foundation: Basement

Livability
at a Glance™

Storing
Entertaining
Flexible Living
De-Stressing

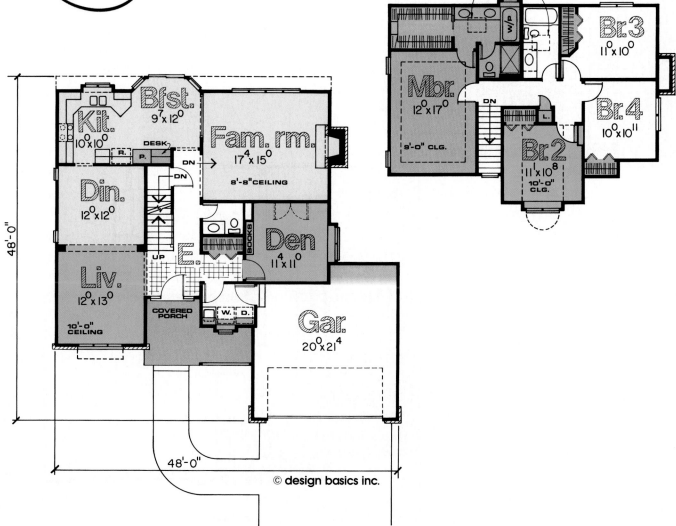

Kit.
10⁰x10⁰

Bfst.
9⁷x12⁰

Fam. rm.
17⁴x15⁰

8'-8" CEILING

Din.
12⁰x12⁰

DESK

R. P.

DN

DN

UP

BOOKS

Den
11⁴x11⁰

Liv.
12⁰x13⁰

10'-0" CEILING

COVERED PORCH

W. D.

Gar.
20⁰x21⁴

48'-0"

48'-0"

SKYLIGHTS

w/p

Mbr.
12⁰x17⁰

9'-0" CLG.

DN

L.

Br. 3
11⁰x10⁰

Br. 4
10⁰x10¹¹

Br. 2
11¹x10⁸
10'-0" CLG.

the Castalia
8500-9JJ
pricecode 22

Main Level	**1130**
Second Level	**1070**
Total Square Ft.	**2200**

Standard Foundation: Basement

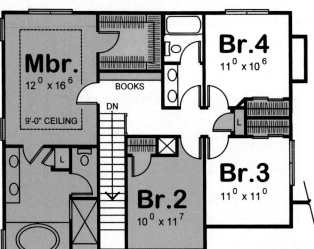

Mbr.
12^0 x 16^6

9'-0" CEILING

BOOKS

DN

L

Br.4
11^0 x 10^6

L

Br.3
11^0 x 11^0

Br.2
10^0 x 11^7

Livability
at a Glance™

Storing
Entertaining
Flexible Living
De-Stressing

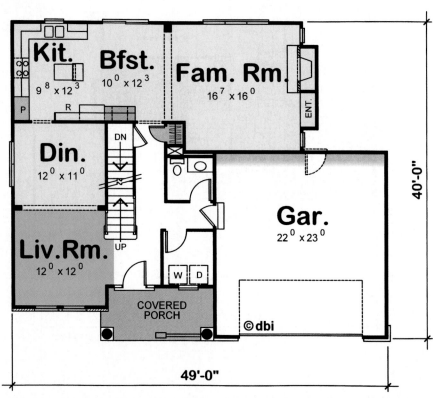

Kit.
9^8 x 12^3

Bfst.
10^0 x 12^3

Fam. Rm.
16^7 x 16^0

ENT.

P

R

Din.
12^0 x 11^0

DN

Gar.
22^0 x 23^0

40'-0"

Liv.Rm.
12^0 x 12^0

UP

W D

COVERED PORCH

©dbi

49'-0"

the
Hazelton
1019-9JJ
pricecode 22

Main Level	**1132**
Second Level	**1087**
Total Square Ft.	**2219**

Standard Foundation: Basement

Livability
at a Glance™

- Storing
- Entertaining
- Flexible Living
- De-Stressing

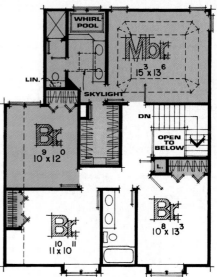

WHIRL POOL

Mbr
15³ x 13⁶

LIN.

SKYLIGHT

Br
10⁹ x 12⁰

DN

OPEN TO BELOW

L.

Br
10 11
11 x 10

Br
10⁸ x 13³

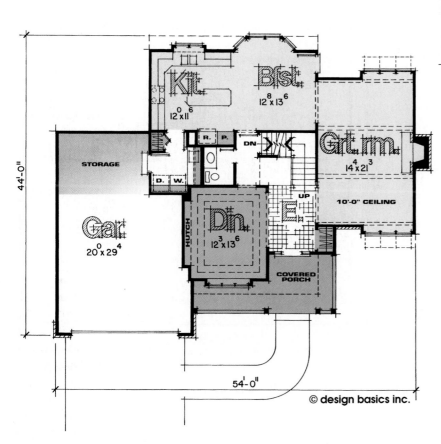

STORAGE

Gar
20⁰ x 29⁴

44'-0"

Kit
12⁰ x 11⁶

Bfst
12⁸ x 13⁶

R. P.

DN

Grt. rm.
14⁴ x 21³

10'-0" CEILING

D. W.

HUTCH

Dn
12³ x 13⁶

UP

COVERED PORCH

54'-0"

© design basics inc.

the Crawford
2408-9JJ
pricecode 22

Main Level	1150
Second Level	1120
Total Square Ft.	2270

Standard Foundation: Basement

Livability at a Glance

- Storing
- Entertaining
- Flexible Living
- De-Stressing

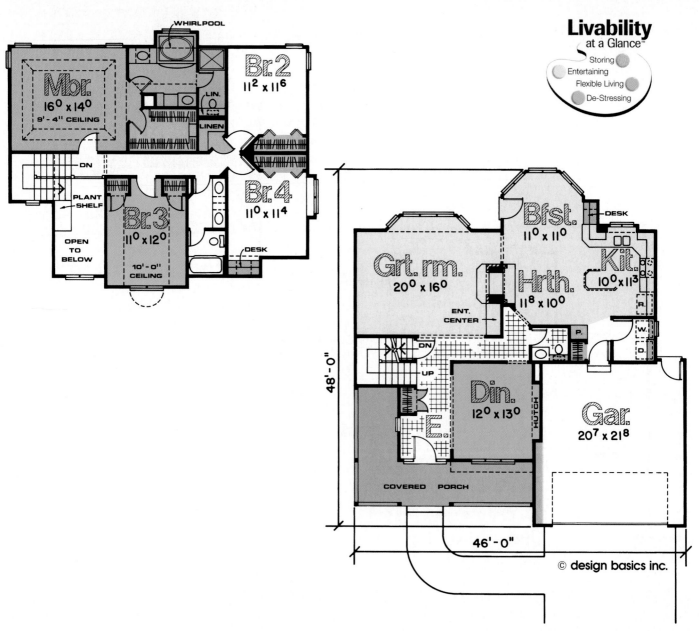

© design basics inc.

the
Eldon
4105-9JJ
price code 22

Main Level	**1098**
Second Level	**1184**
Total Square Ft.	**2282**

Standard Foundation: Basement

Livability
at a Glance™

- Storing
- Entertaining
- Flexible Living
- De-Stressing

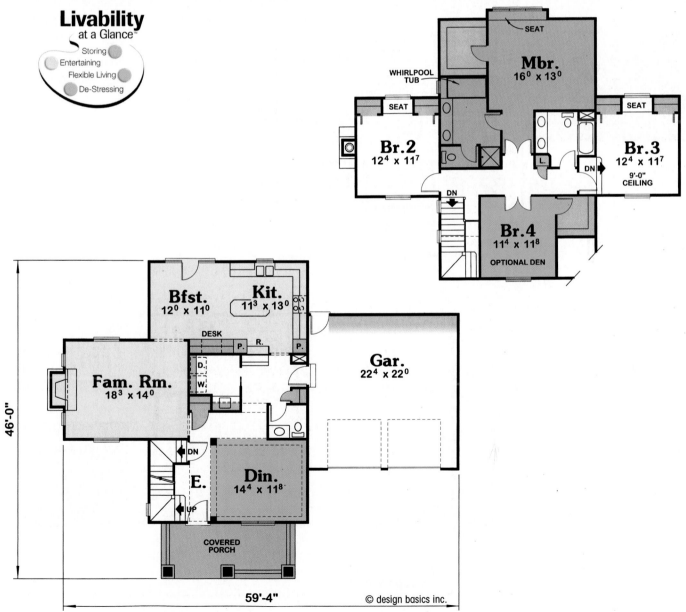

SEAT

WHIRLPOOL TUB

Mbr.
16⁰ x 13⁰

SEAT

Br.2
12⁴ x 11⁷

SEAT

Br.3
12⁴ x 11⁷

9'-0" CEILING

DN

DN

Br.4
11⁴ x 11⁸

OPTIONAL DEN

Bfst.
12⁰ x 11⁰

Kit.
11³ x 13⁰

DESK

Gar.
22⁴ x 22⁰

Fam. Rm.
18³ x 14⁰

P. R.

D.
W.

P.

DN

46'-0"

E.

Din.
14⁴ x 11⁸

UP

COVERED PORCH

59'-4"

© design basics inc.

the
Millard Oaks
8024-9JJ
price code 22

Main Level	**1000**
Second Level	**1298**
Total Square Ft.	**2298**

Standard Foundation: Basement

Livability
at a Glance™

- Storing
- Entertaining
- Flexible Living
- De-Stressing

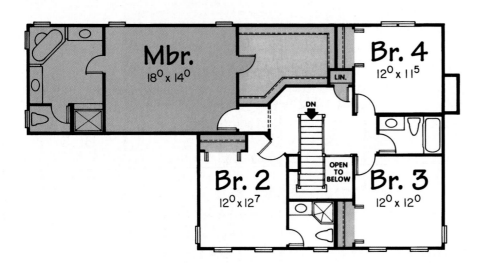

Mbr.
18⁰ x 14⁰

Br. 4
12⁰ x 11⁵

LIN.

DN

Br. 2
12⁰ x 12⁷

OPEN TO BELOW

Br. 3
12⁰ x 12⁰

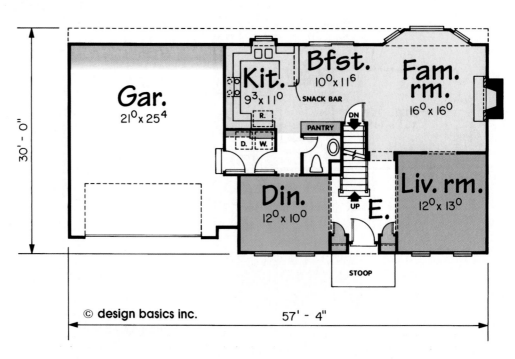

Gar.
21⁰ x 25⁴

Kit.
9³ x 11⁰

R.

D. W.

Bfst.
10⁰ x 11⁶

SNACK BAR

PANTRY

DN

Fam. rm.
16⁰ x 16⁰

Din.
12⁰ x 10⁰

UP

E.

Liv. rm.
12⁰ x 13⁰

STOOP

30' - 0"

© design basics inc.

57' - 4"

the
Hartman

3333-9JJ

price code 23

Main Level	**1273**
Second Level	**1035**
Total Square Ft.	**2308**

Standard Foundation: Basement

Livability
at a Glance™

- Storing
- Entertaining
- Flexible Living
- De-Stressing

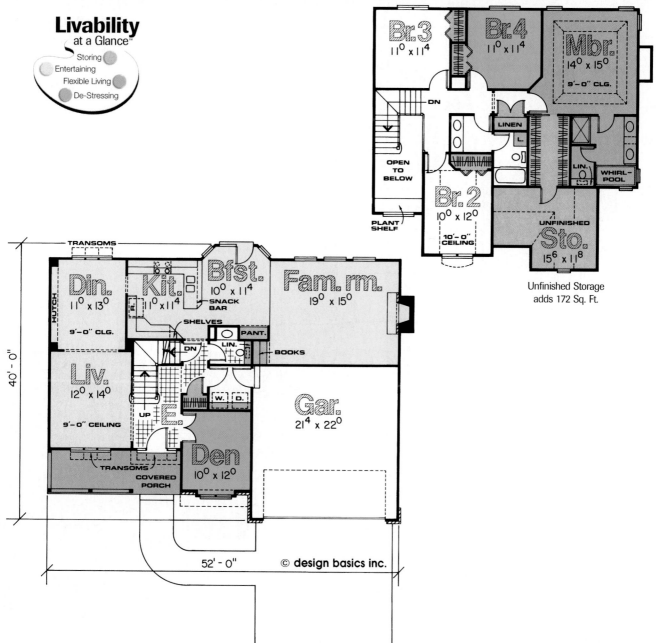

Br. 3
11⁰ x 11⁴

Br. 4
11⁰ x 11⁴

Mbr.
14⁰ x 15⁰
9'-0" CLG.

DN

OPEN
TO
BELOW

LINEN
L

Br. 2
10⁰ x 12⁰
10'-0" CEILING

PLANT
SHELF

LIN.

WHIRL-
POOL

UNFINISHED

Sto.
15⁶ x 11⁸

Unfinished Storage
adds 172 Sq. Ft.

TRANSOMS

Din.
11⁰ x 13⁰
9'-0" CLG.

HUTCH

Kit.
11⁰ x 11⁴

R

Bfst.
10⁰ x 11⁴
SNACK
BAR

SHELVES

Fam. rm.
19⁰ x 15⁰

PANT.

DN

LIN.

BOOKS

Liv.
12⁰ x 14⁰
9'-0" CEILING

UP

W. D.

Gar.
21⁴ x 22⁰

Den
10⁰ x 12⁰

TRANSOMS

COVERED
PORCH

40' - 0"

52' - 0"

© design basics inc.

the Elgin
8524-9JJ

pricecode 23

Main Level	**1036**
Second Level	**1295**
Total Square Ft.	**2331**

Standard Foundation: Basement

Livability
at a Glance™

Storing
Entertaining
Flexible Living
De-Stressing

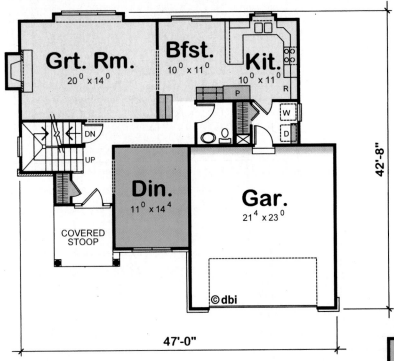

Grt. Rm.
20⁰ x 14⁰

Bfst.
10⁰ x 11⁰

Kit.
10⁰ x 11⁰

P

R

W

D

DN

UP

Din.
11⁰ x 14⁴

Gar.
21⁴ x 23⁰

COVERED STOOP

©dbi

42'-8"

47'-0"

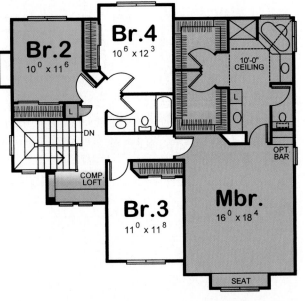

Br.2
10⁰ x 11⁶

Br.4
10⁶ x 12³

10'-0" CEILING

L

L

DN

COMP. LOFT

OPT. BAR

Br.3
11⁰ x 11⁸

Mbr.
16⁰ x 18⁴

SEAT

the Stanton
2414-9JJ
pricecode 23

Main Level	**1075**
Second Level	**1268**
Total Square Ft.	**2343**

Standard Foundation: Basement

Livability
at a Glance™

Storing
Entertaining
Flexible Living
De-Stressing

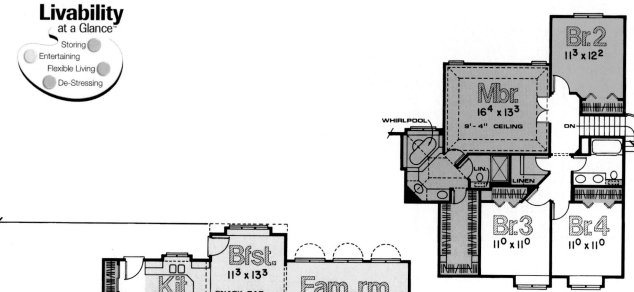

Br.2
11³ x 12²

Mbr.
16⁴ x 13³
9'-4" CEILING

WHIRLPOOL

LIN.

DN.

LINEN

Br.3
11⁰ x 11⁰

Br.4
11⁰ x 11⁰

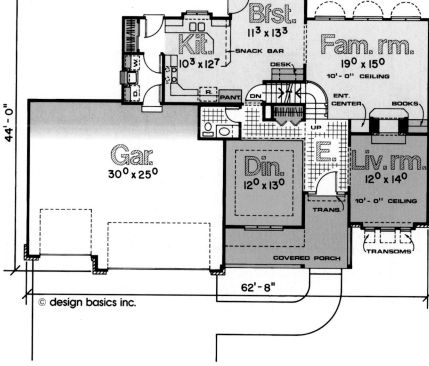

Bfst.
11³ x 13³

SNACK BAR

Kit.
10³ x 12⁷

Fam. rm.
19⁰ x 15⁰
10'-0" CEILING

DESK

PANT.

DN

ENT. CENTER

BOOKS

UP

R

44'-0"

Gar.
30⁰ x 25⁰

Din.
12⁰ x 13⁰

E.

Liv.rm.
12⁰ x 14⁰
10'-0" CEILING

TRANS.

COVERED PORCH

TRANSOMS

62'-8"

© design basics inc.

the
Franklin
2316-9JJ
price code 23

Main Level	**1000**
Second Level	**1345**
Total Square Ft.	**2345**

Standard Foundation: Basement

Livability
at a Glance™

- Storing
- Entertaining
- Flexible Living
- De-Stressing

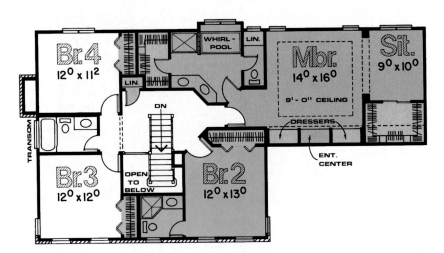

Br.4
12⁰ x 11²

WHIRL-POOL   LIN.

Mbr.
14⁰ x 16⁰

9'-0" CEILING

Sit.
9⁰ x 10⁰

LIN.

TRANSOM

DN

DRESSERS

ENT. CENTER

Br.3
12⁰ x 12⁰

OPEN TO BELOW

Br.2
12⁰ x 13⁰

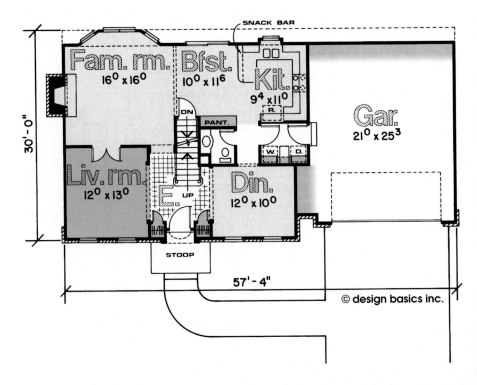

SNACK BAR

Fam. rm.
16⁰ x 16⁰

Bfst.
10⁰ x 11⁶

Kit.
9⁴ x 11⁰

R.

Gar.
21⁰ x 25³

30'-0"

DN

PANT.

W.   D.

Liv. rm.
12⁰ x 13⁰

UP

Din.
12⁰ x 10⁰

STOOP

57'-4"

© design basics inc.

the
Gerard
4135-9JJ
pricecode 23

Main Level	**1199**
Second Level	**1150**
Total Square Ft.	**2349**

Standard Foundation: Basement

Livability
at a Glance™

- Storing
- Entertaining
- Flexible Living
- De-Stressing

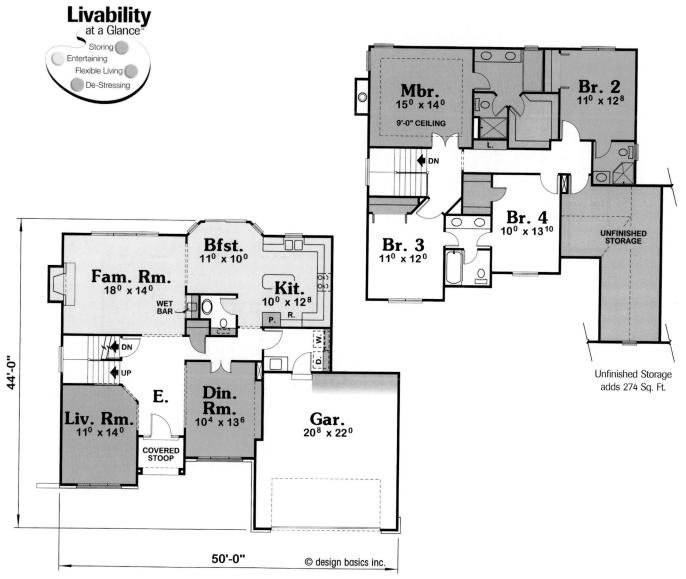

Mbr.
15^0 x 14^0
9'-0" CEILING

Br. 2
11^0 x 12^8

DN

Br. 3
11^0 x 12^0

Br. 4
10^0 x 13^{10}

UNFINISHED STORAGE

Unfinished Storage
adds 274 Sq. Ft.

Fam. Rm.
18^0 x 14^0

Bfst.
11^0 x 10^0

WET BAR

Kit.
10^0 x 12^8

P. R.

DN
UP

D. W.

E.

Liv. Rm.
11^0 x 14^0

COVERED STOOP

Din. Rm.
10^4 x 13^6

Gar.
20^8 x 22^0

44'-0"

50'-0"

© design basics inc.

the
Glendon
8515-9JJ
price code 23

Main Level	**1207**
Second Level	**1147**
Total Square Ft.	**2354**

Standard Foundation: Basement

Livability
at a Glance™

Storing
Entertaining
Flexible Living
De-Stressing

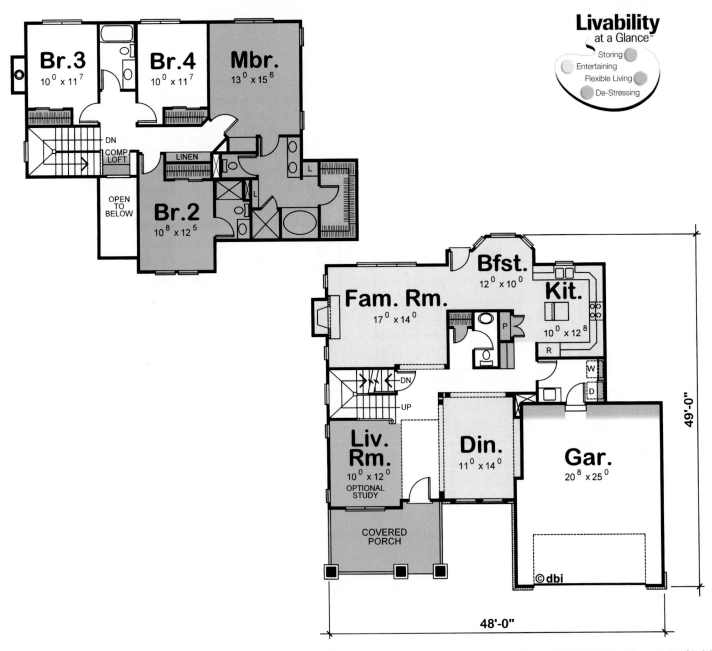

Br.3
10^0 x 11^7

Br.4
10^0 x 11^7

Mbr.
13^0 x 15^6

DN
COMP LOFT

LINEN

OPEN TO BELOW

Br.2
10^8 x 12^5

L

L

Bfst.
12^0 x 10^0

Fam. Rm.
17^0 x 14^0

Kit.
10^0 x 12^8

P

R

DN

UP

W

D

Liv. Rm.
10^0 x 12^0
OPTIONAL STUDY

Din.
11^0 x 14^0

Gar.
20^8 x 25^0

COVERED PORCH

©dbi

49'-0"

48'-0"

the
Kendall
1553-9JJ
price code 23

Main Level	**1303**
Second Level	**1084**
Total Square Ft.	**2387**

Standard Foundation: Basement

Livability
at a Glance™

- Storing
- Entertaining
- Flexible Living
- De-Stressing

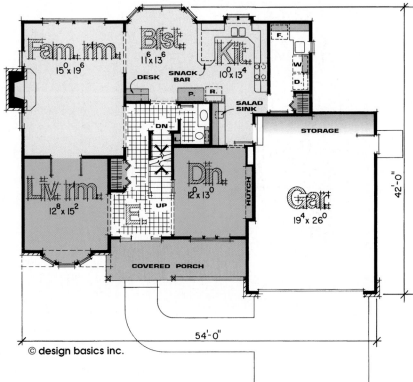

Fam. rm. 15⁰ x 19⁶

Bfst. 11⁶ x 13⁶

Kit. 10⁰ x 13⁴

F.

DESK

SNACK BAR

P. R.

SALAD SINK

W. D.

STORAGE

DN

Liv. rm. 12⁸ x 15²

Dn. 12⁰ x 13⁰

HUTCH

Gar. 19⁴ x 26⁰

UP

COVERED PORCH

42'-0"

54'-0"

© design basics inc.

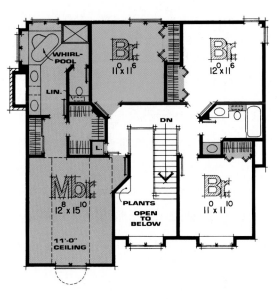

WHIRL-POOL

Br 11⁰ x 11⁶

Br 12⁰ x 11⁶

LIN.

DN

Mbr 12⁸ x 15¹⁰

PLANTS
OPEN TO BELOW

Br 11⁰ x 11⁰

11'-0" CEILING

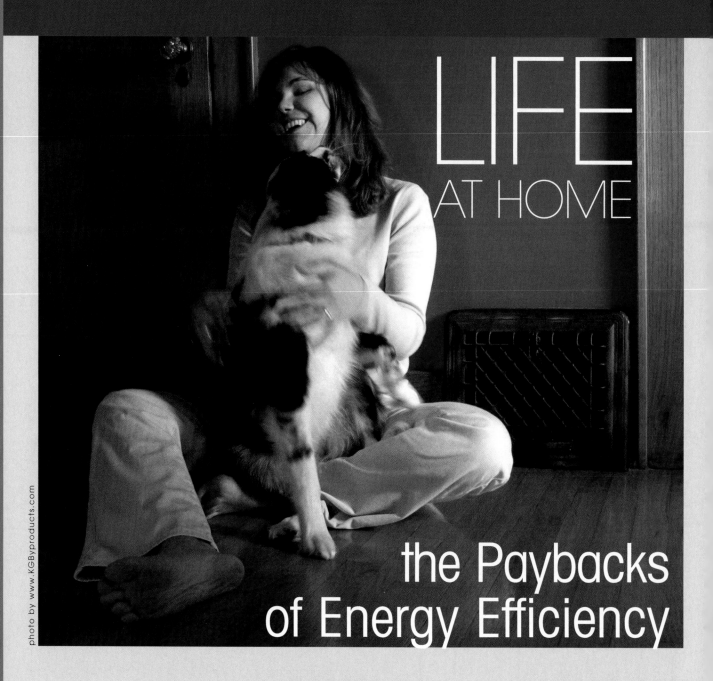

LIFE
AT HOME

the Paybacks of Energy Efficiency

Totaling up the costs of building a new home can be intimidating. For most of us, it's one of the most expensive things we will do in our lifetime. Consequently, it's often necessary to scale back some dreams and make compromises along the way. But one of the places it's important not to cut corners is energy efficiency. That's an area where spending more up front can pay off in years of savings and higher resale value.

INSULATION AND SEALING Nearly half of the average family's energy consumption is used heating and cooling their home. It's easy to understand why, when studies show 75 - 100% of the air inside a typical new home escapes every hour (with all windows and doors tightly closed). The importance of effective insulation and air sealing is clear.

Conventionally framed homes require superb attention and advanced products to minimize air leakage. This may take the form of a housewrap + extensive caulking + a high performance insulation or expanding foams which fill nooks and crevices in wall and attic cavities and surround plumbing and electrical penetrations. Insulated siding (typically vinyl siding) is another emerging approach.

Two building systems which merit special mention for their superior insulating abilities are Structurally Insulated Panels (SIPs) for exterior walls and roofs, and Insulated Concrete Forms (ICFs) for basement and exterior walls. SIPs consist of a thick slab of insulating foam sandwiched between two structural "skins" (usually OSB or plywood). Because the insulation is not interrupted every 16 inches by wooden studs, SIP homes have minimal air leaks and high R-values. ICFs use lightweight, hollow insulating foam blocks which are stacked like Legos® and are then filled with concrete. Continuous insulating foam on both sides of the concrete makes for a highly energy-efficient wall system.

Attic and roof insulation do double duty. In the winter, as warm air rises, it seeks to escape into the attic. In summer, sunshine can raise attic temps to 140° - 170° when outside temps are in the 90's. Attic insulation helps keep heat from entering your living space. (That's also why correct attic/roof ventilation is essential.)

DOORS AND WINDOWS When it comes to doors, insulated steel and fiberglass doors typically have five times the insulating capability of solid wood doors. Windows in the door will reduce this potential somewhat. Most hinged (swing-type) patio doors are much tighter than sliding patio doors.

Window efficiency is measured in terms of U-factors, with the lower numbers representing less heat loss. Many aspects affect a window's U-factor, including the number of panes (referred to as glazing). Double glazing (two panes of glass) is the most common, but triple glazing is gaining popularity. The glass itself may be tinted or include reflective coatings or films to reduce heat gain and glare. Low-emittance coatings (called Low-E) actually reflect heat. In the summer heat is reflected away from the house; in the winter the home's heat is reflected back inside. Some windows also have Argon gas between the panes which further reduces heat transfer. The material used to create the window's frame or "cladding" and the spacers between the panes can affect its performance as well. (Some cladding materials, such as aluminum, absorb heat and transfer it inside.)

HEATING, VENTILATION AND AIR CONDITIONING EQUIPMENT Any new home presents the opportunity to select more efficient HVAC equipment. A well-sealed home allows a smaller furnace, air conditioner or heat pump to perform adequately.

There has been a tendency to oversize furnaces and air conditioners, but it's important to know that doing so can be costly. Units that are too large not only cost more initially, they also don't run long enough to reach operating efficiency and they may wear out sooner because they start and stop so frequently. What's more, they are often louder and they may not dehumidify homes sufficiently in hot weather (because they don't run long enough to remove sufficient amounts of water).

DUCTWORK Another way to maximize the HVAC equipment's efficiency is to locate it to minimize the length of the duct runs. In addition, it's wise to keep duct runs away from exterior walls and out of unconditioned spaces (such as attics or crawl spaces) and to ensure all ductwork is sized properly and well-sealed.

PROPER HUMIDITY In colder climates, indoor air in many homes is too dry. Even if the relative humidity outside is 70%, by the time the outside air passes through the furnace to be heated, the humidity in the hot air may be down to just 7%. Because moist air feels warmer than dry air, adding a power humidifier to the furnace system can create a comfortable environment with the thermostat a couple of degrees lower than normal.

EFFICIENT APPLIANCES While building a new home, don't forget to choose efficient appliances. As the second largest area of power consumption in the home, wise appliance choices can have a major impact on energy consumption. The federal government's ENERGY STAR® program currently has ratings for refrigerators, clothes washers and dishwashers that make it easy to choose energy-smart appliances.

Building an energy-efficient home requires well-informed decisions, detailed planning and in some cases, a willingness to pay more for higher quality products. But the special attention and extra investments will reap benefits for years to come – in your family's comfort, in considerable utility savings and in your home's resale value. ■

For more energy saving tips, and to find out about building an ENERGY STAR® rated home, visit HerHome.com/energystar

Other Ways to Save Energy

1. Choose an efficient, sealed, direct-vent fireplace.

2. Use a ceiling fan to draw cool air which has settled upward in the summer and reverse it in the winter to push warm air downward.

3. Replace standard incandescent light bulbs with compact fluorescent light bulbs.

4. Avoid dark exterior colors (which absorb heat), especially on roofs.

photos by www.KGByproducts.com

The dollars you invest into your home's energy efficiency will begin paying back immediately – and more importantly; can make life at home more comfortable for you and your family for years to come.

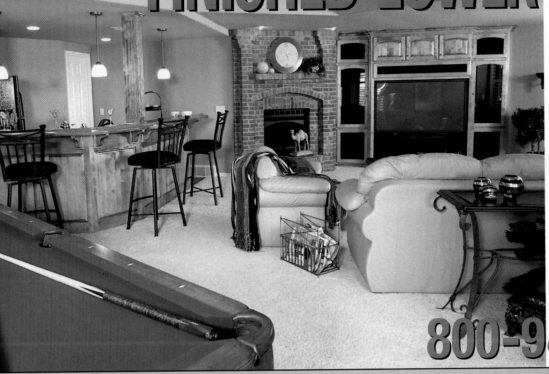

the Hartley
2949-9JJ
price code 24

Main Level	**1216**
Second Level	**1188**
Total Square Ft.	**2404**

Standard Foundation: Basement

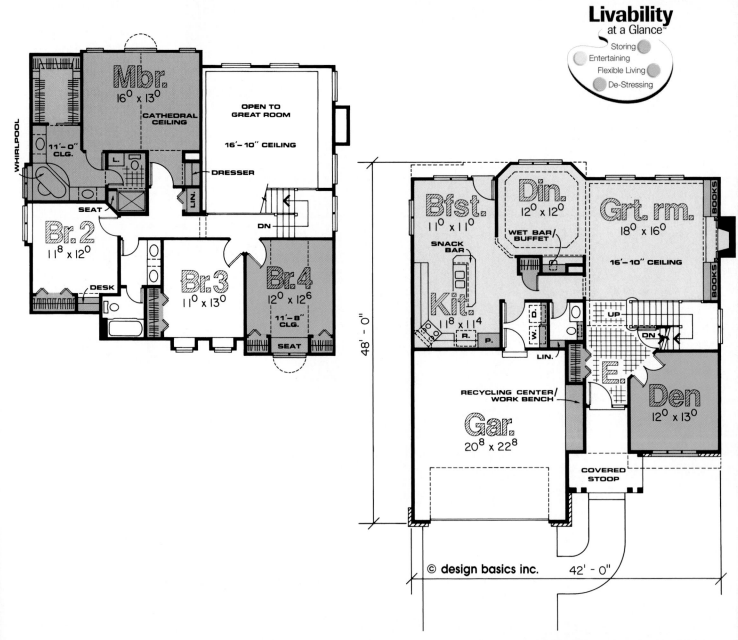

Livability at a Glance™
- Storing
- Entertaining
- Flexible Living
- De-Stressing

Mbr. 16⁰ x 13⁰
CATHEDRAL CEILING

OPEN TO GREAT ROOM
16'-10" CEILING

WHIRLPOOL

11'-0" CLG.

DRESSER

SEAT

DN

Br. 2 11⁸ x 12⁰

DESK

Br. 3 11⁰ x 13⁰

Br. 4 12⁰ x 12⁶

11'-8" CLG.

SEAT

Bfst. 11⁰ x 11⁰

Din. 12⁰ x 12⁰

WET BAR/ BUFFET

Grt. rm. 18⁰ x 16⁰

16'-10" CEILING

BOOKS

SNACK BAR

Kit. 11⁸ x 11⁴

R.   P.   W/ D   LIN.

UP

DN

Den 12⁰ x 13⁰

RECYCLING CENTER/ WORK BENCH

Gar. 20⁸ x 22⁸

COVERED STOOP

48' - 0"

42' - 0"

© design basics inc.

the
Fulton
2919-9JJ
pricecode 24

Main Level	**1277**
Second Level	**1135**
Total Square Ft.	**2412**

Standard Foundation: Basement

Livability
at a Glance™

- Storing
- Entertaining
- Flexible Living
- De-Stressing

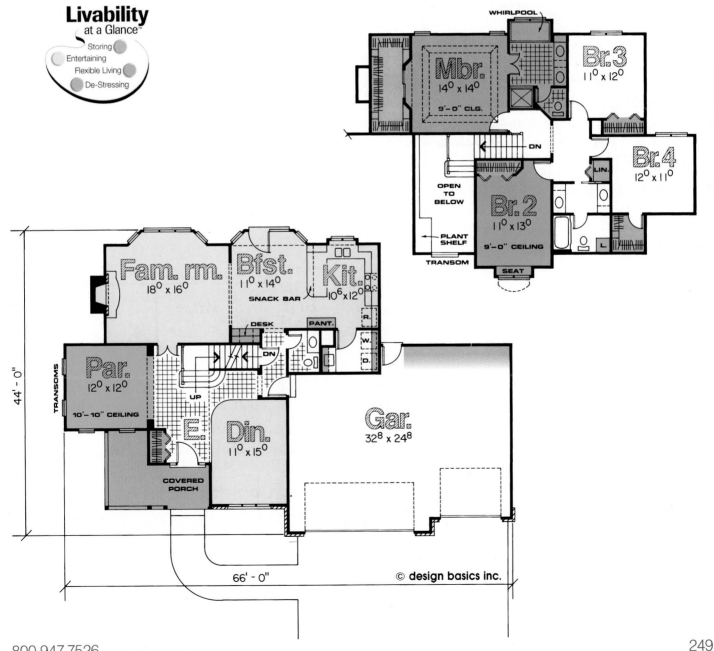

WHIRLPOOL

Mbr.
14⁰ x 14⁰
9'-0" CLG.

Br.3
11⁰ x 12⁰

DN

Br.4
12⁰ x 11⁰

OPEN TO BELOW

LIN.

Br.2
11⁰ x 13⁰
9'-0" CEILING

PLANT SHELF

TRANSOM

SEAT

L.

Fam. rm.
18⁰ x 16⁰

Bfst.
11⁰ x 14⁰

SNACK BAR

Kit.
10⁶ x 12⁰

DESK

PANT.

R.

DN

W.

D.

Par.
12⁰ x 12⁰
10'-10" CEILING

TRANSOMS

UP

E

Din.
11⁰ x 15⁰

Gar.
32⁸ x 24⁸

COVERED PORCH

44' - 0"

66' - 0"

© design basics inc.

the
Patagonia
5086-9JJ

pricecode 24

Main Level	**1162**
Second Level	**1255**
Total Square Ft.	**2417**

Standard Foundation: Basement

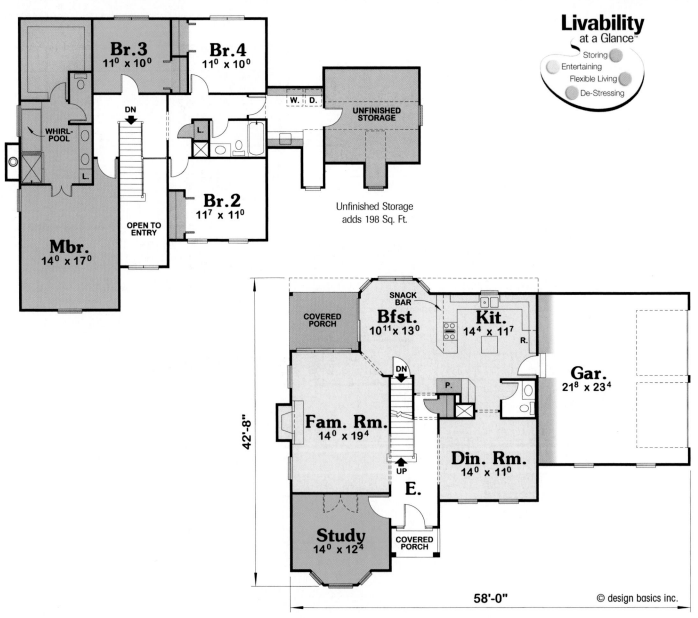

Br.3
11⁰ x 10⁰

Br.4
11⁰ x 10⁰

DN

W. D.

UNFINISHED STORAGE

WHIRL-POOL

L.

L.

Br.2
11⁷ x 11⁰

OPEN TO ENTRY

Mbr.
14⁰ x 17⁰

Unfinished Storage
adds 198 Sq. Ft.

Livability
at a Glance™

Storing
Entertaining
Flexible Living
De-Stressing

COVERED PORCH

SNACK BAR

Bfst.
10¹¹ x 13⁰

Kit.
14⁴ x 11⁷

R.

Gar.
21⁸ x 23⁴

DN

P.

Fam. Rm.
14⁰ x 19⁴

Din. Rm.
14⁰ x 11⁰

UP

E.

42'-8"

Study
14⁰ x 12⁴

COVERED PORCH

58'-0"

© design basics inc.

the Drifton
43014-9JJ
pricecode 24

Main Level	**1044**
Second Level	**1385**
Total Square Ft.	**2429**

Standard Foundation: Slab

Livability
at a Glance™

- Storing
- Entertaining
- Flexible Living
- De-Stressing

Den
11⁴ x 12⁰

Optional Den

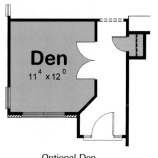

UP
DN
D
W
DROP ZONE

Optional Basement Stair Location

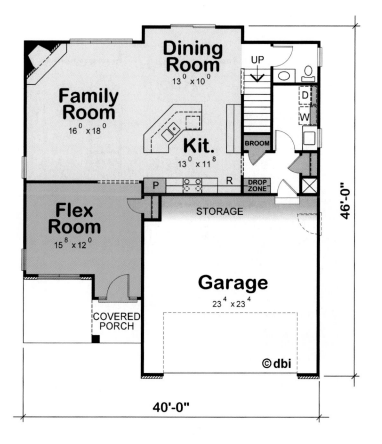

Dining Room 13⁰ x 10⁰

UP

Family Room 16⁰ x 18⁰

Kit. 13⁰ x 11⁸

BROOM

D
W

DROP ZONE

Flex Room 15⁸ x 12⁰

P   R

STORAGE

Garage 23⁴ x 23⁴

COVERED PORCH

©dbi

46'-0"

40'-0"

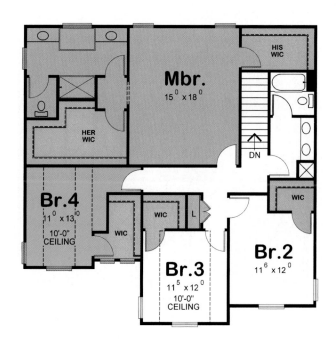

HIS WIC

Mbr. 15⁰ x 18⁰

HER WIC

DN

WIC

Br.4 11⁰ x 13¹⁰
10'-0" CEILING

WIC

WIC

L

Br.3 11⁵ x 12⁰
10'-0" CEILING

Br.2 11⁶ x 12⁰

the
Moss Bluff
43013-9JJ
pricecode 24

Main Level	**1044**
Second Level	**1385**
Total Square Ft.	**2429**

Standard Foundation: Slab

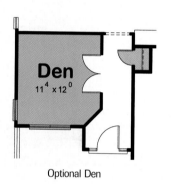

Optional Den

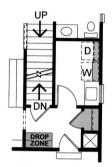

Optional Basement Stair Location

Livability
at a Glance™

Storing
Entertaining
Flexible Living
De-Stressing

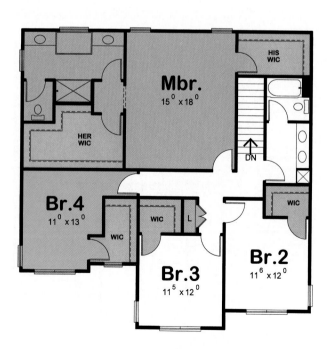

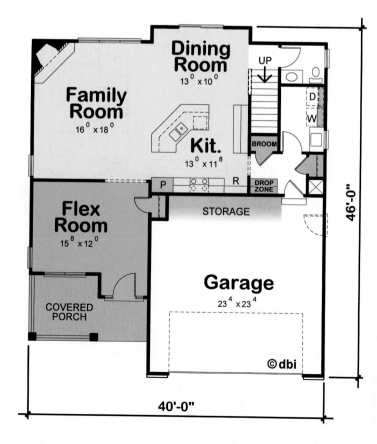

the Bibury Manor

9172-9JJ

price code 24

Main Level	**1280**
Second Level	**1158**
Total Square Ft.	**2438**

Standard Foundation: Slab

Livability
at a Glance™

- Storing
- Entertaining
- Flexible Living
- De-Stressing

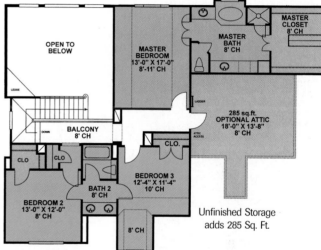

OPEN TO BELOW

LEDGE

MASTER BEDROOM
13'-0" X 17'-0"
8'-11' CH

MASTER BATH
8' CH

MASTER CLOSET
8' CH

BALCONY
8' CH

DOWN

LADDER

285 sq.ft.
OPTIONAL ATTIC
18'-0" X 13'-8"
8' CH

ATTIC ACCESS

CLO

CLO

CLO.

BATH 2
8' CH

BEDROOM 3
12'-4" X 11'-4"
10' CH

BEDROOM 2
13'-0" X 12'-0"
8' CH

8' CH

Unfinished Storage
adds 285 Sq. Ft.

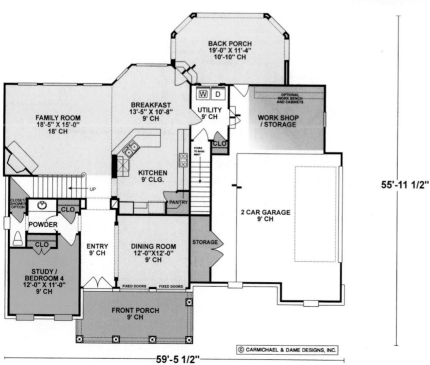

BACK PORCH
19'-0" X 11'-4"
10'-10" CH

FAMILY ROOM
18'-5" X 15'-0"
18' CH

BREAKFAST
13'-5" X 10'-8"
9' CH

W D

UTILITY
9' CH

OPTIONAL WORK BENCH AND CABINETS

WORK SHOP / STORAGE

KITCHEN
9' CLG.

CLO

STAIRS TO BASEMENT

PANTRY

UP

CLOSET & SHOWER OPTION

CLO

POWDER

CLO

STORAGE

2 CAR GARAGE
9' CH

ENTRY
9' CH

DINING ROOM
12'-0" X 12'-0"
9' CH

STUDY / BEDROOM 4
12'-0" X 11'-0"
9' CH

FIXED DOORS   FIXED DOORS

FRONT PORCH
9' CH

55'-11 1/2"

59'-5 1/2"

© CARMICHAEL & DAME DESIGNS, INC.

the
Fayette
2346-9JJ
pricecode 24

Main Level	**1369**
Second Level	**1111**
Total Square Ft.	**2480**

Standard Foundation: Basement

Livability
at a Glance™

- Storing
- Entertaining
- Flexible Living
- De-Stressing

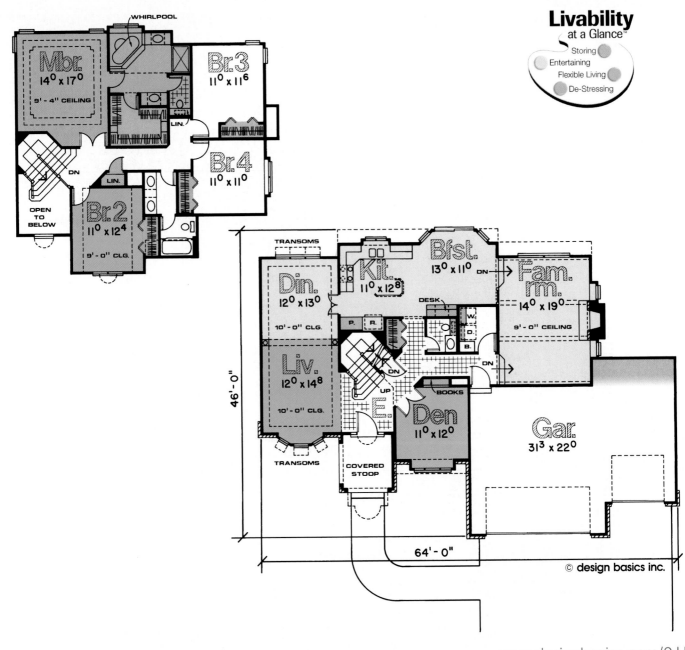

© design basics inc.

the Lawler

2898-9JJ

pricecode 24

Main Level	**1553**
Second Level	**962**
Total Square Ft.	**2497**

Standard Foundation: Basement

Livability at a Glance™

- Storing
- Entertaining
- Flexible Living
- De-Stressing

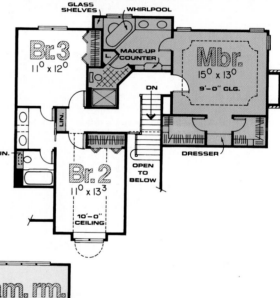

GLASS SHELVES
WHIRLPOOL

Br. 3
11⁰ x 12⁰

MAKE-UP COUNTER

Mbr.
15⁰ x 13⁰

9'-0" CLG.

DN

LIN.

LIN.

DRESSER

OPEN TO BELOW

Br. 2
11⁰ x 13³

10'-0" CEILING

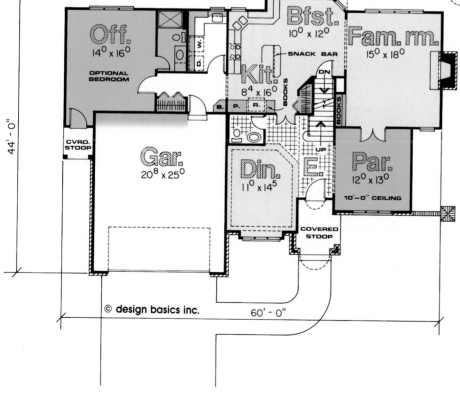

Off.
14⁰ x 16⁰

OPTIONAL BEDROOM

Bfst.
10⁰ x 12⁰

Fam. rm.
15⁰ x 18⁰

SNACK BAR

Kit.
8⁴ x 16⁰

BOOKS

DN

BOOKS

B. P. R.

UP

CVRD. STOOP

Gar.
20⁸ x 25⁰

Din.
11⁰ x 14⁵

F.

Par.
12⁰ x 13⁰

10'-0" CEILING

COVERED STOOP

44' - 0"

© design basics inc.

60' - 0"

the
Kinnersley
29507-9JJ
pricecode 24

Main Level	**1178**
Second Level	**1321**
Total Square Ft.	**2499**

Standard Foundation: Slab

Livability
at a Glance™

- Storing
- Entertaining
- Flexible Living
- De-Stressing

Br.4
11⁴×13⁰

Master
15⁴×16⁰
9'-0" CEILING

Br.3
13⁴×11⁰

WIC

WIC

LINEN

DN

SHELF

WIC

L

OPEN TO BELOW

Br.2
13⁴×11⁰
10'-0" CEILING

Study
13³×13⁰

Optional Study

UP   DN

Optional Basement Stair Location

Dining
11⁴×11

Kitchen
12⁰×12¹

Family
17⁰×15¹

Laun.
7⁶×11⁰

DROP ZONE

D W

R

UP

PANT

Flex
13³×13⁰

Entry
9⁷×6⁰

SEAT

2 Car Garage
23⁸×23⁸

COVERED PORCH

©prime designs, inc.

44'-0"

50'-0"

the
Whiteville
43049-9JJ
price**code** 25

Main Level	**1248**
Second Level	**1253**
Total Square Ft.	**2501**

Standard Foundation: Slab

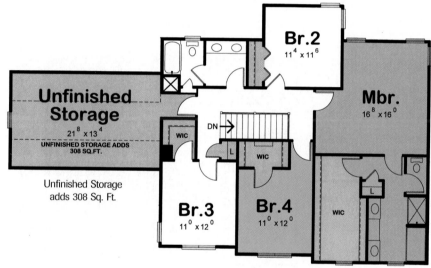

Livability
at a Glance™

- Storing
- Entertaining
- Flexible Living
- De-Stressing

Unfinished Storage
21⁸ x 13⁴

UNFINISHED STORAGE ADDS 308 SQ.FT.

Unfinished Storage adds 308 Sq. Ft.

Br.2 11⁴ x 11⁶

Mbr. 16⁸ x 16⁰

WIC

DN

L

WIC

Br.3 11⁰ x 12⁰

Br.4 11⁰ x 12⁰

WIC

L

WIC

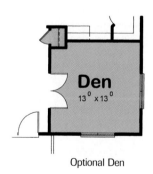

Den 13⁰ x 13⁰

Optional Den

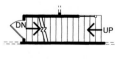

DN   UP

Optional Basement Stair Location

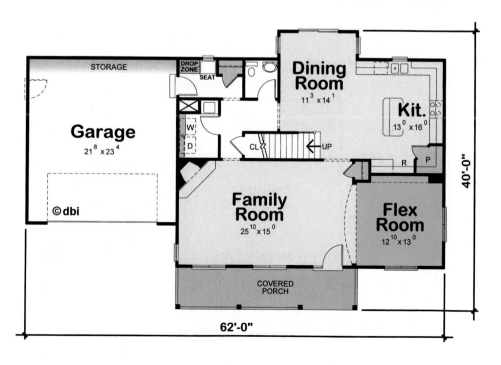

STORAGE

DROP ZONE

SEAT

Dining Room 11³ x 14¹

Kit. 13⁰ x 16⁰

Garage 21⁸ x 23⁴

W

D

CL

UP

R   P

©dbi

Family Room 25¹⁰ x 15⁰

Flex Room 12¹⁰ x 13⁰

COVERED PORCH

40'-0"

62'-0"

the
Keene
43050-9JJ

pricecode 25

Main Level	1248
Second Level	1257
Total Square Ft.	2505

Standard Foundation: Slab

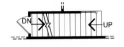

Livability
at a Glance™

- Storing
- Entertaining
- Flexible Living
- De-Stressing

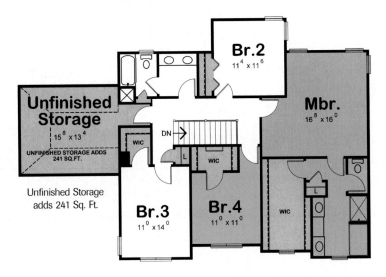

Br.2
11⁴ x 11⁶

Unfinished Storage
15⁸ x 13⁴

UNFINISHED STORAGE ADDS 241 SQ.FT.

Unfinished Storage adds 241 Sq. Ft.

DN

WIC

Mbr.
16⁸ x 16⁰

WIC

Br.3
11⁰ x 14⁰

Br.4
11⁰ x 11⁰

WIC

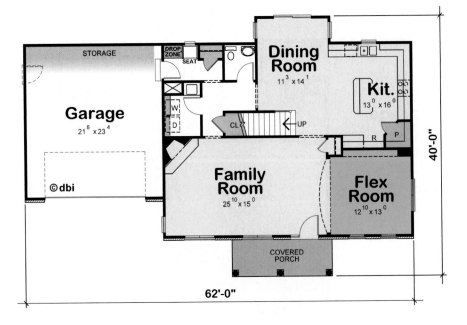

STORAGE

DROP ZONE

SEAT

Dining Room
11³ x 14¹

Kit.
13⁰ x 16⁰

Garage
21⁸ x 23⁴

W
D

CL

UP

R   P

©dbi

Family Room
25¹⁰ x 15⁰

Flex Room
12¹⁰ x 13⁰

COVERED PORCH

40'-0"

62'-0"

Den
13⁰ x 13⁰

Optional Den

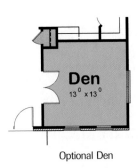

DN   UP

Optional Basement Stair Location

the
Morrison
2229-9JJ
pricecode 25

Main Level	**1392**
Second Level	**1153**
Total Square Ft.	**2545**

Standard Foundation: Basement

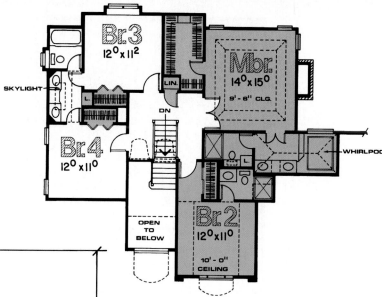

Livability at a Glance™
- Storing
- Entertaining
- Flexible Living
- De-Stressing

Second Level

Br.3 12⁰x11²

Mbr. 14⁰x15⁰ 9'-6" CLG.

SKYLIGHT

LIN.

DN

L.

Br.4 12⁰x11⁰

WHIRLPOOL

L.

OPEN TO BELOW

Br.2 12⁰x11⁰ 10'-0" CEILING

Main Level

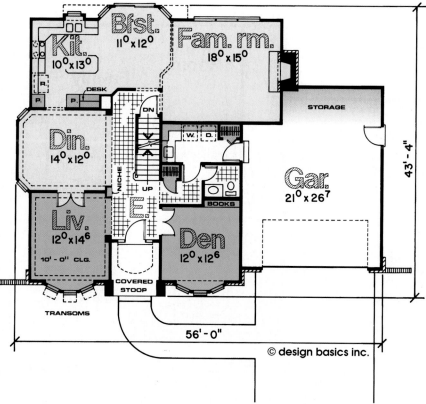

Kit. 10⁰x13⁰

Bfst. 11⁰x12⁰

Fam. rm. 18⁰x15⁰

DESK

R.

P. P.

STORAGE

Din. 14⁰x12⁰

DN

W. D.

Gar. 21⁰x26⁷

NICHE

UP

E.

BOOKS

Liv. 12⁰x14⁶ 10'-0" CLG.

Den 12⁰x12⁶

COVERED STOOP

43'-4"

56'-0"

TRANSOMS

© design basics inc.

the
Waterloo
43025-9JJ
price code 25

Main Level	**1301**
Second Level	**1248**
Total Square Ft.	**2549**

Standard Foundation: Slab

Livability
at a Glance™

Storing
Entertaining
Flexible Living
De-Stressing

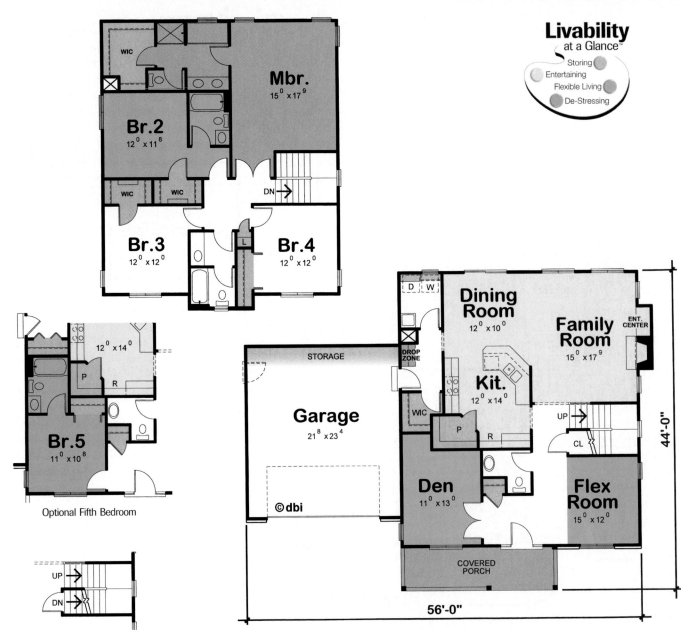

WIC

Mbr.
15⁰ x 17⁹

Br.2
12⁰ x 11⁸

WIC   WIC

DN →

Br.3
12⁰ x 12⁰

L

Br.4
12⁰ x 12⁰

12⁰ x 14⁰

P   R

Br.5
11⁰ x 10⁸

Optional Fifth Bedroom

UP →
DN →

Optional Basement Stair Location

STORAGE

DROP ZONE

D W

Dining Room
12⁰ x 10⁰

Family Room
15⁰ x 17⁹

ENT. CENTER

Kit.
12⁰ x 14⁰

Garage
21⁸ x 23⁴

WIC

P   R

UP →

CL

Den
11⁰ x 13⁰

Flex Room
15⁰ x 12⁰

©dbi

COVERED PORCH

44'-0"

56'-0"

the
Karlynda
4156-9JJ

pricecode 25

Main Level	**1266**
Second Level	**1292**
Total Square Ft.	**2558**

Standard Foundation: Basement

Livability
at a Glance™

- Storing
- Entertaining
- Flexible Living
- De-Stressing

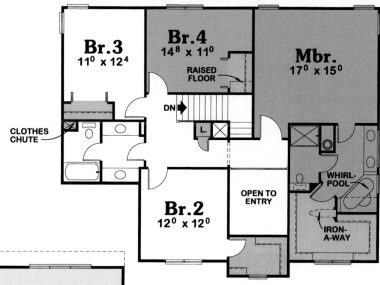

Br.3 11⁰ x 12⁴

Br.4 14⁸ x 11⁰

RAISED FLOOR

DN

Mbr. 17⁰ x 15⁰

CLOTHES CHUTE

L.

WHIRL-POOL

Br.2 12⁰ x 12⁰

OPEN TO ENTRY

IRON-A-WAY

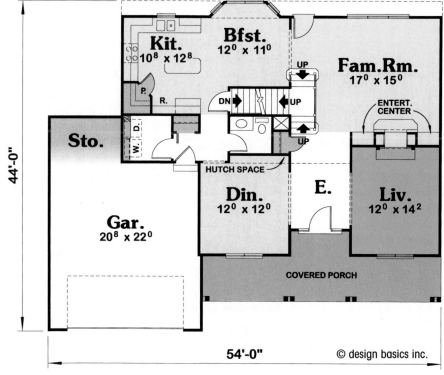

Kit. 10⁸ x 12⁸

Bfst. 12⁰ x 11⁰

Fam.Rm. 17⁰ x 15⁰

UP

P.

R.

DN

UP

ENTERT. CENTER

UP

Sto.

W. D.

HUTCH SPACE

Din. 12⁰ x 12⁰

E.

Liv. 12⁰ x 14²

Gar. 20⁸ x 22⁰

COVERED PORCH

44'-0"

54'-0"

© design basics inc.

the
Algona
43026-9JJ

price code 25

Main Level	**1301**
Second Level	**1273**
Total Square Ft.	**2574**

Standard Foundation: Slab

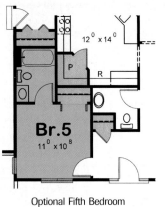

Br.5
11⁰ x 10⁸

12⁰ x 14⁰

P   R

Optional Fifth Bedroom

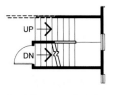

UP
DN

Optional Basement Stair Location

Livability
at a Glance™

Storing
Entertaining
Flexible Living
De-Stressing

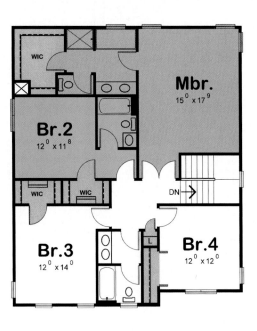

WIC

Mbr.
15⁰ x 17⁹

Br.2
12⁰ x 11⁸

WIC   WIC

DN

Br.3
12⁰ x 14⁰

Br.4
12⁰ x 12⁰

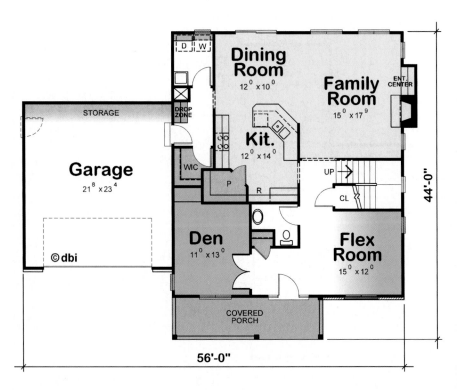

D W

Dining Room
12⁰ x 10⁰

Family Room
15⁰ x 17⁹

ENT. CENTER

STORAGE

DROP ZONE

Kit.
12⁰ x 14⁰

WIC

Garage
21⁸ x 23⁴

P   R

UP

CL

© dbi

Den
11⁰ x 13⁰

Flex Room
15⁰ x 12⁰

COVERED PORCH

44'-0"

56'-0"

the Castelar
2656-9JJ

pricecode 25

Main Level **1362**

Second Level **1223**

Total Square Ft. **2585**

Standard Foundation: Basement

Livability
at a Glance™

- Storing
- Entertaining
- Flexible Living
- De-Stressing

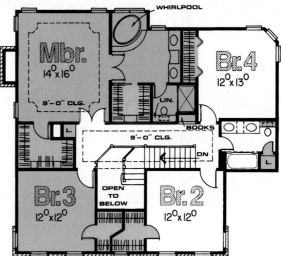

WHIRLPOOL

Mbr.
14⁰x16⁰

9'-0" CLG.

Br.4
12⁰x13⁰

LIN.

BOOKS

9'-0" CLG.

DN

Br.3
12⁰x12⁰

OPEN TO BELOW

Br.2
12⁰x12⁰

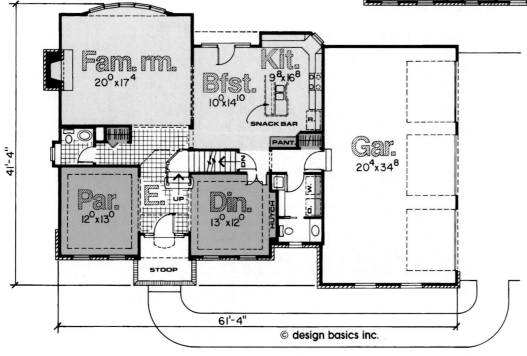

Fam. rm.
20⁰x17⁴

Kit.
9⁸x16⁸

Bfst.
10⁰x14¹⁰

SNACK BAR

PANT.

Gar.
20⁴x34⁸

Par.
12⁰x13⁰

DN

UP

Din.
13⁰x12⁰

HUTCH

STOOP

41'-4"

61'-4"

© design basics inc.

the
Newberry
1455-9JJ
price code 25

Main Level	**1322**
Second Level	**1272**
Total Square Ft.	**2594**

Standard Foundation: Basement

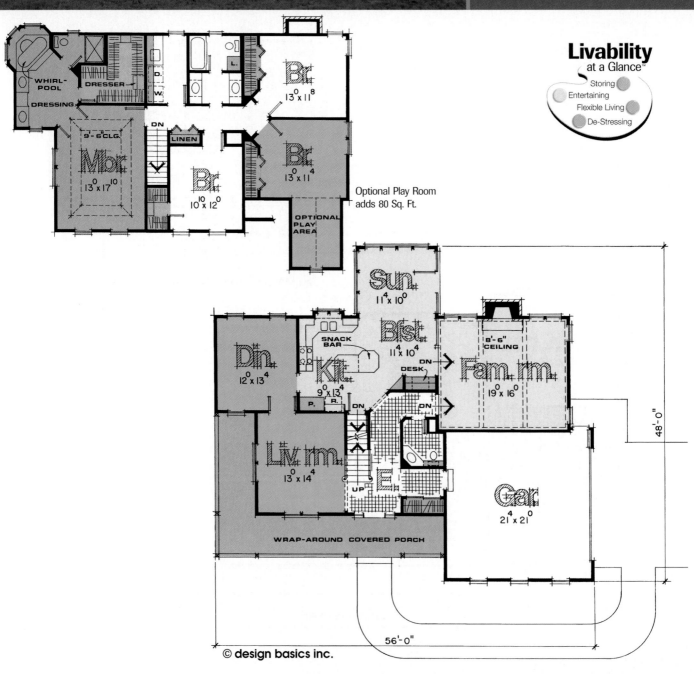

Optional Play Room adds 80 Sq. Ft.

Livability
at a Glance™

- Storing
- Entertaining
- Flexible Living
- De-Stressing

WHIRL-POOL
DRESSER
DRESSING
9'- 6" CLG.
Mbr 13⁰ x 17⁰
DN
LINEN
Br 10⁴ x 12⁰
Br 13⁰ x 11⁸
Br 13⁰ x 11⁴
OPTIONAL PLAY AREA

Sun 11⁴ x 10⁰
Bfst 11⁴ x 10⁴
8'- 6" CEILING
Fam. rm. 19⁰ x 16⁰
SNACK BAR
Kit 9⁰ x 13⁰
DESK
Dn. 12⁰ x 13⁴
P. R.
DN
DN
Liv. rm. 13⁰ x 14⁰
UP
Gar 21⁴ x 21⁰
48'- 0"
56'- 0"
WRAP-AROUND COVERED PORCH

© design basics inc.

the
Kirksville
43055-9JJ
pricecode 26

Main Level	**1149**
Second Level	**1460**
Total Square Ft.	**2609**

Standard Foundation: Slab

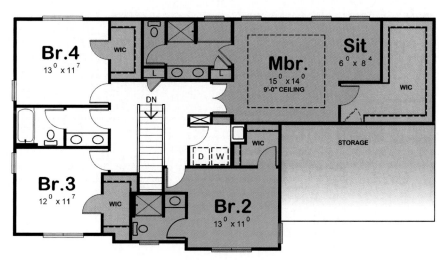

Livability
at a Glance™

Storing
Entertaining
Flexible Living
De-Stressing

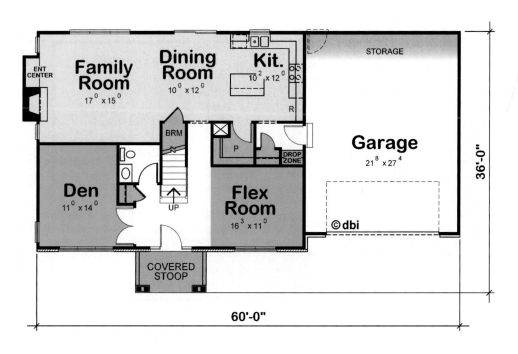

Br.4
13⁰ x 11⁷

WIC

Mbr.
15⁰ x 14⁰
9'-0" CEILING

Sit
6⁰ x 8⁴

WIC

DN

D   W

WIC

STORAGE

Br.3
12⁰ x 11⁷

WIC

Br.2
13⁰ x 11⁰

STORAGE

Family Room
17⁰ x 15⁰

Dining Room
10⁰ x 12⁰

Kit.
10² x 12⁰

ENT CENTER

BRM

P

DROP ZONE

Garage
21⁸ x 27⁴

Den
11⁰ x 14⁰

UP

Flex Room
16³ x 11⁰

©dbi

COVERED STOOP

60'-0"

36'-0"

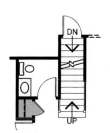

DN

UP

Optional Basement Stair Location

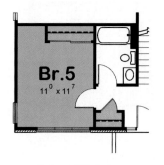

Br.5
11⁰ x 11⁷

Optional Fifth Bedroom

the
Westboro
43056-9JJ

price code 26

Main Level	1149
Second Level	1460
Total Square Ft.	2609

Standard Foundation: Slab

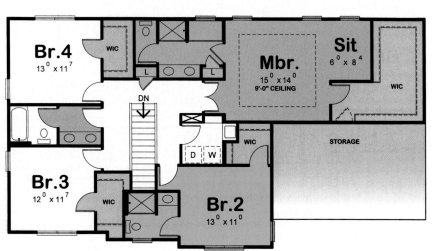

Br.4 13⁰ x 11⁷

WIC

DN

Mbr. 15⁰ x 14⁰ 9'-0" CEILING

Sit 6⁰ x 8⁴

WIC

STORAGE

WIC

D W

Br.3 12⁰ x 11⁷

WIC

Br.2 13⁰ x 11⁰

Livability
at a Glance™

Storing
Entertaining
Flexible Living
De-Stressing

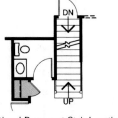

DN

UP

Optional Basement Stair Location

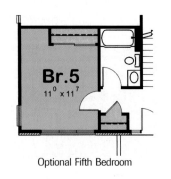

Br.5 11⁰ x 11⁷

Optional Fifth Bedroom

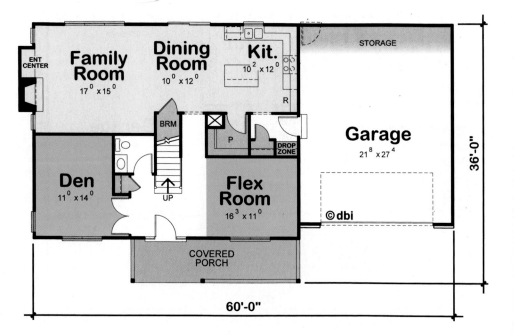

ENT CENTER

Family Room 17⁰ x 15⁰

Dining Room 10⁰ x 12⁰

Kit. 10² x 12⁰

STORAGE

BRM

P

DROP ZONE

Den 11⁰ x 14⁰

UP

Flex Room 16³ x 11⁰

Garage 21⁸ x 27⁴

© dbi

R

36'-0"

COVERED PORCH

60'-0"

the
Calabretta
4106-9JJ
pricecode 26

Main Level	**1333**
Second Level	**1280**
Total Square Ft.	**2613**

Standard Foundation: Basement

Livability
at a Glance™

- Storing
- Entertaining
- Flexible Living
- De-Stressing

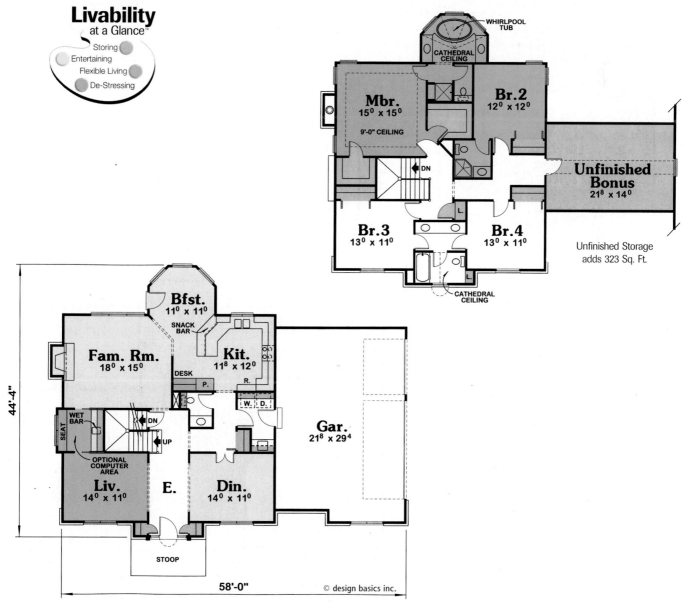

WHIRLPOOL TUB

CATHEDRAL CEILING

Mbr.
15^0 x 15^0

9'-0" CEILING

Br.2
12^0 x 12^0

DN

Unfinished Bonus
21^8 x 14^0

Br.3
13^0 x 11^0

L.

Br.4
13^0 x 11^0

L.

Unfinished Storage
adds 323 Sq. Ft.

CATHEDRAL CEILING

Bfst.
11^0 x 11^0

SNACK BAR

Fam. Rm.
18^0 x 15^0

Kit.
11^8 x 12^0

DESK

P.

R.

W. D.

Gar.
21^8 x 29^4

WET BAR

SEAT

DN

UP

OPTIONAL COMPUTER AREA

Liv.
14^0 x 11^0

E.

Din.
14^0 x 11^0

44'-4"

STOOP

58'-0"

© design basics inc.

the
Jennings
3246-9JJ
price code 26

Main Level	**1366**
Second Level	**1278**
Total Square Ft.	**2644**

Standard Foundation: Basement

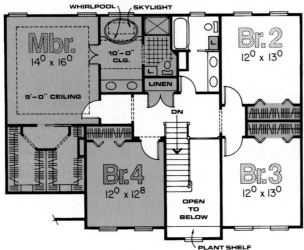

WHIRLPOOL — SKYLIGHT

Mbr.
14⁰ x 16⁰

9'-0" CEILING

10'-0" CLG.

LINEN

Br. 2
12⁰ x 13⁰

L.

DN

Br. 4
12⁰ x 12⁸

Br. 3
12⁰ x 13⁰

OPEN
TO
BELOW

PLANT SHELF

Livability
at a Glance™

Storing
Entertaining
Flexible Living
De-Stressing

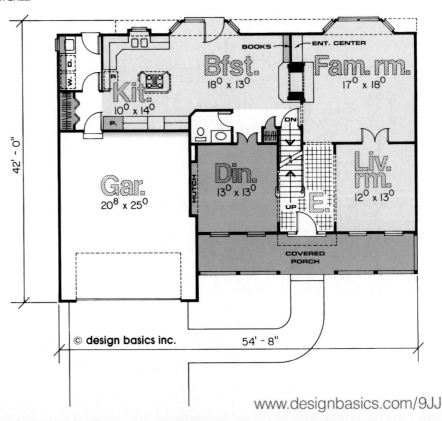

BOOKS   ENT. CENTER

Bfst.
18⁰ x 13⁰

Fam. rm.
17⁰ x 18⁰

Kit.
10⁰ x 14⁰

R.

P.

DN

Liv.
rm.
12⁰ x 13⁰

Gar.
20⁸ x 25⁰

HUTCH

Din.
13⁰ x 13⁰

UP

42' - 0"

COVERED
PORCH

© design basics inc.

54' - 8"

the
Leawood
2779-9JJ
price code 26

Main Level	**1415**
Second Level	**1274**
Total Square Ft.	**2689**

Standard Foundation: Basement

Livability at a Glance™

- Storing
- Entertaining
- Flexible Living
- De-Stressing

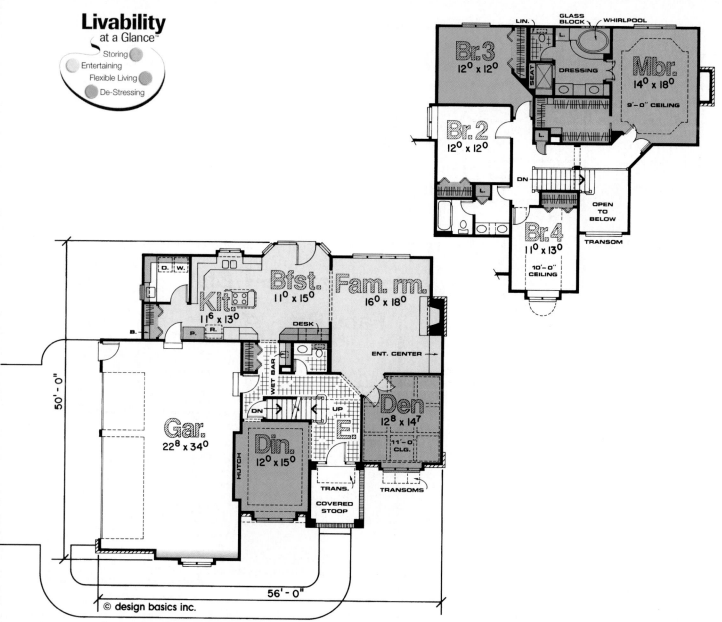

the Oakboro
8512-9JJ
price code 27

Main Level	**1369**
Second Level	**1336**
Total Square Ft.	**2705**

Standard Foundation: Basement

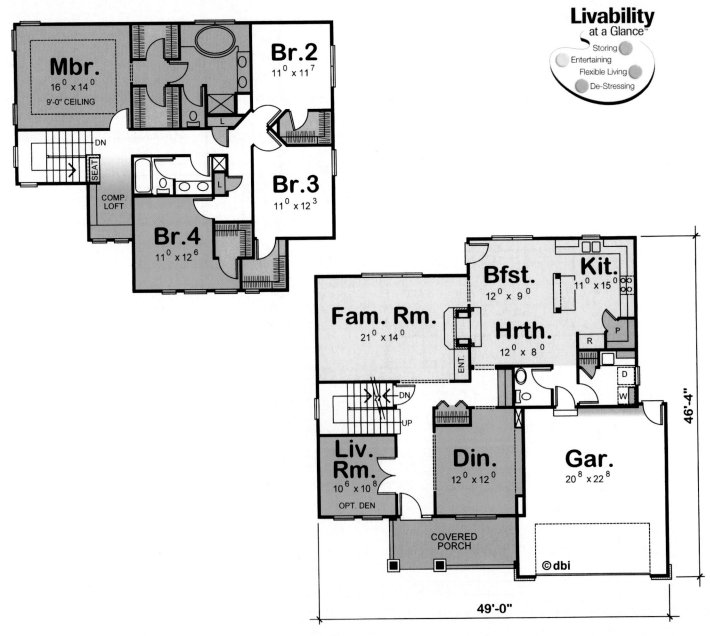

Livability
at a Glance™

- Storing
- Entertaining
- Flexible Living
- De-Stressing

Mbr.
16⁰ x 14⁰
9'-0" CEILING

Br.2
11⁰ x 11⁷

Br.3
11⁰ x 12³

Br.4
11⁰ x 12⁶

DN

SEAT

COMP. LOFT

L

L

Bfst.
12⁰ x 9⁰

Kit.
11⁰ x 15⁰

Fam. Rm.
21⁰ x 14⁰

Hrth.
12⁰ x 8⁰

R

P

D

W

ENT.

DN

UP

Liv. Rm.
10⁶ x 10⁸
OPT. DEN

Din.
12⁰ x 12⁰

Gar.
20⁸ x 22⁸

COVERED PORCH

©dbi

46'-4"

49'-0"

the Woodvine Manor

9161-9JJ

pricecode 27

Main Level	**1400**
Second Level	**1315**
Total Square Ft.	**2715**

Standard Foundation: Slab

Livability at a Glance™

- Storing
- Entertaining
- Flexible Living
- De-Stressing

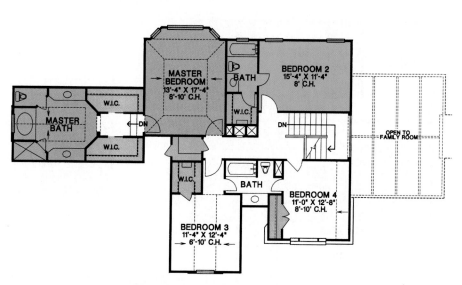

MASTER BEDROOM
13'-4" X 17'-4"
8'-10" C.H.

W.I.C.

MASTER BATH

W.I.C.

DN

BATH

W.I.C.

BEDROOM 2
15'-4" X 11'-4"
8' C.H.

DN

OPEN TO FAMILY ROOM

W.I.C.

BATH

BEDROOM 4
11'-0" X 12'-8"
8'-10" C.H.

BEDROOM 3
11'-4" X 12'-4"
6'-10" C.H.

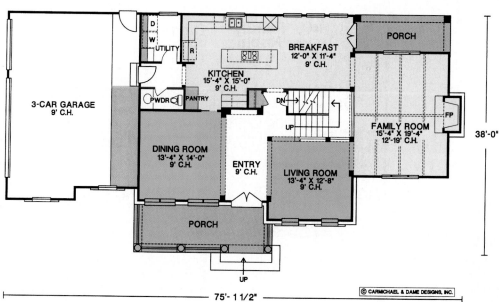

3-CAR GARAGE
9' C.H.

D
W
UTILITY
R

BREAKFAST
12'-0" X 11'-4"
9' C.H.

PORCH

KITCHEN
15'-4" X 15'-0"
9' C.H.

PWDR

PANTRY

DN

UP

FAMILY ROOM
15'-4" X 19'-4"
12'-19' C.H.

FP

DINING ROOM
13'-4" X 14'-0"
9' C.H.

ENTRY
9' C.H.

LIVING ROOM
13'-4" X 12'-8"
9' C.H.

38'-0"

PORCH

UP

75'- 1 1/2"

the Chestnut Knoll
43001-9JJ
price code 27

Main Level	**1436**
Second Level	**1300**
Total Square Ft.	**2736**

Standard Foundation: Slab

Livability
at a Glance™

- Storing
- Entertaining
- Flexible Living
- De-Stressing

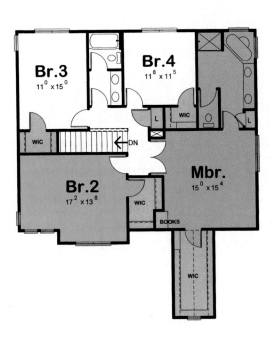

Br.3 11⁰ x 15⁰
Br.4 11⁸ x 11⁵
Br.2 17² x 13⁸
Mbr. 15⁰ x 15⁴
WIC · DN · L · BOOKS

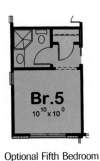

Br.5 10¹⁰ x 10⁰

Optional Fifth Bedroom

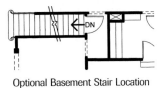

Optional Basement Stair Location

Optional Bathroom

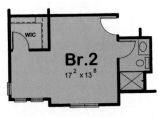

Br.2 17² x 13⁸

Optional Second Bedroom

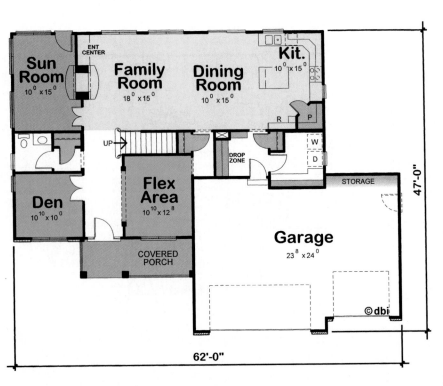

Sun Room 10⁰ x 15⁰
Family Room 18⁰ x 15⁰
Dining Room 10⁰ x 15⁰
Kit. 10⁰ x 15⁰
ENT CENTER
Den 10¹⁰ x 10⁰
Flex Area 10¹⁰ x 12⁸
UP · DROP ZONE · W · D · STORAGE · R · P
Garage 23⁸ x 24⁰
COVERED PORCH
©dbi

47'-0"

62'-0"

the Dublin Hill

43002-9JJ

pricecode 27

Main Level	**1436**
Second Level	**1306**
Total Square Ft.	**2742**

Standard Foundation: Slab

Livability
at a Glance™

Storing
Entertaining
Flexible Living
De-Stressing

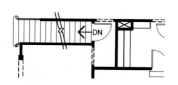

Optional Basement Stair Location

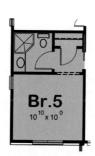

Br.5
10¹⁰ x 10⁰

Optional Fifth Bedroom

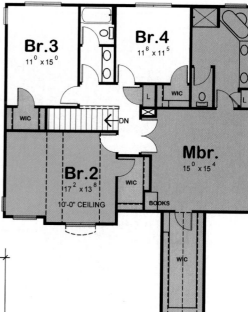

Br.3
11⁰ x 15⁰

Br.4
11⁸ x 11⁵

WIC

DN

Br.2
17² x 13⁸
10'-0" CEILING

Mbr.
15⁰ x 15⁴

WIC

BOOKS

WIC

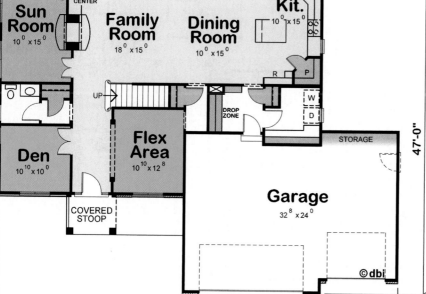

Sun Room
10⁰ x 15⁰

ENT CENTER

Family Room
18⁰ x 15⁰

Dining Room
10⁰ x 15⁰

Kit.
10⁰ x 15⁰

R   P

UP

DROP ZONE

W   D

Den
10¹⁰ x 10⁰

Flex Area
10¹⁰ x 12⁸

STORAGE

Garage
32⁸ x 24⁰

COVERED STOOP

©dbi

47'-0"

62'-0"

Optional Bathroom

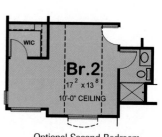

WIC

Br.2
17² x 13⁸
10'-0" CEILING

Optional Second Bedroom

the
Attleboro
5083-9JJ
price code 27

Main Level	**1582**
Second Level	**1170**
Total Square Ft.	**2752**

Standard Foundation: Basement

Livability
at a Glance™

- Storing
- Entertaining
- Flexible Living
- De-Stressing

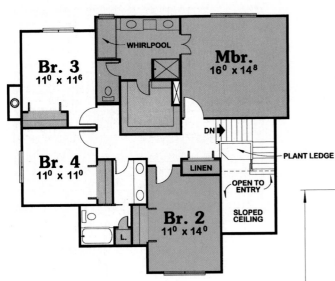

WHIRLPOOL

Br. 3
11⁰ x 11⁶

Mbr.
16⁰ x 14⁸

Br. 4
11⁰ x 11⁰

DN

LINEN

PLANT LEDGE

OPEN TO ENTRY

Br. 2
11⁰ x 14⁰

SLOPED CEILING

L.

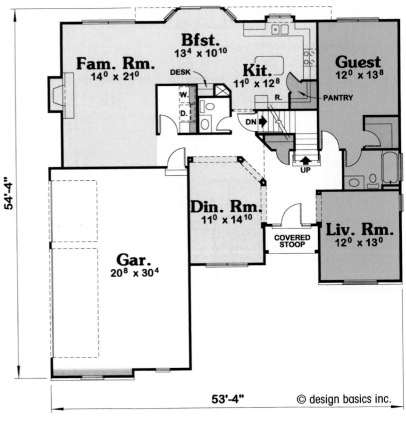

Fam. Rm.
14⁰ x 21⁰

Bfst.
13⁴ x 10¹⁰

Kit.
11⁰ x 12⁸

Guest
12⁰ x 13⁸

DESK

W.

D.

PANTRY

R.

DN

UP

54'-4"

Din. Rm.
11⁰ x 14¹⁰

Gar.
20⁸ x 30⁴

COVERED STOOP

Liv. Rm.
12⁰ x 13⁰

© design basics inc.

53'-4"

the
Broadmead
Court

9265-9JJ
price code 27

Main Level	**1305**
Second Level	**1461**
Total Square Ft.	**2766**

Standard Foundation: Basement

Livability
at a Glance™

- Storing
- Entertaining
- Flexible Living
- De-Stressing

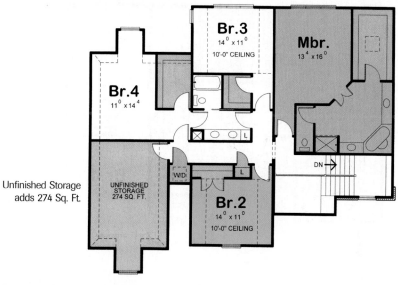

Br.3
14⁰ x 11⁰
10'-0" CEILING

Mbr.
13⁴ x 16⁰

Br.4
11⁰ x 14⁴

Unfinished Storage
adds 274 Sq. Ft.

UNFINISHED
STORAGE
274 SQ. FT.

W/D

DN →

Br.2
14⁰ x 11⁰
10'-0" CEILING

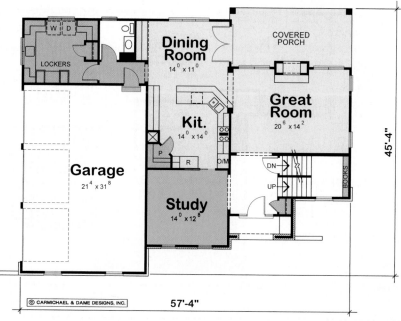

W D

LOCKERS

Dining Room
14⁰ x 11⁰

COVERED PORCH

Kit.
14⁰ x 14⁰

Great Room
20⁶ x 14²

Garage
21⁴ x 31⁸

P

R

D/W

DN →

UP →

BOOKS

Study
14⁰ x 12⁸

45'-4"

57'-4"

© CARMICHAEL & DAME DESIGNS, INC.

the
Alloway
43004-9JJ
price code 27

Main Level	**1337**
Second Level	**1460**
Total Square Ft.	**2797**

Standard Foundation: Slab

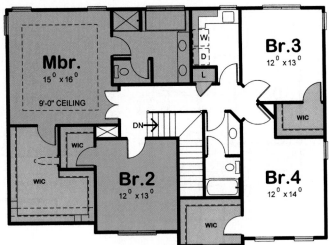

Livability
at a Glance™

- Storing
- Entertaining
- Flexible Living
- De-Stressing

Mbr.
15⁰ x 16⁰
9'-0" CEILING

Br.3
12⁰ x 13⁰

WIC

DN →

WIC

WIC

Br.2
12⁰ x 13⁰

Br.4
12⁰ x 14⁰

WIC

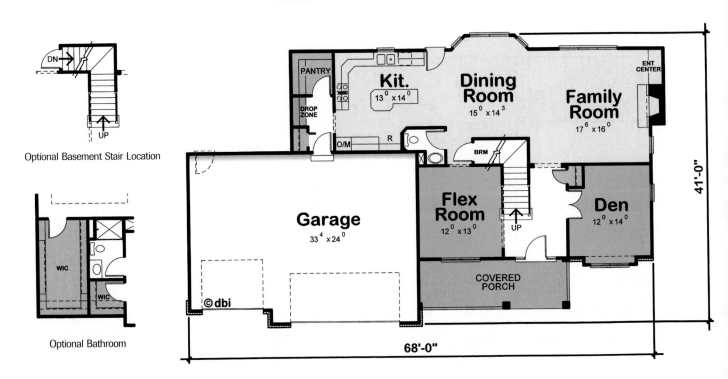

DN →

UP

Optional Basement Stair Location

WIC

WIC

Optional Bathroom

PANTRY

DROP ZONE

Kit.
13⁰ x 14⁰

Dining Room
15⁰ x 14³

Family Room
17⁶ x 16⁰

ENT CENTER

O/M

R

BRM

Garage
33⁴ x 24⁰

Flex Room
12⁰ x 13⁰

UP

Den
12⁰ x 14⁰

COVERED PORCH

©dbi

41'-0"

68'-0"

the
Hitchins
43005-9JJ
pricecode 28

Main Level	**1329**
Second Level	**1521**
Total Square Ft.	**2850**

Standard Foundation: Slab

Livability
at a Glance™

Storing
Entertaining
Flexible Living
De-Stressing

Mbr.
15⁰ x 16⁰
9'-0" CEILING

W
D
L

Br.3
12⁰ x 13⁰

WIC

WIC

DN→

WIC

Br.2
12⁰ x 15⁰
10'-0"
CEILING

Br.4
12⁰ x 13⁰

DESK

WIC

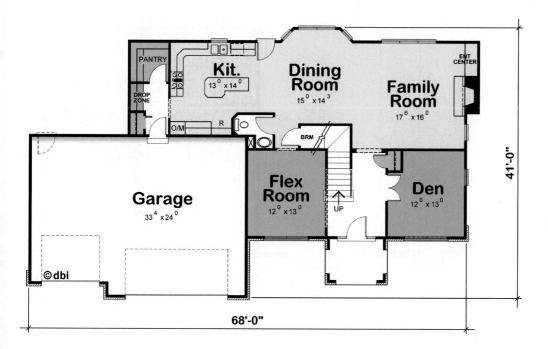

PANTRY

Kit.
13⁰ x 14⁰

DROP ZONE

O/M   R

BRM

Dining Room
15⁰ x 14³

ENT CENTER

Family Room
17⁶ x 16⁰

Garage
33⁴ x 24⁰

Flex Room
12⁰ x 13⁰

UP

Den
12⁰ x 13⁰

©dbi

41'-0"

68'-0"

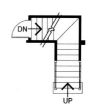

DN→

UP

Optional Basement Stair Location

WIC

WIC

Optional Bathroom

the
Newport
2293-9JJ
pricecode 28

Main Level	**1501**
Second Level	**1389**
Total Square Ft.	**2890**

Standard Foundation: Basement

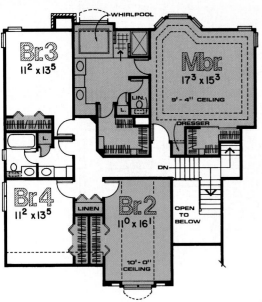

Br.3
11² x 13⁵

WHIRLPOOL

Mbr.
17³ x 15³
9'-4" CEILING

DRESSER

LIN.

DN

Br.4
11² x 13⁵

LINEN

Br.2
11⁰ x 16¹
10'-0" CEILING

OPEN TO BELOW

Livability
at a Glance™

Storing
Entertaining
Flexible Living
De-Stressing

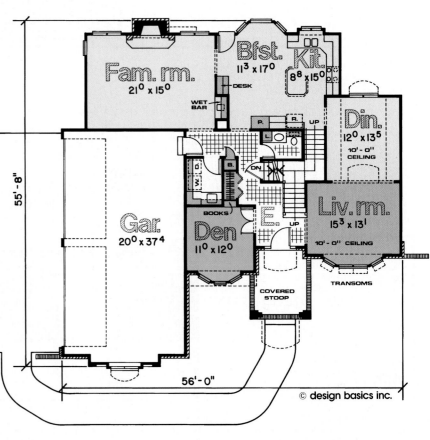

Fam. rm.
21⁰ x 15⁰

Bfst.
11³ x 17⁰

Kit.
8⁸ x 15⁰

DESK

WET BAR

Din.
12⁰ x 13⁵
10'-0" CEILING

P. R. UP

L

DN

55'-8"

Gar.
20⁰ x 37⁴

W.D.

BOOKS

Den
11⁰ x 12⁰

E.

UP

Liv. rm.
15³ x 13¹
10'-0" CEILING

COVERED STOOP

TRANSOMS

56'-0"

© design basics inc.

the Somersworth

43052-9JJ

pricecode 28

Main Level **1410**

Second Level **1482**

Total Square Ft. **2892**

Standard Foundation: Slab

Livability
at a Glance™

- Storing
- Entertaining
- Flexible Living
- De-Stressing

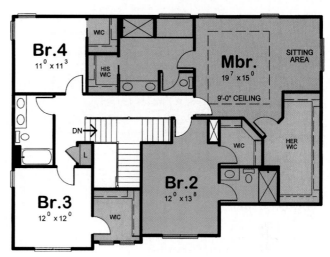

Br.4
11⁰ x 11³

WIC

HIS WIC

Mbr.
19⁷ x 15⁰

SITTING AREA

9'-0" CEILING

DN →

L

HER WIC

WIC

Br.2
12⁰ x 13⁸

Br.3
12⁰ x 12⁰

WIC

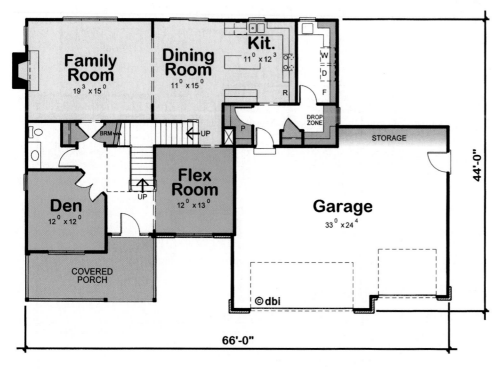

Family Room
19³ x 15⁰

Dining Room
11⁰ x 15⁰

Kit.
11⁰ x 12³

W
D

R

F

BRM

UP

P

DROP ZONE

STORAGE

Den
12⁰ x 12⁰

Flex Room
12⁰ x 13⁰

Garage
33⁰ x 24⁴

UP

COVERED PORCH

44'-0"

©dbi

66'-0"

Optional Bathroom

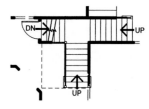

Optional Basement Stair Location

DN

UP

UP

the
Manning
2207-9JJ

price code 29

Main Level	**1583**
Second Level	**1331**
Total Square Ft.	**2914**

Standard Foundation: Basement

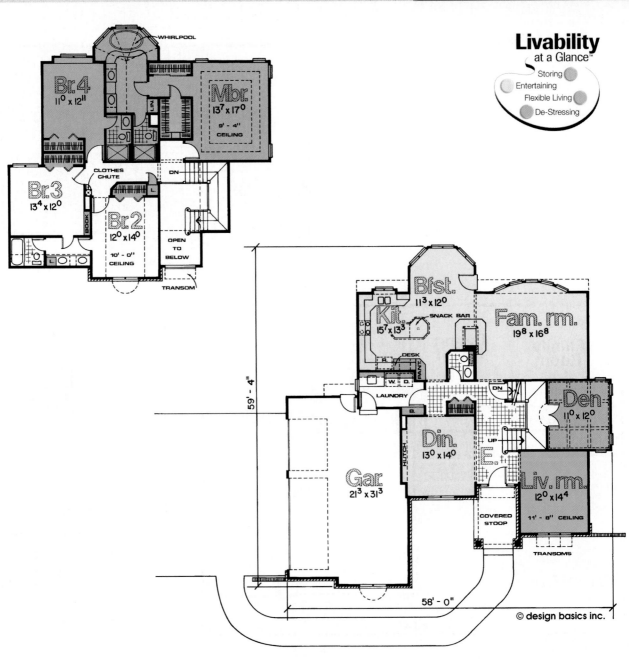

Livability
at a Glance™

Storing
Entertaining
Flexible Living
De-Stressing

www.designbasics.com/9JJ

© design basics inc.

the Karli Rose

43053-9JJ

pricecode 29

Main Level	**1418**
Second Level	**1499**
Total Square Ft.	**2917**

Standard Foundation: Slab

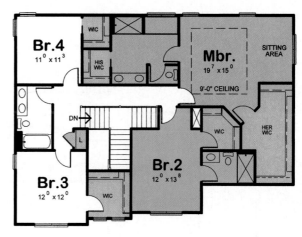

Livability at a Glance™

- Storing
- Entertaining
- Flexible Living
- De-Stressing

Br.4
11⁰ x 11³

WIC

HIS WIC

Mbr.
19⁷ x 15⁰

SITTING AREA

9'-0" CEILING

DN

HER WIC

WIC

Br.2
12⁰ x 13⁸

Br.3
12⁰ x 12⁰

WIC

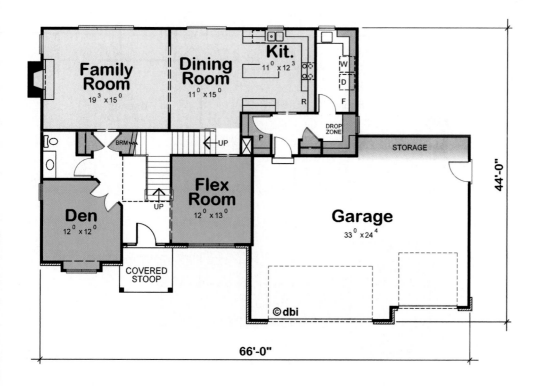

Family Room
19³ x 15⁰

Dining Room
11⁰ x 15⁰

Kit.
11⁰ x 12³

W
D

BRM

UP

P

DROP ZONE

R
F

STORAGE

UP

Flex Room
12⁰ x 13⁰

Den
12⁰ x 12⁰

COVERED STOOP

Garage
33⁰ x 24⁴

©dbi

44'-0"

66'-0"

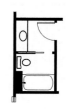

Optional Bathroom

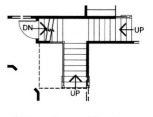

DN

UP

UP

Optional Basement Stair Location

the
Goldendale
24052-9JJ
price code 30

Main Level **1303**

Second Level **1699**

Total Square Ft. **3002**

Standard Foundation: Slab

Livability at a Glance™
- Storing
- Entertaining
- Flexible Living
- De-Stressing

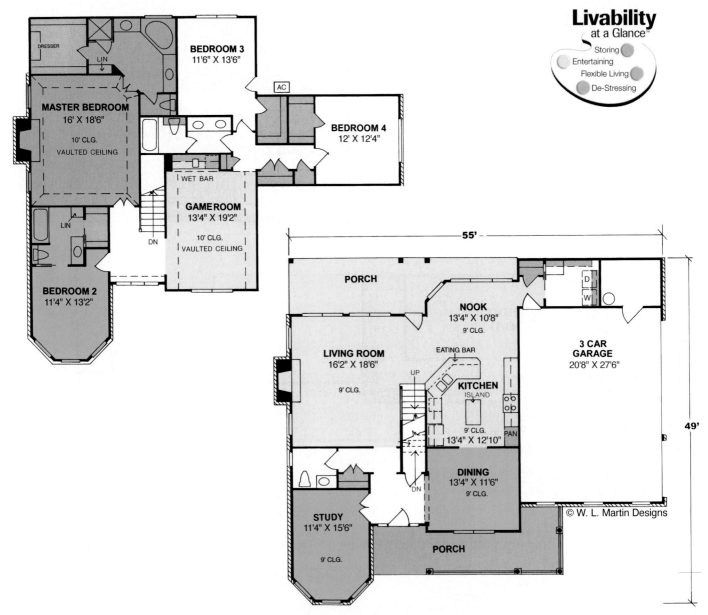

DRESSER

LIN

MASTER BEDROOM
16' X 18'6"
10' CLG.
VAULTED CEILING

BEDROOM 3
11'6" X 13'6"

AC

BEDROOM 4
12' X 12'4"

LIN

WET BAR

GAME ROOM
13'4" X 19'2"
10' CLG.
VAULTED CEILING

DN

BEDROOM 2
11'4" X 13'2"

55'

49'

PORCH

NOOK
13'4" X 10'8"
9' CLG.

D
W

3 CAR GARAGE
20'8" X 27'6"

LIVING ROOM
16'2" X 18'6"
9' CLG.

EATING BAR

UP

KITCHEN
ISLAND
9' CLG.
13'4" X 12'10"

PAN

DN

DINING
13'4" X 11'6"
9' CLG.

STUDY
11'4" X 15'6"
9' CLG.

PORCH

© W. L. Martin Designs

the Santa Ana
987-9JJ
pricecode 30

Main Level **1583**

Second Level **1442**

Total Square Ft. **3025**

Standard Foundation: Basement

Livability
at a Glance™

- Storing
- Entertaining
- Flexible Living
- De-Stressing

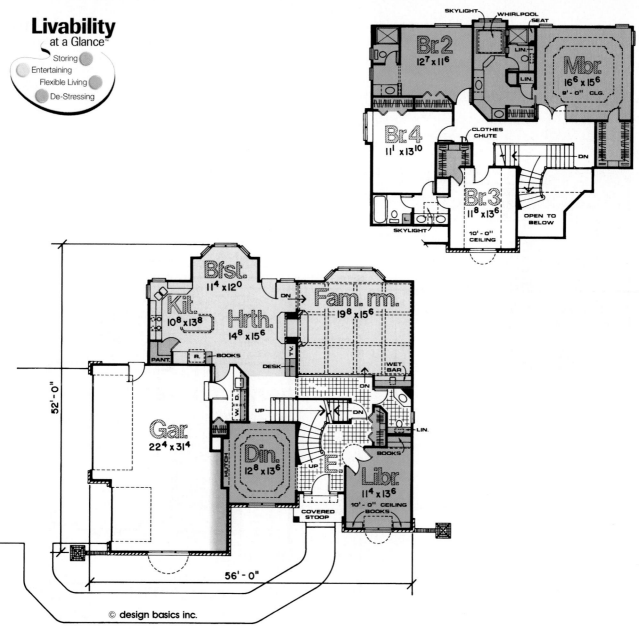

© design basics inc.

Main Level	**1631**
Second Level	**1426**
Total Square Ft.	**3057**

Standard Foundation: Basement

Livability
at a Glance™

- Storing
- Entertaining
- Flexible Living
- De-Stressing

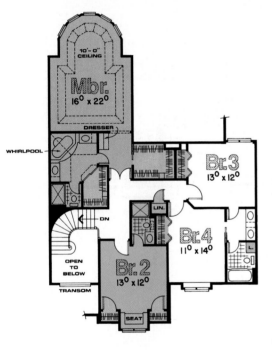

10'-0" CEILING

Mbr.
16⁰ x 22⁰

DRESSER

WHIRLPOOL

Br. 3
13⁰ x 12⁰

LIN.

Br. 4
11⁰ x 14⁰

DN

OPEN TO BELOW

Br. 2
13⁰ x 12⁰

TRANSOM

SEAT

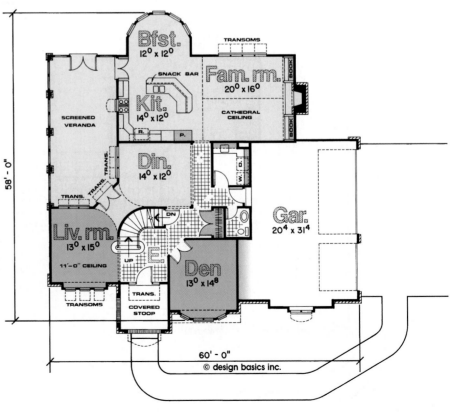

58' - 0"

Bfst.
12⁰ x 12⁰

TRANSOMS

SNACK BAR

Fam. rm.
20⁰ x 16⁰

BOOK

SCREENED VERANDA

Kit.
14⁰ x 12⁰

CATHEDRAL CEILING

BOOK

Din.
14⁰ x 12⁰

W. D.

TRANS. TRANS.

TRANS.

Liv. rm.
13⁰ x 15⁰

11'-0" CEILING

Gar.
20⁴ x 31⁴

DN

UP

E.

Den
13⁰ x 14⁸

TRANS.

TRANSOMS

COVERED STOOP

60' - 0"

© design basics inc.

the Jacksonville

3156-9JJ

pricecode 32

Main Level	**1598**
Second Level	**1675**
Total Square Ft.	**3273**

Standard Foundation: Basement

Livability
at a Glance™

- Storing
- Entertaining
- Flexible Living
- De-Stressing

Unfinished Storage
adds 534 Sq. Ft.

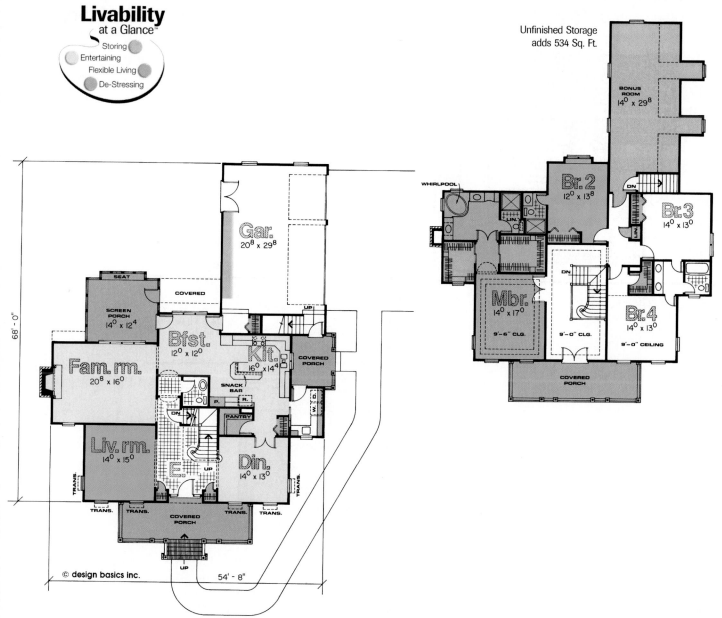

© design basics inc.

the Abbey
1510-9JJ
price code 33

Main Level	**1709**
Second Level	**1597**
Total Square Ft.	**3306**

Standard Foundation: Basement

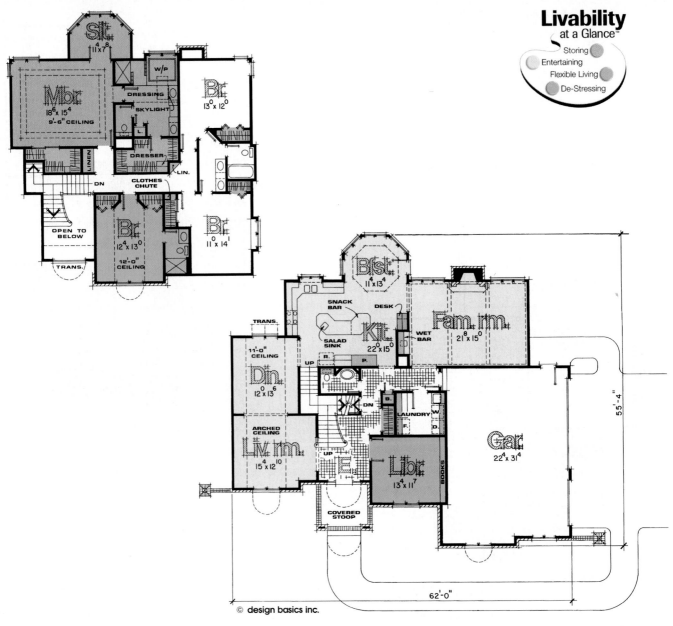

Livability
at a Glance™

Storing
Entertaining
Flexible Living
De-Stressing

Sit.
11⁴ x 7⁸

Mbr
18⁶ x 15⁴
9'-6" CEILING

DRESSING

W/P

Br.
13⁰ x 12⁰

SKYLIGHT

LINEN

DRESSER

LIN.

CLOTHES CHUTE

DN

OPEN TO BELOW

Br.
12⁴ x 13⁰
12'-0" CEILING

Br.
11⁰ x 14

TRANS.

Bfst.
11⁴ x 13⁴

SNACK BAR

DESK

Kit.
22⁴ x 15⁰

WET BAR

Fam. rm.
21⁸ x 15⁰

SALAD SINK

TRANS.

Dn.
12⁰ x 13⁶
11'-0" CEILING

UP

R.

P.

DN

B.

LAUNDRY

W

F

D

Gar.
22⁴ x 31⁴

Liv. rm.
15⁴ x 12¹⁰
ARCHED CEILING

UP

Libr.
13⁴ x 11⁷

BOOKS

COVERED STOOP

55'-4"

62'-0"

© design basics inc.

the Harrison

3174-9JJ

pricecode 34

Main Level	**1824**
Second Level	**1580**
Total Square Ft.	**3404**

Standard Foundation: Basement

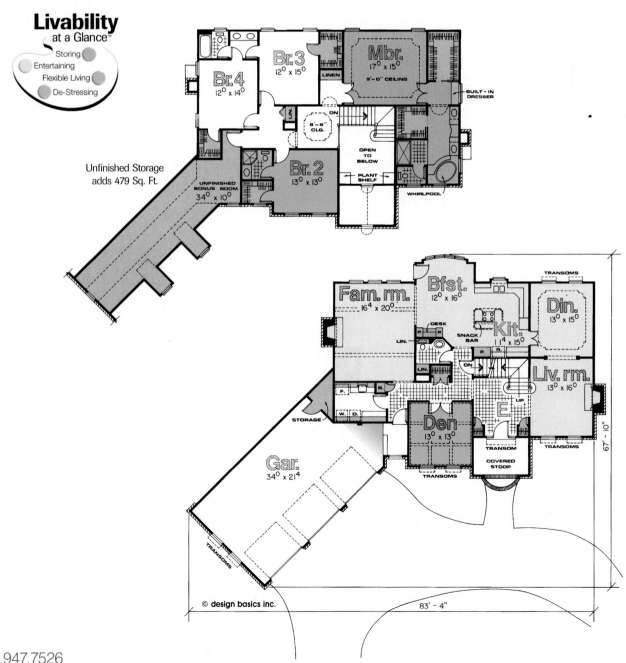

Livability at a Glance™

- Storing
- Entertaining
- Flexible Living
- De-Stressing

Br. 4
12⁰ x 14⁰

Br. 3
12⁰ x 15⁰

Mbr.
17⁰ x 15⁰
9'-0" CEILING

LINEN

BUILT - IN DRESSER

DN

LIN.

8'-8" CLG.

Br. 2
13⁰ x 13⁰

OPEN TO BELOW

PLANT SHELF

WHIRLPOOL

Unfinished Storage adds 479 Sq. Ft.

UNFINISHED BONUS ROOM
34⁰ x 10⁰

Fam. rm.
16⁴ x 20⁰

Bfst.
12⁰ x 16⁰

TRANSOMS

Din.
13⁰ x 15⁰

DESK

LIN.

SNACK BAR

Kit.
11⁴ x 15⁰

Liv. rm.
13⁰ x 16⁰

LIN.

DN

UP

STORAGE

F.

W. D.

Den
13⁰ x 13⁰

COVERED STOOP

TRANSOM

TRANSOMS

TRANSOMS

Gar.
34⁰ x 21⁴

TRANSOMS

67' - 10"

83' - 4"

© design basics inc.

the
Briarglan
Estate
9263-9JJ
price**code** 34

Main Level	**1719**
Second Level	**1735**
Total Square Ft.	**3454**

Standard Foundation: Basement

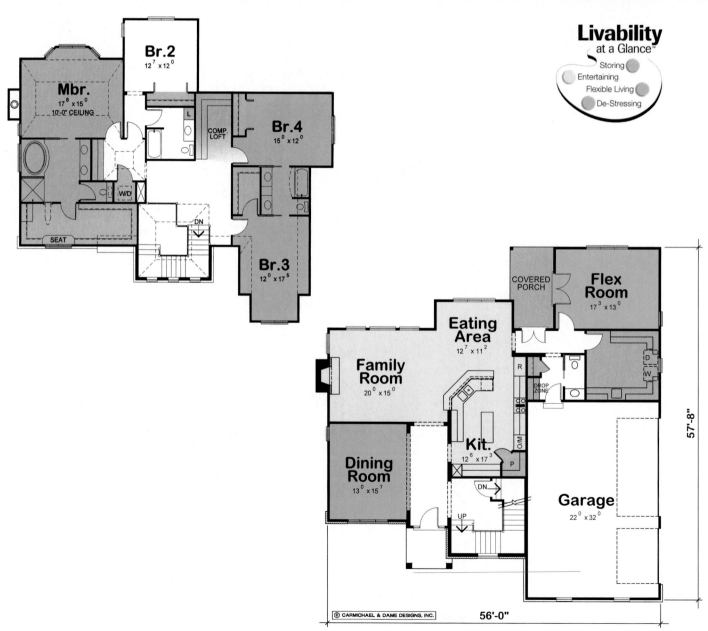

Livability
at a Glance™

Storing
Entertaining
Flexible Living
De-Stressing

Br.2
12⁷ x 12⁰

Mbr.
17⁸ x 15⁰
10'-0" CEILING

COMP.
LOFT

Br.4
15⁰ x 12⁰

W/D

SEAT

DN

Br.3
12⁰ x 17⁵

COVERED
PORCH

Flex
Room
17³ x 13⁰

Eating
Area
12⁷ x 11²

Family
Room
20⁰ x 15⁰

R

DROP
ZONE

D
W

Kit.
12⁶ x 17³

O/M

P

Dining
Room
13⁰ x 15⁷

DN

UP

Garage
22⁰ x 32⁰

57'-8"

56'-0"

© CARMICHAEL & DAME DESIGNS, INC.

www.designbasics.com/9JJ

the
Glencross
3388-9JJ
price code 36

Main Level	**1857**
Second Level	**1754**
Total Square Ft.	**3611**

Standard Foundation: Basement

Livability
at a Glance™

- Storing
- Entertaining
- Flexible Living
- De-Stressing

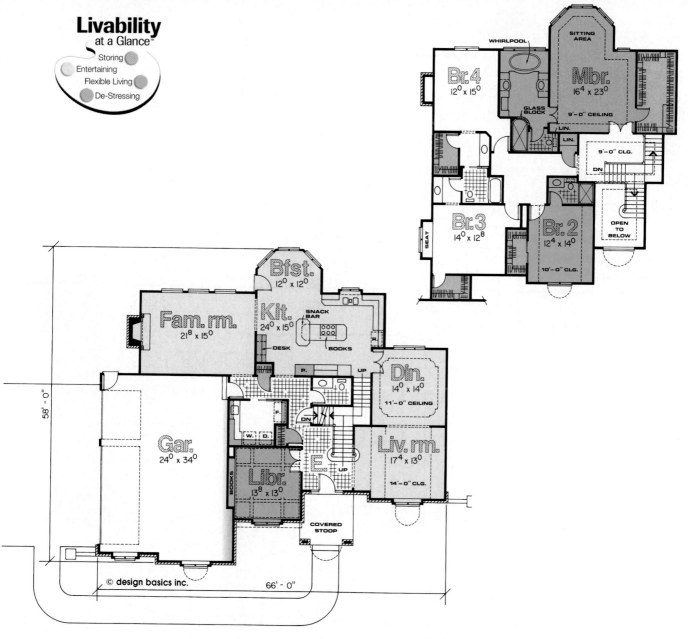

WHIRLPOOL

SITTING AREA

Br. 4
12⁰ x 15⁰

Mbr.
16⁴ x 23⁰

GLASS BLOCK

9'-0" CEILING

LIN.

LIN.

9'-0" CLG.

DN

Br. 3
14⁰ x 12⁸

SEAT

Br. 2
12⁴ x 14⁰

10'-0" CLG.

OPEN TO BELOW

Bfst.
12⁰ x 12⁰

Fam. rm.
21⁸ x 15⁰

Kit.
24⁰ x 15⁰

SNACK BAR

DESK

BOOKS

P.

UP

Din.
14⁰ x 14⁰

11'-0" CEILING

DN

F.

W. D.

Gar.
24⁰ x 34⁰

BOOKS

Libr.
13⁸ x 13⁰

E.

UP

Liv. rm.
17⁴ x 13⁰

14'-0" CLG.

COVERED STOOP

58'-0"

© design basics inc.

66'-0"

the
Corinth
2332-9JJ

pricecode 37

Main Level	**1923**
Second Level	**1852**
Total Square Ft.	**3775**

Standard Foundation: Basement

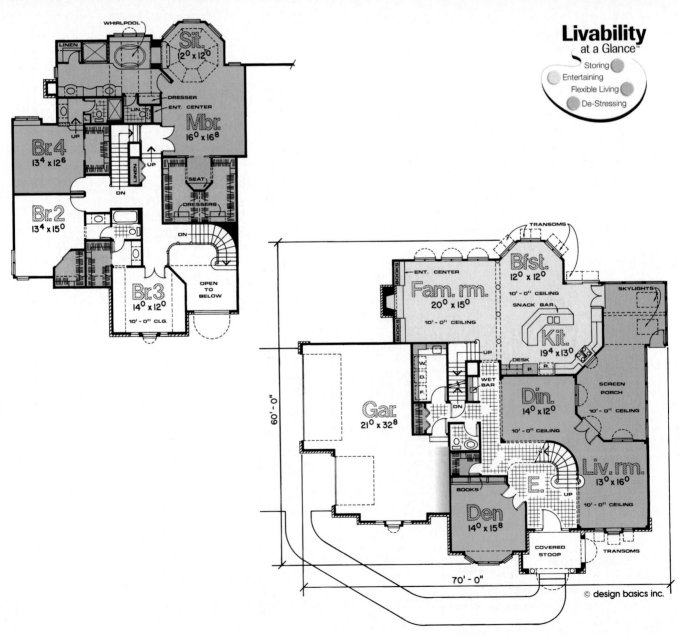

Livability
at a Glance™

Storing
Entertaining
Flexible Living
De-Stressing

www.designbasics.com/9JJ

© design basics inc.

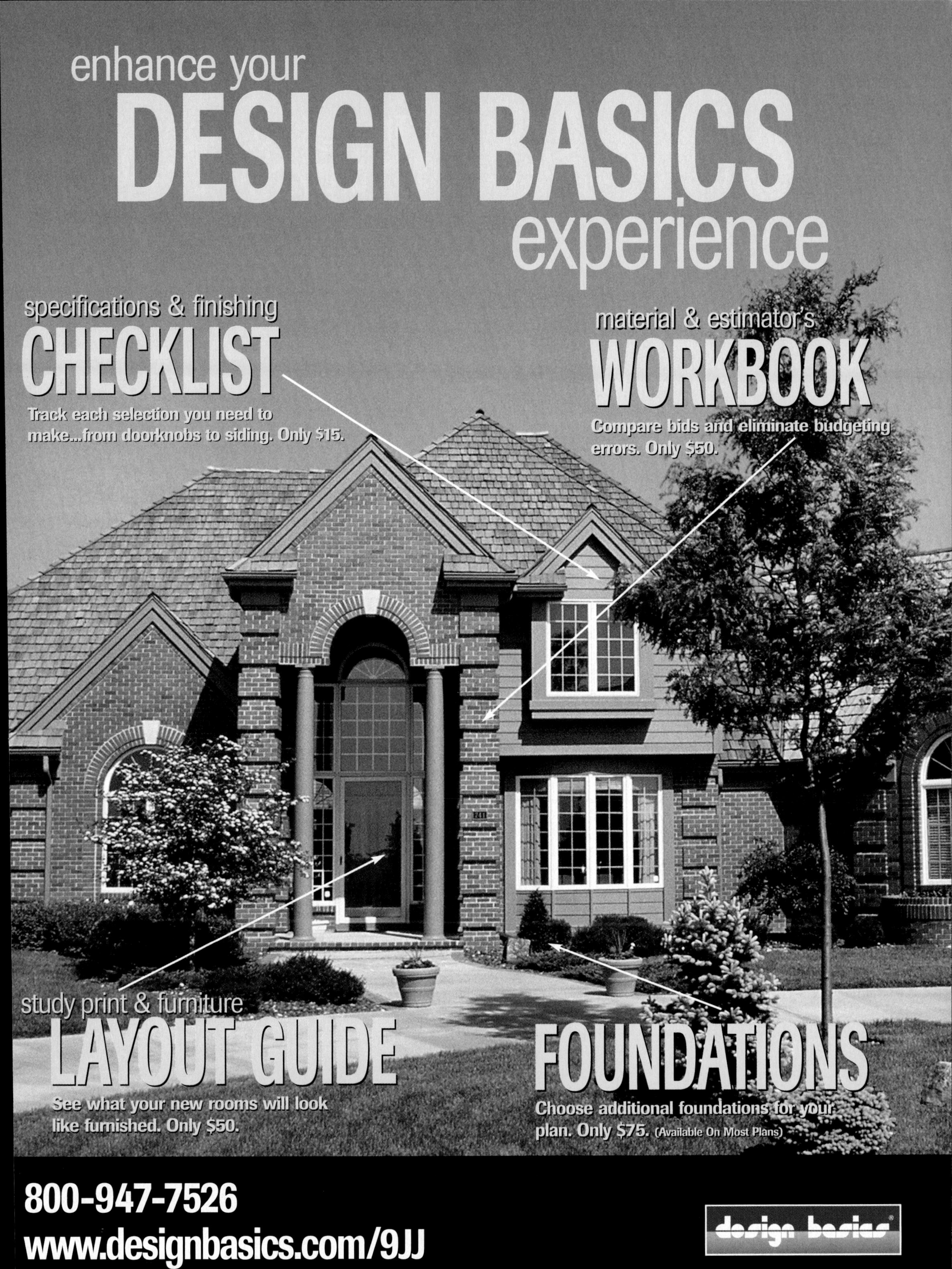
enhance your
DESIGN BASICS
experience
specifications & finishing
CHECKLIST
Track each selection you need to make...from doorknobs to siding. Only $15.
material & estimator's
WORKBOOK
Compare bids and eliminate budgeting errors. Only $50.
study print & furniture
LAYOUT GUIDE
See what your new rooms will look like furnished. Only $50.
FOUNDATIONS
Choose additional foundations for your plan. Only $75. (Available On Most Plans)
800-947-7526
www.designbasics.com/9JJ
design basics

Lisa Albrecht shares lessons she's learned while building her dream home.

10 Things to Consider BEFORE Signing on the Dotted Line

Making the decision to build a new home is a thrilling prospect. For many, it is the realization of a dream. But many potential new home owners don't realize that some of the decisions made after signing a contract would be less expensive and better negotiated if they researched their needs before inking the deal.

Her Home spoke to one woman who, in the process of considering her building project, took extra steps to research what she wanted. She ultimately saved thousands of dollars in "up charges" – changes or additions made by the builder once a contract is signed. Here are the ten items she considered before signing, and what she learned in the process.

1 Pre-qualify for a mortgage.

- Get credit information in order.
- Check out several lenders.
- Review needs for a construction loan or a bridge loan.
- Understand mortgage products; energy efficient, (see *Her Home*, Fall '04) woman-centric aspects (page 20, this issue), etc.

"Pre-qualifying for a mortgage put my mind at ease. I knew how much home I could buy. I wanted to look for homes only within my price range."

2 Review your present home and situation.

- Are room sizes adequate?
- What special needs do you have, such as a blended family or the need for a workshop?
- What furniture will you keep?

"My existing townhouse is great for entertaining. And the master bedroom is separate from the other bedrooms, which works well for my blended family. I wanted to keep most of my furniture, so the rooms in my new house will need to be large."

3 Find a lot.

- Is it close to schools, church, shopping, health care, pizza delivery?
- What direction does the lot face? Do you want morning sun? A special view?
- Do you want a sloping lot for a walkout basement?
- Study covenant and community restrictions.
- What is the tax levy?
- Look around the neighborhood. What do you like? What bothers you?

"Trees are very important to me, and also a private backyard – so that I am not looking at my neighbor's house. My location was also determined by good pizza delivery service!"

4 Find a home plan by asking the following questions:

- How do I want to entertain?
- How much storage will I need? What kind?
- Does the plan have flexibility for special rooms or situations (exercise room, craft area, etc.)?
- How does the home help me de-stress? A quiet area for me? Built-in organization like drop zones? Whirlpool bath? Sunroom? Porches?
- Where do I want the master bedroom?
- Is a healthy home important to me? (See *Her Home*, Fall '03)

"Once I identified that I needed an open floor plan with a lot of space in the kitchen and great room, as well as divided bedrooms and storage space, finding a plan was a piece of cake. I walked through a number of model homes to get a sense of room-size proportions and went on www.HerHome.com."

5

Select a builder.

- Is there a builder attached to the lot you want? If so, interview him/her extensively.

- If not, interview several builders. Try to find someone with whom you'll have good chemistry.

- Check references of the builder's former homebuyers, subcontractors and vendors.

"My builder was attached to my lot, which was a big consideration, since I had to work with this person. I drove him crazy asking so many questions. But since this is a huge decision, I — wanted to do it right."

6

Consult with an interior designer for a couple of hours. (See *Her Home*, Summer '04)

- Make sure everything flows; coordinate colors, flooring and countertops; and plan placement of outlets.

"The time I had with an interior design consultant was the best money I spent. I wanted a contemporary look, and she helped me coordinate flooring, countertops and colors. While I have a sense of my style, I am now more confident with my choices."

7

Meet with an electrician and electronic specialists to pre-wire the house properly.

- Consider Christmas lights, other outdoor lighting, accent lighting, security, stereo surround sound, telephones, ample outlets and their placements, Internet and media rooms.

"I walked through the entire plan with an electrician to get advice on lighting, security, outlets, etc. This was time well spent, because I made sure the elements were incorporated before I signed the contract and avoided many upcharges."

8

Talk to as many people as you can who have been through the building process. Be sure to ask what they would do differently.

"I learned a great deal from the mistakes of others – which saved me tons of headaches."

9

Customize your home plan.

- Make sure the working drawings are clear and exactly how you want them.

"I did not want any ambiguity on my working drawings. I made sure everything was how I wanted it. I revised my plans many times; it's worth the hard work to get what I want."

10

Pack Your Survival Kit.

- A sense of humor
- A 12-pack of patience
- Drawers of chocolate
- Bottles of aspirin
- A jump rope for de-stressing

"I'm ready to sign the contract and get started!"

the Clearfield
6789N-9JJ
pricecode 13

Main Level	**978**
Second Level	**417**
Total Square Ft.	**1395**

Standard Foundation: Basement

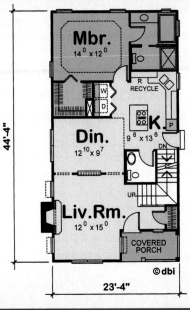

Mbr.
14⁰ x 12⁰

RECYCLE
W
D

Din.
12¹⁰ x 9⁷

K
9⁸ x 13⁶
P

Liv.Rm.
12⁰ x 15⁰

COVERED PORCH

© dbi

44'-4"
23'-4"

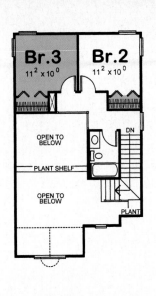

Br.3
11² x 10⁰

Br.2
11² x 10⁰

OPEN TO BELOW

PLANT SHELF

OPEN TO BELOW

DN

PLANT

the Bonneville
6783N-9JJ
pricecode 14

Main Level	**949**
Second Level	**451**
Total Square Ft.	**1400**

Standard Foundation: Basement

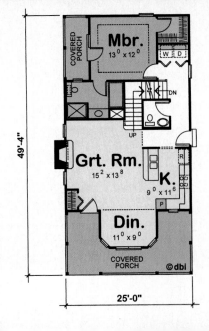

COVERED PORCH

Mbr.
13⁰ x 12⁰

W D

DN

Grt. Rm.
15² x 13⁸

K.
9⁰ x 11⁶
P

UP

Din.
11⁰ x 9⁰

COVERED PORCH

© dbi

49'-4"
25'-0"

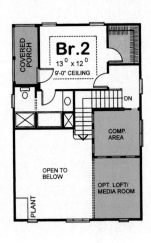

COVERED PORCH

Br.2
13⁰ x 12⁰
9'-0" CEILING

DN

COMP. AREA

OPEN TO BELOW

OPT. LOFT/ MEDIA ROOM

PLANT

Livability at a Glance™

Storing
Entertaining
Flexible Living
De-Stressing

www.designbasics.com/9JJ

the Woodington
6780N-9JJ
pricecode 14

Main Level	**1008**
Second Level	**415**
Total Square Ft.	**1423**

Standard Foundation: Basement

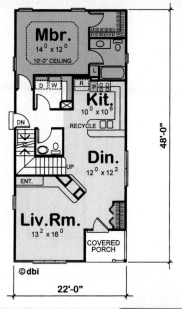

Mbr.
14⁰ x 12⁰
10'-0" CEILING

Kit.
10⁰ x 10⁶

Din.
12⁰ x 12²

Liv.Rm.
13² x 16⁰

COVERED PORCH

©dbi

22'-0"

48'-0"

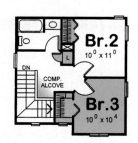

Br.2
10⁰ x 11⁰

COMP. ALCOVE

Br.3
10⁰ x 10⁴

the Wayside
6781N-9JJ
pricecode 14

Main Level	**979**
Second Level	**511**
Total Square Ft.	**1490**

Standard Foundation: Basement

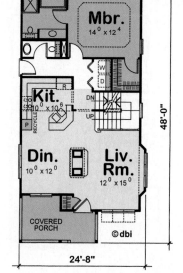

Mbr.
14⁰ x 12⁴

Kit.
10⁰ x 10⁶

Din.
10⁰ x 12⁰

Liv. Rm.
12⁰ x 15⁰

COVERED PORCH

©dbi

24'-8"

48'-0"

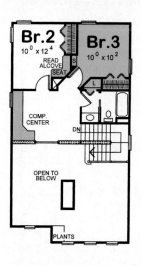

Br.2
10⁰ x 12⁴

Br.3
10⁰ x 10²

READ ALCOVE SEAT

COMP. CENTER

OPEN TO BELOW

PLANTS

Livability
at a Glance™

Storing
Entertaining
Flexible Living
De-Stressing

the
Overbrook
6713N-9JJ

pricecode 15

Main Level	**1055**
Second Level	**525**
Total Square Ft.	**1580**

Standard Foundation: Basement

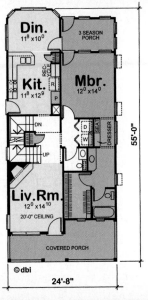

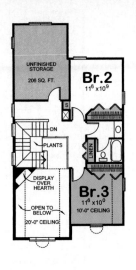

the
Kincaid
6710N-9JJ

pricecode 12

Main Level	**603**
Second Level	**694**
Total Square Ft.	**1297**

Standard Foundation: Basement

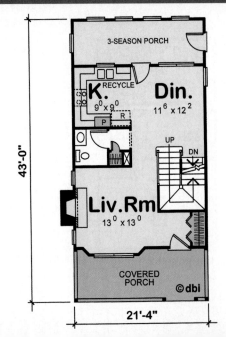

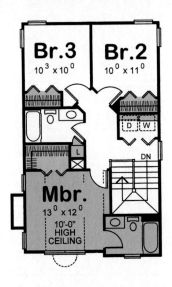

Livability
at a Glance™

Storing
Entertaining
Flexible Living
De-Stressing

www.designbasics.com/9JJ

the Winstrom
29079-9JJ
price code 14

Main Level	**672**
Second Level	**768**
Total Square Ft.	**1440**

Standard Foundation: Basement

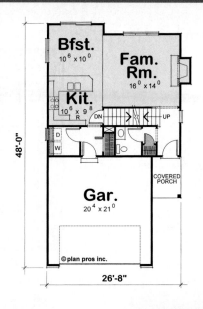

Bfst.
10⁶ x 10⁰

Fam. Rm.
16⁰ x 14⁰

Kit.
10⁶ x 9⁸
R

DN UP

D
W

48'-0"

Gar.
20⁴ x 21⁰

COVERED PORCH

© plan pros inc.

26'-8"

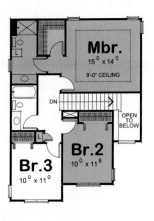

Mbr.
15⁰ x 14⁰
9'-0" CEILING

L

DN

OPEN TO BELOW

Br.3
10⁰ x 11⁰

Br.2
10⁰ x 11⁸

the Kelford
6791N-9JJ
price code 14

Main Level	**762**
Second Level	**691**
Total Square Ft.	**1453**

Standard Foundation: Basement

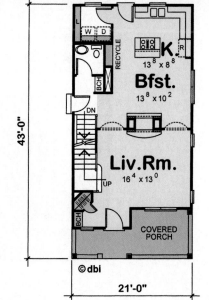

W D

RECYCLE

BCH

K.
13⁸ x 8⁸
R

Bfst.
13⁸ x 10²

DN

Liv. Rm.
16⁴ x 13⁰

UP

BCH

43'-0"

COVERED PORCH

© dbi

21'-0"

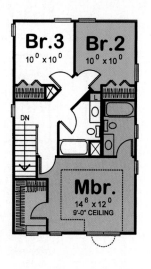

Br.3
10⁰ x 10⁰

Br.2
10⁰ x 10⁰

L

DN

Mbr.
14⁶ x 12⁰
9'-0" CEILING

Livability at a Glance™

Storing
Entertaining
Flexible Living
De-Stressing

800.947.7526

the Copeland
6706N-9JJ
price code 14

Main Level	719
Second Level	752
Total Square Ft.	1471

Standard Foundation: Basement

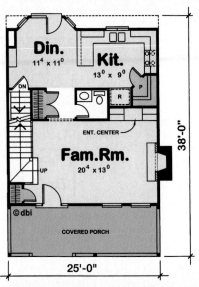

Din. 11⁴ x 11⁰

Kit. 13⁰ x 9⁰

P

R

DN

ENT. CENTER

Fam.Rm. 20⁴ x 13⁰

UP

©dbi

COVERED PORCH

38'-0"

25'-0"

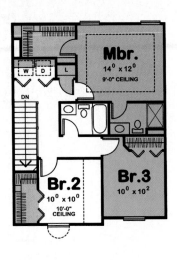

Mbr. 14⁰ x 12⁰
9'-0" CEILING

W D L

DN

L

Br.2 10⁰ x 10⁰
10'-0" CEILING

Br.3 10⁰ x 10²

---

the Erwin
8534N-9JJ
price code 14

Main Level	753
Second Level	720
Total Square Ft.	1473

Standard Foundation: Basement

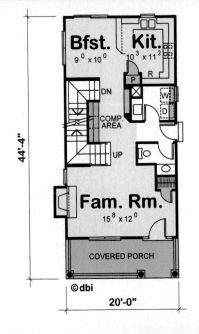

Bfst. 9⁰ x 10⁰

Kit. 10³ x 11²

P

R

DN

W D

COMP. AREA

UP

Fam. Rm. 15⁸ x 12⁰

COVERED PORCH

©dbi

44'-4"

20'-0"

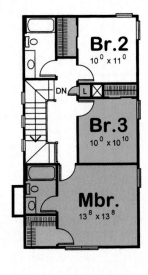

Br.2 10⁰ x 11⁰

DN L

Br.3 10⁰ x 10¹⁰

Mbr. 13⁸ x 13⁸

Livability at a Glance™

Storing
Entertaining
Flexible Living
De-Stressing

www.designbasics.com/9JJ

the
Keiser
8537N-9JJ
pricecode 14

Main Level	753
Second Level	720
Total Square Ft.	1473

Standard Foundation: Basement

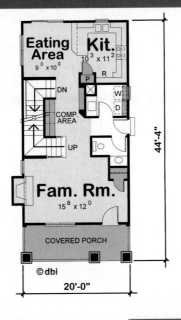

Eating Area 9⁰ x 10⁰

Kit. 10³ x 11²

P R

DN

W D

COMP. AREA

UP

Fam. Rm. 15⁸ x 12⁰

COVERED PORCH

© dbi

20'-0"

44'-4"

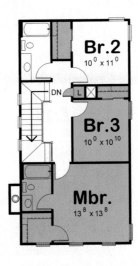

Br.2 10⁰ x 11⁰

DN L

Br.3 10⁰ x 10¹⁰

Mbr. 13⁸ x 13⁸

the
Martelle
6792N-9JJ
pricecode 14

Main Level	750
Second Level	725
Total Square Ft.	1475

Standard Foundation: Basement

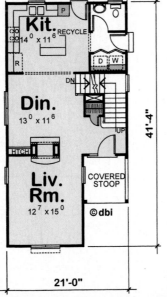

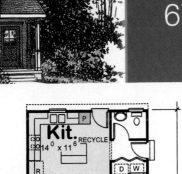

Kit. 14⁰ x 11⁶

P

RECYCLE

R

D W

DN

Din. 13⁰ x 11⁶

UP

HTCH

Liv. Rm. 12⁷ x 15⁰

COVERED STOOP

© dbi

21'-0"

41'-4"

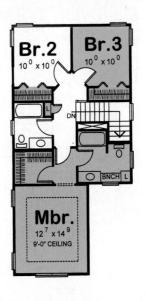

Br.2 10⁰ x 10⁰

Br.3 10⁰ x 10⁰

DN

BNCH L

Mbr. 12⁷ x 14⁹
9'-0" CEILING

Livability at a Glance™

Storing
Entertaining
Flexible Living
De-Stressing

the Sycamore
6715N-9JJ
price code 14

Main Level	**747**
Second Level	**748**
Total Square Ft.	**1495**

Standard Foundation: Basement

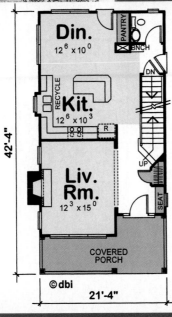

Din.
12⁶ x 10⁰

PANTRY
BNCH

RECYCLE

Kit.
12⁶ x 10³

DN

R

UP

Liv. Rm.
12³ x 15⁰

SEAT

COVERED PORCH

©dbi

42'-4"

21'-4"

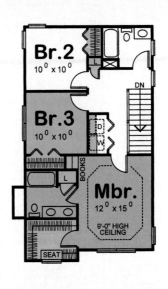

Br.2
10⁰ x 10⁰

DN

Br.3
10⁰ x 10⁰

D
W

BOOKS

L

Mbr.
12⁰ x 15⁰
9'-0" HIGH CEILING

SEAT

the Annapolis
8614-9JJ
price code 15

Main Level	**717**
Second Level	**823**
Total Square Ft.	**1540**

Standard Foundation: Basement

COVERED PORCH

Fam. Rm.
17⁰ x 13⁰

ENT

DN

Bfst.
10⁴ x 10⁰

P

UP

Kit.
11⁴ x 12⁰

R

COVERED PORCH

Gar.
15⁰ x 20⁸

©dbi/HBN

47'-8"

28'-0"

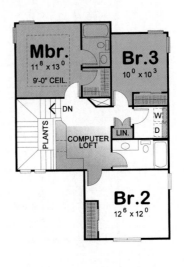

Mbr.
11⁸ x 13⁰
9'-0" CEIL.

Br.3
10⁰ x 10³

DN

PLANTS

W
D

LIN.

COMPUTER LOFT

Br.2
12⁶ x 12⁰

Livability
at a Glance™

Storing
Entertaining
Flexible Living
De-Stressing

the Fairborn
8615-9JJ
price code 15

Main Level	**717**
Second Level	**823**
Total Square Ft.	**1540**

Standard Foundation: Basement

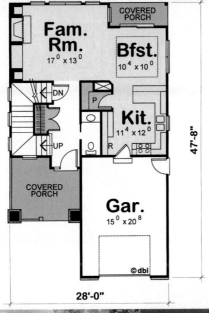

Fam. Rm. 17⁰ x 13⁰
COVERED PORCH
Bfst. 10⁴ x 10⁰
Kit. 11⁴ x 12⁰
DN
UP
P
R
COVERED PORCH
Gar. 15⁰ x 20⁸
© dbi
47'-8"
28'-0"

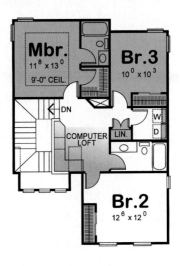

Mbr. 11⁸ x 13⁰ 9'-0" CEIL.
Br.3 10⁰ x 10³
DN
COMPUTER LOFT
LIN.
W D
Br.2 12⁶ x 12⁰

---

the Grosse Point
8616-9JJ
price code 15

Main Level	**717**
Second Level	**823**
Total Square Ft.	**1540**

Standard Foundation: Basement

Livability at a Glance™
- Storing
- Entertaining
- Flexible Living
- De-Stressing

ENT
Fam. Rm. 17⁰ x 13⁰
COVERED PORCH
Bfst. 10⁴ x 10⁰
DN
Kit. 11⁴ x 12⁰
UP
P
R
COVERED PORCH
Gar. 15⁰ x 20⁸
© dbi/HBN
47'-8"
28'-0"

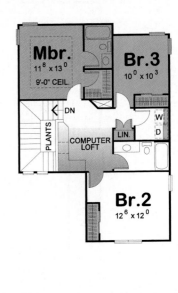

Mbr. 11⁸ x 13⁰ 9'-0" CEIL.
Br.3 10⁰ x 10³
DN
PLANTS
COMPUTER LOFT
LIN.
W D
Br.2 12⁶ x 12⁰

the Potomac
8613-9JJ
pricecode 15

Main Level	**717**
Second Level	**823**
Total Square Ft.	**1540**

Standard Foundation: Basement

Fam. Rm. 17⁰ x 13⁰
Bfst. 10⁴ x 10⁰
COVERED PORCH
ENT
DN
UP
P
Kit. 11⁴ x 12⁰
R
COVERED PORCH
Gar. 15⁰ x 20⁸
© dbi/HBN
28'-0"
47'-8"

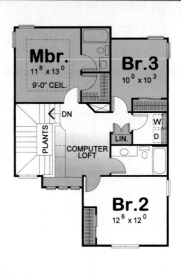

Mbr. 11⁸ x 13⁰ 9'-0" CEIL.
Br.3 10⁰ x 10³
DN
PLANTS
LIN.
W D
COMPUTER LOFT
Br.2 12⁸ x 12⁰

the Chenoweth
43044-9JJ
pricecode 15

Main Level	**733**
Second Level	**817**
Total Square Ft.	**1550**

Standard Foundation: Slab

UP DN

Optional Basement Stair Location

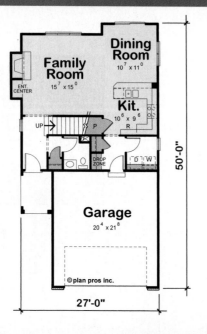

Family Room 15⁷ x 15⁰
Dining Room 10⁷ x 11⁰
ENT. CENTER
UP
P
Kit. 10⁶ x 9⁶
R
DROP ZONE
D W
Garage 20⁴ x 21⁸
© plan pros inc.
27'-0"
50'-0"

HIS WIC

Optional Closet adds 59 sq. ft.

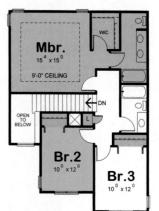

Mbr. 15⁴ x 15⁰ 9'-0" CEILING
WIC
DN
OPEN TO BELOW
L
Br.2 10⁰ x 12⁰
Br.3 10⁰ x 12⁰

Optional Bathroom

Livability at a Glance™
Storing
Entertaining
Flexible Living
De-Stressing

the
Colbourne
43043-9JJ
price code 15

Main Level	733
Second Level	817
Total Square Ft.	1550

Standard Foundation: Slab

Optional Basement Stair Location

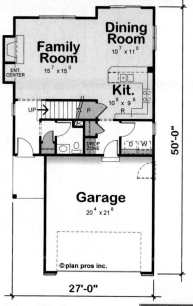

UP → ← DN

Family Room
15⁷ x 15⁰

ENT. CENTER

Dining Room
10⁷ x 11⁰

UP →

Kit.
10⁶ x 9⁶
R
P

DROP ZONE

D W

50'-0"

Garage
20⁴ x 21⁸

© plan pros inc.

27'-0"

HIS WIC

Optional Closet
adds 59 sq. ft.

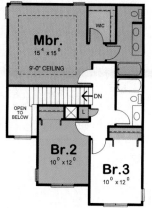

Mbr.
15⁴ x 15⁰
9'-0" CEILING

WIC

DN

OPEN TO BELOW

L

Br.2
10⁰ x 12⁰

Br.3
10⁰ x 12⁰

Optional Bathroom

the
Joliet
8554N-9JJ
price code 15

Main Level	787
Second Level	773
Total Square Ft.	1560

Standard Foundation: Basement

DESK

Eating Area
9⁸ x 12⁰

D W

P

Kit.
11⁸ x 10³
R

DN

UP

Fam. Rm.
17⁰ x 14⁰

COVERED PORCH

© dbi

20'-0"

46'-0"

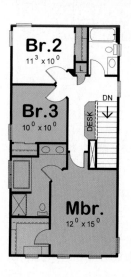

Br.2
11³ x 10⁰

L

Br.3
10⁰ x 10⁰

DESK

DN

Mbr.
12⁰ x 15⁰

Livability
at a Glance™

- Storing
- Entertaining
- Flexible Living
- De-Stressing

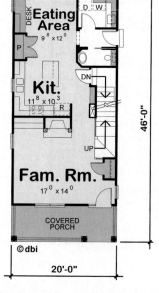

the Ravena
8535N-9JJ
pricecode 15

Main Level	**788**
Second Level	**773**
Total Square Ft.	**1561**

Standard Foundation: Basement

Eating Area 9⁰ x 10⁰
Kit. 10³ x 11²
DN
P
R
W
D
COMPUTER AREA
UP
Family Room 15⁸ x 14⁶
COVERED STOOP
©dbi
44'-4"
20'-0"

Br.2 10⁰ x 13⁰
DN
L
Br.3 10⁰ x 10¹⁰
Mbr. 13⁸ x 14⁸

the Ansley
8555N-9JJ
pricecode 15

Main Level	**787**
Second Level	**781**
Total Square Ft.	**1568**

Standard Foundation: Basement

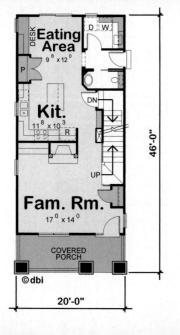

DESK
Eating Area 9⁸ x 12⁰
D W
P
Kit. 11⁸ x 10³
DN
R
UP
Fam. Rm. 17⁰ x 14⁰
COVERED PORCH
©dbi
46'-0"
20'-0"

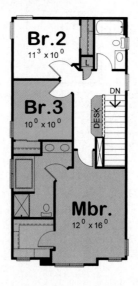

Br.2 11³ x 10⁰
L
Br.3 10⁰ x 10⁰
DN
DESK
Mbr. 12⁰ x 16⁰

Livability at a Glance™
- Storing
- Entertaining
- Flexible Living
- De-Stressing

www.designbasics.com/9JJ

the
Hollister
8553N-9JJ
pricecode 15

Main Level	**787**
Second Level	**788**
Total Square Ft.	**1575**

Standard Foundation: Basement

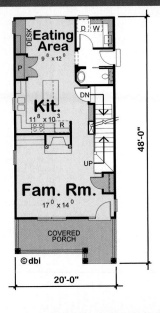

Main Level floor plan:
- Eating Area 9⁸ x 12⁰
- DESK, P, D, W
- Kit. 11⁸ x 10³, R
- DN, UP
- Fam. Rm. 17⁰ x 14⁰
- COVERED PORCH
- 48'-0"
- 20'-0"
- ©dbi

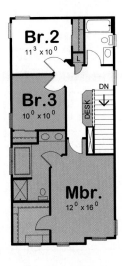

Second Level floor plan:
- Br.2 11³ x 10⁰
- Br.3 10⁰ x 10⁰
- DESK, DN, L
- Mbr. 12⁰ x 16⁰

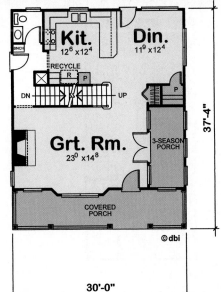

the
Hopewell
6705N-9JJ
pricecode 16

Main Level	**838**
Second Level	**803**
Total Square Ft.	**1641**

Standard Foundation: Basement

Main Level floor plan:
- Kit. 12⁶ x 12⁴
- Din. 11⁹ x 12⁴
- RECYCLE, R, P, BNCH
- DN, UP, P
- Grt. Rm. 23⁰ x 14⁸
- 3-SEASON PORCH
- COVERED PORCH
- 37'-4"
- 30'-0"
- ©dbi

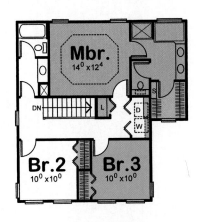

Second Level floor plan:
- Mbr. 14⁰ x 12⁴
- DN, L, D, W, S
- Br.2 10⁰ x 10⁰
- Br.3 10⁰ x 10⁰

Livability
at a Glance™
- Storing
- Entertaining
- Flexible Living
- De-Stressing

the Gardena
8558N-9JJ
pricecode 16

Main Level	**853**
Second Level	**796**
Total Square Ft.	**1649**

Standard Foundation: Basement

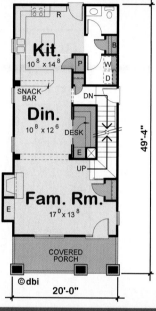

Kit.
$10^8 \times 14^8$

R

B

P

W
D

SNACK BAR

Din.
$10^8 \times 12^6$

DESK

DN

E

UP

Fam. Rm.
$17^0 \times 13^8$

E

COVERED PORCH

©dbi

20'-0"

49'-4"

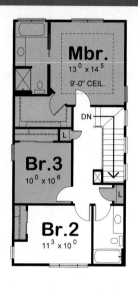

Mbr.
$13^0 \times 14^5$
9'-0" CEIL.

DN

L

Br.3
$10^0 \times 10^6$

L

Br.2
$11^3 \times 10^0$

---

the Wellman
8556N-9JJ
pricecode 16

Main Level	**853**
Second Level	**796**
Total Square Ft.	**1649**

Standard Foundation: Basement

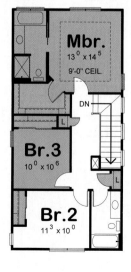

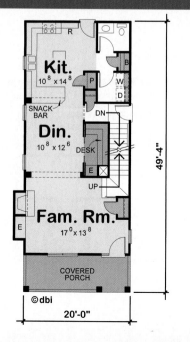

Kit.
$10^8 \times 14^8$

R

B

P

W
D

SNACK BAR

DN

Din.
$10^8 \times 12^6$

DESK

E

UP

Fam. Rm.
$17^0 \times 13^8$

E

COVERED PORCH

©dbi

20'-0"

49'-4"

Mbr.
$13^0 \times 14^5$
9'-0" CEIL.

DN

L

Br.3
$10^0 \times 10^6$

L

Br.2
$11^3 \times 10^0$

Livability
at a Glance™

Storing
Entertaining
Flexible Living
De-Stressing

www.designbasics.com/9JJ

the Edinburg
8557N-9JJ
pricecode 17

Main Level	879
Second Level	824
Total Square Ft.	1703

Standard Foundation: Basement

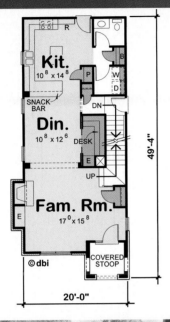

Kit. 10⁸ x 14⁸

R, P, B, W, D

SNACK BAR

Din. 10⁸ x 12⁶

DESK, E, DN, UP

Fam. Rm. 17⁰ x 15⁸

E

© dbi

COVERED STOOP

49'-4"

20'-0"

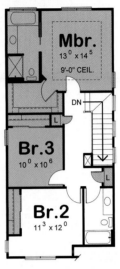

Mbr. 13⁰ x 14⁵ 9'-0" CEIL.

DN, L

Br.3 10⁰ x 10⁶

Br.2 11³ x 12⁰

L

the Bloomington
8631-9JJ
pricecode 23

Main Level	1135
Second Level	1190
Total Square Ft.	2325

Standard Foundation: Basement

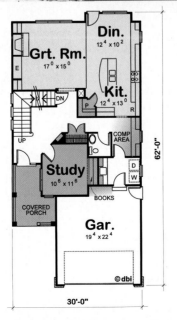

Grt. Rm. 17⁰ x 15⁰

E

Din. 12⁴ x 10²

Kit. 12⁴ x 13⁰

P, DN

COMP AREA

UP

Study 10⁶ x 11⁶

COVERED PORCH

BOOKS

D, W

Gar. 19⁴ x 22⁴

© dbi

62'-0"

30'-0"

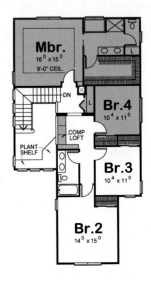

Mbr. 16⁰ x 15⁰ 9'-0" CEIL.

DN, L

Br.4 10⁴ x 11⁰

COMP LOFT

PLANT SHELF

Br.3 10⁴ x 11⁰

Br.2 14⁰ x 15⁰

Livability at a Glance™

- Storing
- Entertaining
- Flexible Living
- De-Stressing

the Tiburon
8632-9JJ
price code 23

Main Level	**1161**
Second Level	**1183**
Total Square Ft.	**2344**

Standard Foundation: Basement

Mbr.
19⁸ x 15⁰
9'-0" CEIL

DN   L

COMP LOFT

Optional Master Bedroom

D W

Optional Laundry Room

Din.
12⁴ x 10²

Grt. Rm.
17⁰ x 15⁰

Kit.
12⁴ x 13⁰

P   R

DN

UP

COMP AREA

Study
10⁶ x 11⁸

D W

BOOKS

COVERED PORCH

Gar.
19⁴ x 22⁴

62'-0"

30'-0"

© dbi/HBN

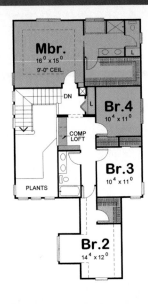

Mbr.
16⁰ x 15⁰
9'-0" CEIL

DN   L

COMP LOFT

Br.4
10⁴ x 11⁰

Br.3
10⁴ x 11⁰

PLANTS

Br.2
14⁴ x 12⁰

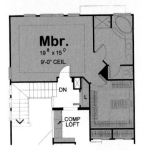

Br.5
10⁶ x 11⁶

D W

Optional Fifth Bedroom

---

the Urbandale
8633-9JJ
price code 23

Main Level	**1135**
Second Level	**1211**
Total Square Ft.	**2346**

Standard Foundation: Basement

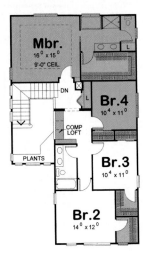

Mbr.
19⁸ x 15⁰
9'-0" CEIL

DN   L

COMP LOFT

Optional Master Bedroom

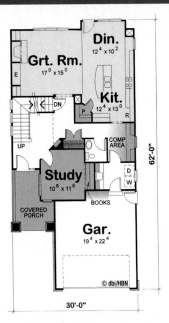

Din.
12⁴ x 10²

Grt. Rm.
17⁰ x 15⁰

Kit.
12⁴ x 13⁰

P   R

DN

UP

COMP AREA

Study
10⁶ x 11⁶

D W

BOOKS

COVERED PORCH

Gar.
19⁴ x 22⁴

62'-0"

30'-0"

© dbi/HBN

Mbr.
16⁰ x 15⁰
9'-0" CEIL

DN   L

COMP LOFT

Br.4
10⁴ x 11⁰

Br.3
10⁴ x 11⁰

PLANTS

Br.2
14⁰ x 12⁰

D W

Optional Laundry Room

Br.5
10⁶ x 11⁶

D W

Optional Fifth Bedroom

Livability
at a Glance™

Storing
Entertaining
Flexible Living
De-Stressing

www.designbasics.com/9JJ

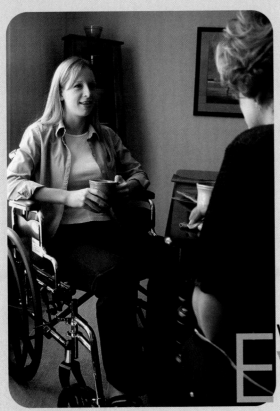

Most everyone wants their new home to be very hospitable and inviting, to provide a sense of warmth, starting with the front door and continuing from room to room.

But have you given any thought to whether your home will welcome everyone in a real, practical sense? What about those who may come into your life who depend on the use of a walker or wheelchair? Will they be able to even enter your home? Will there be at least one bathroom on the main floor for them to use?

Unfortunately, these are issues that are usually not considered by able-bodied homebuyers. But for anyone faced with the challenges of limited mobility, the humiliation and frustration of being unable to visit friends' or relatives' homes is often very real.

Taking measures before construction to ensure your home will be visit-able by everyone is very cost-effective and actually makes anyone's home more practical and liveable. Incorporating them after construction is considerably more involved and more expensive.

Will Your Home Welcome Everyone?

Steps to take before you build to make your home visit-able^{cm}*

The three keys to creating a visit-able home are:

1| Provide at least one zero-step entrance (with a shallow slope) into the home.

2| Make all main-floor doors (including closets and bathrooms) no less than 2'-10" wide. This step can also enhance resale values by making the home seem larger and more spacious.

3| Choose a home plan that includes a main-floor bathroom that is large enough to accommodate a wheelchair.

If you see a possible need for your home to be even more accessible in the future, you may want to consider incorporating these additional recommendations:

• Rooms need to be large enough to allow a wheelchair to pass through after furniture has been brought in.

• Bathrooms must be roomy, with adequate access to toilets and proper backing in the walls where hand rails will be installed or added later if needed. Showers should be roll-in or have built-in seats. Tubs need generous clearances and a seat on the edge. Linen closets and cabinets should accommodate height limitations.

• Inside, there should be few or no surface level changes. If stairs are included, they should be in a straight run to accommodate a chair lift.

• All doors must have sufficient clearance (on the door handle side) to allow a person in a wheelchair to pull them open.

• Garages should be sized to offer greater mobility around vehicles.

• Hallways must be wide enough for a wheelchair to turn into rooms.

• In the kitchen, aisles should be at least 40 inches wide. Raised dishwashers and side-by-side refrigerators provide greater accessibility. Ovens that open from the side eliminate the need to reach over a hot door. Drawer cabinets, Lazy Susans and

pull-out shelves add convenience for everyone. A counter portion 30 inches wide and 28-32 inches high, with no cabinet beneath it, can be used as a work station by anyone seated in a chair or wheelchair.

• In the laundry room, choose appliances with controls in front. The washer should also be front loading.

• Throughout the home, single-lever hardware, easy-to-reach switches, outlets and appliance controls add ease. Using layered closet rods adds storage and accessibility.

To learn more about the differences between universal, accessible, adaptable and visit-able design, see www.resna.org/taproject/policy/community/HMRG.htm#target4

*Visit-able is a term coined by Concrete Change, an international advocacy group working to make all homes visit-able.

Discover many more wheelchair accessible designs at www.designbasics.com. Click on "Universal Design" in our section "Design - For Homebuilders."

Can Luxury Showering be Green?

by Stephanie A. Young

photos courtesy of MOEN® Incorporated

Luxury living and environmentalism. Now there's a pair that belongs on opposite ends of the spectrum – or so we've always thought. As we've become more aware of today's environmental issues, many of us have begun to think more responsibly when it comes to building a new home. At the same time, however, an ever-growing array of pampering amenities keeps us enticed with visions of our "dream home."

So, can a green home also be a dream home? It can, because more and more of today's luxury products are also friendly to our natural resources. As a result, many homebuilders are going "green," not because of the global warming crisis, but instead, to satisfy the growing consumer trend of luxurious environmental living.

A prime example of earth-friendly indulgence is found in the realm of today's sumptuous shower systems. Whether your lifestyle is running a business, staying at home with the kids, hustling as a hectic executive, or enjoying retirement, there's nothing better than pampering yourself with a shower system that works just like a jetted tub. The best part is that it will take up less time and waste less water.

There are several showering systems on the market in varying price points and configurations. Kohler® offers the BodySpa as well as the MasterShower Tower. Grohe's® system is called the Amera Shower System. The MOEN® vertical spa, however, is an example of a showering experience that truly is a vertical bath. This type of system will isolate more of your stressed sensory points by jetting forced water on parts of your lower back and kneading your scalp with a swirling, spinning, massaging spray. To top it off, you can dial up your favorite hot water temperature instantly with a touch of a knob.

Because the heart of the system begins with Moen's own ExactTemp pressure-balanced thermostatic valve, the water temperature doesn't fluctuate – even as the hot water in the tank gets lower. Users can dial up the same shower temperature day after day, just like a thermostat. Temperature settings on the dial correspond to water temperatures between 85 and 115 degrees. This product features pressure-balancing, which maintains water pressure so effectively you will never feel a hot or cold surge in water, also known as "shower shock." The valve ensures that water temperature remains a constant ±2º F.

Installation is a cinch. The advanced engineering means that the $^1/_2$" valves create a luxurious experience while using plumbing lines common to the majority of households. The benefit of the $^1/_2$" valve also means that the shower is using less water while still pro-viding the feel of a system plumbed with a $^3/_4$" valve. The Moen vertical spa delivers maximum force at standard gallons per minute, without the additional expense of larger or multiple water tanks or larger capacity drainage systems. And best of all, there's still enough hot water for the next person in your family to take a shower or do several loads of laundry!

With any of today's showering systems, it is easy to add different showerheads for additional effects of spinning, twisting or spiraling that twirls the water for phenomenal coverage. Body sprays – large or small, single or multi-function showerheads, hand showers, multi-function transfer valves and even rainfall-like showerheads are all designed to operate within federal guidelines imposed on faucet and showering devices since 1994.

So whether you're building a new home or remodeling your current one, remember to include one of today's water-friendly showering systems. Finally, you can de-stress your body without re-stressing your mind. ∎

Stephanie A. Young is a specialist in kitchen and bath lifestyle trends. Based in Houston, TX, she works as a builder sales consultant with MOEN® Incorporated. Please email comments and questions to her at syoung@HerHome.com

the
Deerfield
4614-9JJ
pricecode 2X

Left Side
Total Square Ft. **1218**

Right Side
Total Square Ft. **1218**

Standard Foundation: Basement

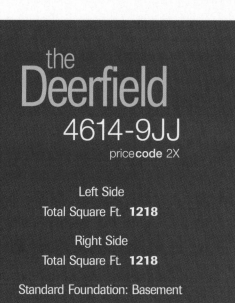

Livability
at a Glance™

Storing
Entertaining
Flexible Living
De-Stressing

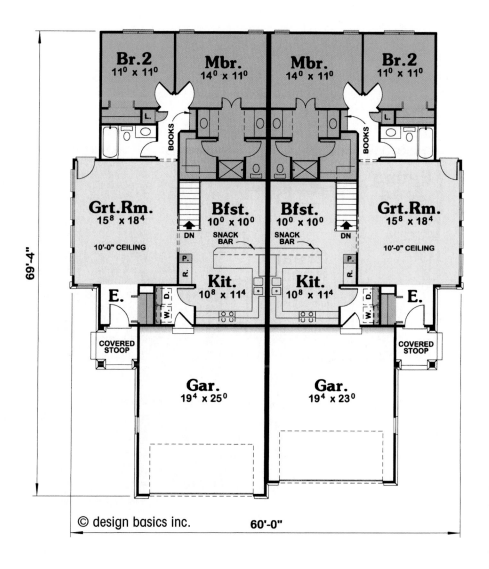

Br. 2
11⁰ x 11⁰

Mbr.
14⁰ x 11⁰

Mbr.
14⁰ x 11⁰

Br. 2
11⁰ x 11⁰

BOOKS

BOOKS

L.

L.

Grt. Rm.
15⁸ x 18⁴

10'-0" CEILING

Bfst.
10⁰ x 10⁰

Bfst.
10⁰ x 10⁰

Grt. Rm.
15⁸ x 18⁴

10'-0" CEILING

DN

DN

SNACK BAR

SNACK BAR

P.

R.

P.

R.

Kit.
10⁸ x 11⁴

Kit.
10⁸ x 11⁴

E.

W. D.

W. D.

E.

COVERED STOOP

COVERED STOOP

Gar.
19⁴ x 25⁰

Gar.
19⁴ x 23⁰

69'-4"

60'-0"

© design basics inc.

the
Crimson Creek
8174-9JJ

price**code** 2X

Left Side
Total Square Ft. **1212**

Right Side
Total Square Ft. **1233**

Standard Foundation: Basement

Livability
at a Glance™

Storing
Entertaining
Flexible Living
De-Stressing

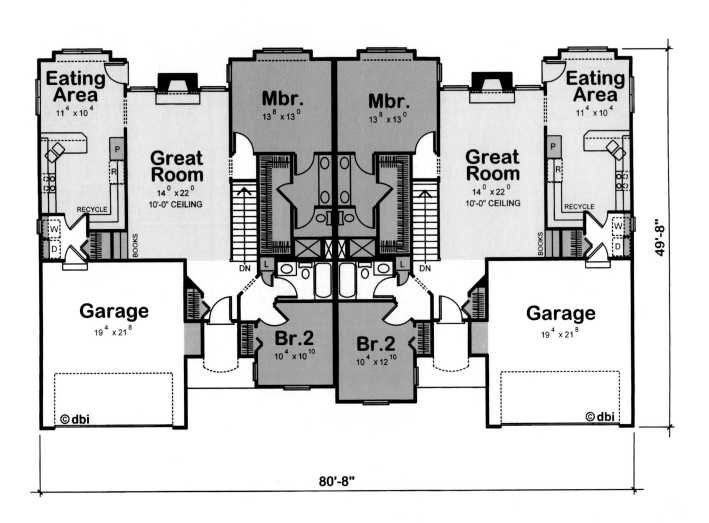

Eating Area
11⁴ x 10⁴

Mbr.
13⁸ x 13⁰

Mbr.
13⁸ x 13⁰

Eating Area
11⁴ x 10⁴

Great Room
14⁰ x 22⁰
10'-0" CEILING

Great Room
14⁰ x 22⁰
10'-0" CEILING

RECYCLE

RECYCLE

P
R

P
R

BOOKS

BOOKS

W
D

W
D

DN

DN

L

L

Garage
19⁴ x 21⁸

Garage
19⁴ x 21⁸

Br.2
10⁴ x 10¹⁰

Br.2
10⁴ x 12¹⁰

© dbi

© dbi

49'-8"

80'-8"

the Allston

7603-9JJ

pricecode 2X

Left Side
Total Square Ft. **1311**

Right Side
Total Square Ft. **1311**

Standard Foundation: Basement

Livability
at a Glance™

- Storing
- Entertaining
- Flexible Living
- De-Stressing

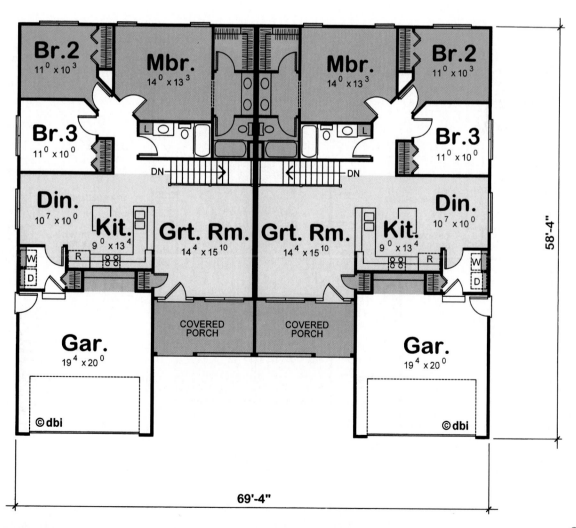

Br.2
11⁰ x 10³

Mbr.
14⁰ x 13³

Mbr.
14⁰ x 13³

Br.2
11⁰ x 10³

Br.3
11⁰ x 10⁰

Br.3
11⁰ x 10⁰

DN

DN

Din.
10⁷ x 10⁰

Kit.
9⁰ x 13⁴

Grt. Rm.
14⁴ x 15¹⁰

Grt. Rm.
14⁴ x 15¹⁰

Kit.
9⁰ x 13⁴

Din.
10⁷ x 10⁰

W
D

R

R

W
D

Gar.
19⁴ x 20⁰

COVERED
PORCH

COVERED
PORCH

Gar.
19⁴ x 20⁰

©dbi

©dbi

58'-4"

69'-4"

the
Landsford
4625-9JJ
price code 2X

Left Side
Total Square Ft. **1344**

Right Side
Total Square Ft. **1344**

Standard Foundation: Basement

Livability
at a Glance™

Storing
Entertaining
Flexible Living
De-Stressing

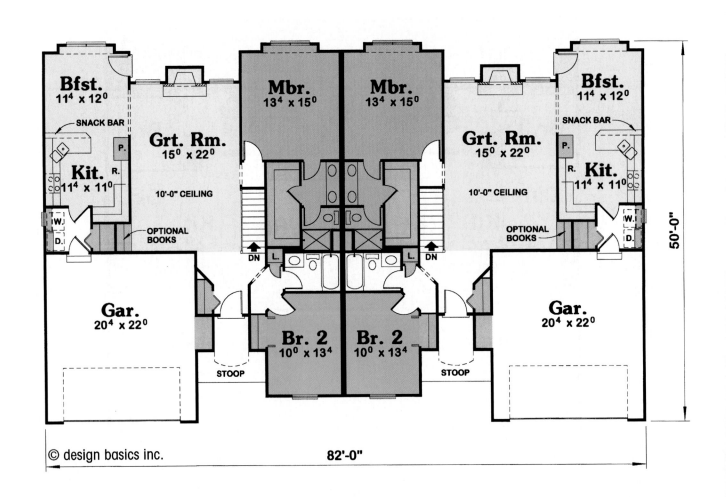

Bfst.
11⁴ x 12⁰

SNACK BAR

Kit.
11⁴ x 11⁰

Grt. Rm.
15⁰ x 22⁰

10'-0" CEILING

OPTIONAL BOOKS

P.

R.

W.
D.

Gar.
20⁴ x 22⁰

DN L.

Mbr.
13⁴ x 15⁰

Mbr.
13⁴ x 15⁰

L. DN

Grt. Rm.
15⁰ x 22⁰

10'-0" CEILING

OPTIONAL BOOKS

Bfst.
11⁴ x 12⁰

SNACK BAR

P.

R.

Kit.
11⁴ x 11⁰

W.
D.

Gar.
20⁴ x 22⁰

STOOP

Br. 2
10⁰ x 13⁴

Br. 2
10⁰ x 13⁴

STOOP

50'-0"

© design basics inc.

82'-0"

www.designbasics.com/9JJ

the
Fairhope
4618-9JJ
pricecode 2X

Left Side
Total Square Ft. **1392**

Right Side
Total Square Ft. **1392**

Standard Foundation: Basement

Livability
at a Glance™

Storing
Entertaining
Flexible Living
De-Stressing

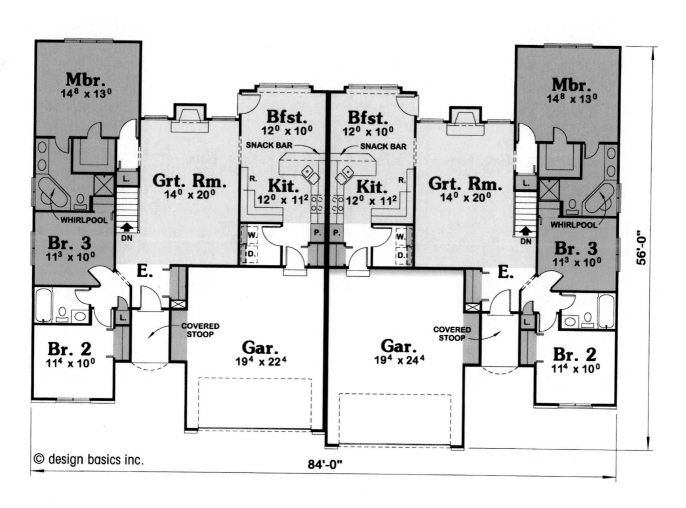

© design basics inc.

the
Ellington
4632-9JJ
price**code** 2X

Left Side
Total Square Ft. **1478**

Right Side
Total Square Ft. **1478**

Standard Foundation: Basement

Livability
at a Glance™

Storing
Entertaining
Flexible Living
De-Stressing

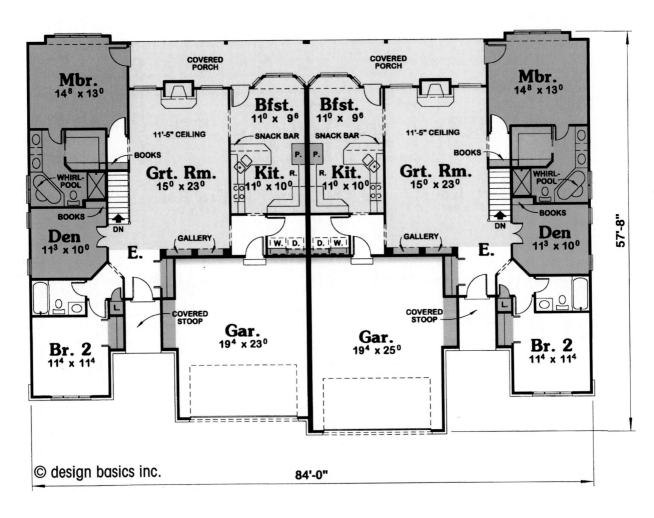

Mbr.
14⁸ x 13⁰

COVERED PORCH

COVERED PORCH

Mbr.
14⁸ x 13⁰

11'-5" CEILING

BOOKS

Bfst.
11⁰ x 9⁶

Bfst.
11⁰ x 9⁶

BOOKS

11'-5" CEILING

WHIRL-POOL

SNACK BAR

SNACK BAR

WHIRL-POOL

BOOKS

Grt. Rm.
15⁰ x 23⁰

Kit.
11⁰ x 10⁰

Kit.
11⁰ x 10⁰

Grt. Rm.
15⁰ x 23⁰

BOOKS

Den
11³ x 10⁰

DN

DN

Den
11³ x 10⁰

E.

GALLERY

W. D.   D. W.

GALLERY

E.

COVERED STOOP

COVERED STOOP

Br. 2
11⁴ x 11⁴

Gar.
19⁴ x 23⁰

Gar.
19⁴ x 25⁰

Br. 2
11⁴ x 11⁴

57'-8"

84'-0"

© design basics inc.

the
Clarendon
4011-9JJ
pricecode 2X

Left Side		Right Side	
Main	**1308** sq. ft.	Main	**1284** sq. ft.
Second	**645** sq. ft.	Second	**645** sq. ft.
Total	**1953** sq. ft.	Total	**1929** sq. ft.

Standard Foundation: Basement

Livability
at a Glance™
- Storing
- Entertaining
- Flexible Living
- De-Stressing

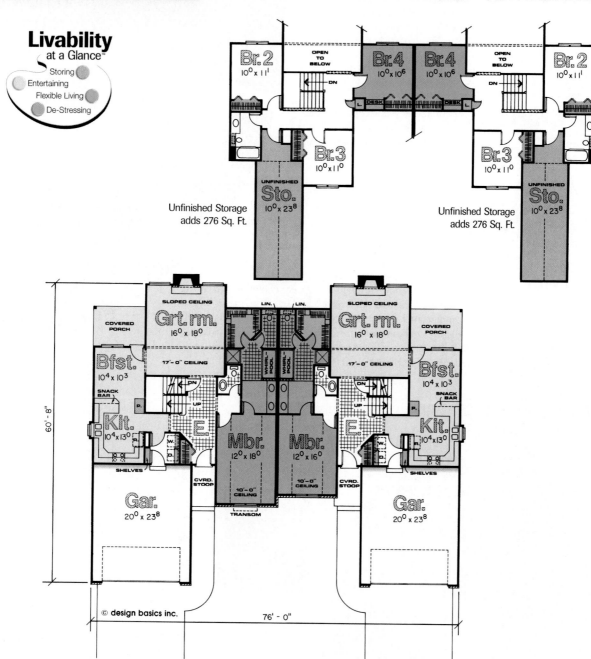

Unfinished Storage
adds 276 Sq. Ft.

Unfinished Storage
adds 276 Sq. Ft.

© design basics inc.

76' - 0"

Color

by Erika Woelfel

Why your walls don't always match those little color chips from the paint store.

It had happened again. There we were, knee deep in drop cloths, paint brushes, masking tape and ladders – and the color on the paint chip did not resemble what was going on the walls. My friend had decided to go with a soft pink in her daughter's bedroom. "Ballerina" the color chip was a light pastel, reminiscent of cotton candy. "Ballerina" the paint color looked like Pepto Bismal on the walls. My friend claimed the paint chip looked different at home than it did under the store lights. She was right.

The number one factor in how a color looks in a room is lighting. During the day, natural sunlight gives the truest color. Allow for variances depending on how much daylight comes into a room and what direction the light is coming from. Tip: Southern exposures tend to have brighter, warmer light quality; northern facing rooms that do not get much sun appear cooler and have a blue cast. Painted walls will look darker at night, when incandescent lighting casts many shadows. Fluorescent lighting is slightly cool so it enhances blues and greens, while reds appear more dull. Incandescent lighting sheds a warm, yellow cast light and makes yellows and reds brighter. It will dull the brightness of blue.

"The number [...] in how a colo[...] room is light[...] the day, natu[...] gives the tru[...]

RED-VIOLET

RED

VIOLET

BLUE-VIOLET

BLUE

BLUE-GREEN

GREEN

natural sunlight

at night

fluorescent lighting

Incandescent lighting

Erika Woelfel understands the importance of color in the home. She is Senior Color Designer of the Colwell Color Studio, a company that produces color merchandising tools for the decorative products industry. Her insights on color trends and usage have won her international recognition as a speaker and writer.

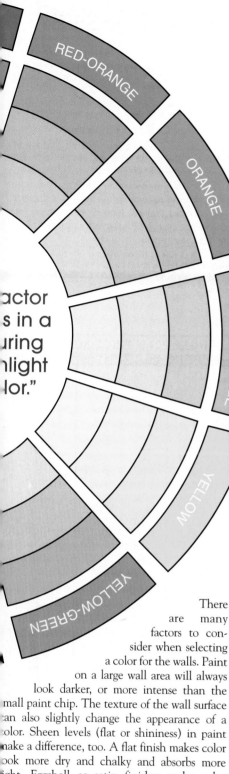

RED-ORANGE

ORANGE

YELLOW-ORANGE

YELLOW

YELLOW-GREEN

actor
s in a
uring
nlight
lor."

to bring down the scale of high ceilings or tall walls. Cool colors such as blue, green and violet visually recede. Use them to make small rooms feel more spacious.

Many new homes today have open floor plans with great expanses of wall, very high ceilings, and large windows which allow in lots of natural daylight. Bright colors are going to look more intense in these spaces. One or two accent walls is a good way to bring brighter or darker colors into your room. For colors that aren't as visually overpowering, try using neutrals, earth tones, or lighter values of your favorite bright/dark hues on tall walls.

Paint manufacturers are coming up with some savvy ways to hurdle these colorful challenges. Large color samples are available in many retail centers. Small samples of liquid paint are also becoming more available, dispensed from jars or pouches that give just enough color to brush out a test swatch on a wall. Leave color swatches on the walls a few days and look at them during different times of day, under different light sources before determining whether you want to live with your new color.

Paint stores provide many handy brochures to provide pre-determined color combination. A dominant color and one or two accents usually serve to balance walls, floors, furnishings and window treatments. Accent colors provide the visual sizzle and can be anything from pillows to artwork to plants. The key to color combinations is determining what colors you already have to work with. Edit your selections. The pieces you choose for the room should determine how your color story develops. If you are keeping the sofa and changing the walls, is there a color in the upholstery pattern you can use for paint? Do you have a particular piece of artwork that would just sing if the wall behind it were painted a color from its palette? Is there a view outside the window that provides color inspiration you would like to bring indoors?

So how did my friend solve her Pepto Bismal color challenge? Aside from the walls, the floor color is often the second largest space of color in a room. A green carpet will reflect a minty shade on white walls. Red carpets will make white walls look pink. Knowing this, she counterbalanced the room by installing an off-white carpet on the floor to reflect light up. The ceiling of the room was finished with a darker shade of pink to make the walls appear lighter. Bright artwork with white frames and mattes completed the feminine effect. ■

There are many factors to consider when selecting a color for the walls. Paint on a large wall area will always look darker, or more intense than the mall paint chip. The texture of the wall surface can also slightly change the appearance of a color. Sheen levels (flat or shininess) in paint make a difference, too. A flat finish makes color ook more dry and chalky and absorbs more ight. Eggshell or satin finishes make color ppear polished and will reflect more light.

he rule of opposites:

The size of your room also affects the final ook of paint. You can use a few tricks to your dvantage. All colors have a temperature – they ll into a warm or cool category. Reds, yellows nd oranges are considered warm – they visually dvance towards you to make a room seem maller. Use them for areas where you want

It has often been said small rooms should never be painted dark or bold colors because it makes them seem smaller. While this is generally true, if you have a small room or back hallway that gets really good light, a dramatic color makes an exciting statement. Another tip for small rooms – don't forget the fifth wall! A ceiling painted bold red, yellow, blue or green draws the eye up for *Aha!* impact.

Designer Sharon Bledsoe Designs

photo by: Robert Hock

Cool colors such as blue, green and violet visually recede. Use them to make rooms feel more spacious.

In open floor plans, colors such as earth-toned neutrals, grays and off whites work well because they aren't visually overpowering.

What Do I Get With a Plan from Design Basics?

CONSTRUCTION LICENSE

When you purchase a Design Basics home plan, you receive a Construction License which gives you certain rights in building the home depicted in that plan, including:

No Re-Use Fee. As the original purchaser of a Design Basics home plan, the Construction License permits you to build the plan as many times as you like.

Local Modifications. The Construction License allows you to make modifications to your Design Basics plans. We offer a complete plan alteration service, or you may have the desired changes done locally by a qualified draftsman, designer, architect or engineer.

Running Blueprints. Your plans are sent to you on vellum paper that reproduces well on your blueprint machine. The Construction License authorizes you or your blueprint facility, at your direction, to make as many copies of the plan from the vellum masters as you need for construction purposes.

CONSTRUCTION DRAWINGS

1. Cover Page. Each Design Basics home plan features the rendered elevation and informative reference sections including: general notes and design criteria;* abbreviations; and symbols for your plan.

2. Elevations. Drafted at $1/4$" scale for the front and $1/8$" scale for the rear and sides. All elevations are detailed and an aerial view of the roof is provided, showing all framing members.

3. Foundations. Drafted at $1/4$" scale. Foundations are fully engineered for each design, whether slab or basement.

4. Main Level Floor Plan. Drafted at $1/4$" scale. Fully dimensioned from stud to stud for ease of framing. 2x4 walls are standard. The detailed drawings include such things as structural header locations, framing layout and kitchen layout.

5. Second Level Floor Plan. Drafted at $1/4$" scale. Dimensioned from stud to stud and drafted to the same degree of detail as the main level floor plan.*

6. Interior Elevations. Useful for the cabinet and bidding process.

7. Electrical and Sections. Illustrated on a separate page for clarity, the electrical plan shows suggested electrical layout for the main and second level floor plans. Typical wall, cantilever and stair sections are provided to further explain construction of these areas.

Full technical support is available for any plan purchase from Design Basics. Our technical support specialists provide unlimited technical support free of charge and answer questions regarding construction methods, framing techniques and more. Please call **800-947-7526** for more information.

* Design Basics plans are drafted to meet average conditions and codes in the state of Nebraska, at the time they are designed. Because codes and requirements can change and may vary from jurisdiction to jurisdiction, Design Basics Inc. cannot warrant compliance with any specific code or regulation. All Design Basics plans can be adapted to your local building codes and requirements. It is the responsibility of the purchaser and/or builder of each plan to see that the structure is built in strict compliance with all governing municipal codes (city, county, state and federal).

Some of the plans in this book are available on disk.

IF THIS IS NOT RED DO NOT COPY

These days it seems almost everybody has a question about what can or can-not be done with copyrighted home plans. At Design Basics, we know U.S. copyright law can sometimes get complex and confusing, but here are a few of the basic points of the law you'll want to remember.

Once you've purchased a plan from us and have received a construction license from Design Basics:

You Can ...

■ Make duplicate blueprint copies as needed for construction on prints bearing our RED seal (above).

■ Build it as many times as you wish *without* additional re-use fees.

■ Construct the plan as originally designed, or change it to meet your specific needs.

You Cannot ...

■ Build our plans without a construction license from Design Basics.

■ Copy *any* part of our original designs to create another design of your own.

■ Claim copyright on changes you make to our plans.

■ Give a plan to someone else for construction purposes.

■ Sell the plan.

PROTECT YOUR RIGHTS

to build, modify and reproduce our home plans with a Design Basics construction license.

CONSTRUCTION LICENSE

The above points are provided as general guidelines only. Additional information is provided with each home plan purchase, or is available upon request at (800) 947-7526.

SINGLE PLAN PRICE SCHEDULE		
PLAN CODE	**TOTAL SQ. FT.**	**PRICE**
11	1100' - 1199'	$705
12	1200' - 1299'	$715
13	1300' - 1399'	$725
14	1400' - 1499'	$735
15	1500' - 1599'	$745
16	1600' - 1699'	$755
17	1700' - 1799'	$765
18	1800' - 1899'	$775
19	1900' - 1999'	$785
20	2000' - 2099'	$795
21	2100' - 2199'	$805
22	2200' - 2299'	$815
23	2300' - 2399'	$825
24	2400' - 2499'	$835
25	2500' - 2599'	$845
26	2600' - 2699'	$855
27	2700' - 2799'	$865
28	2800' - 2899'	$875
29	2900' - 2999'	$885
30	3000' - 3099'	$895
31	3100' - 3199'	$905
32	3200' - 3299'	$915
33	3300' - 3399'	$925
34	3400' - 3499'	$935
35	3500' - 3599'	$945
36	3600' - 3699'	$955
37	3700' - 3799'	$965
38	3800' - 3899'	$975
39	3900' - 3999'	$985
40	4000' - 4099'	$995
41	4100' - 4199'	$1005
42	4200' - 4299'	$1015
43	4300' - 4399'	$1025
44	4400' - 4499'	$1035
45	4500' - 4599'	$1045
46	4600' - 4699'	$1055
47	4700' - 4799'	$1065
48	4800' - 4899'	$1075
49	4900' - 4999'	$1085
50	5000' - 5099'	$1095
51	5100' - 5199'	$1105
52	5200' - 5299'	$1115
53	5300' - 5399'	$1125
54	5400' - 5499'	$1135
55	5500' - 5599'	$1145
56	5600' - 5699'	$1155
57	5700' - 5799'	$1165
58	5800' - 5899'	$1175
59	5900' - 5999'	$1185
2X	Duplex	$1005

PRICES SUBJECT TO CHANGE

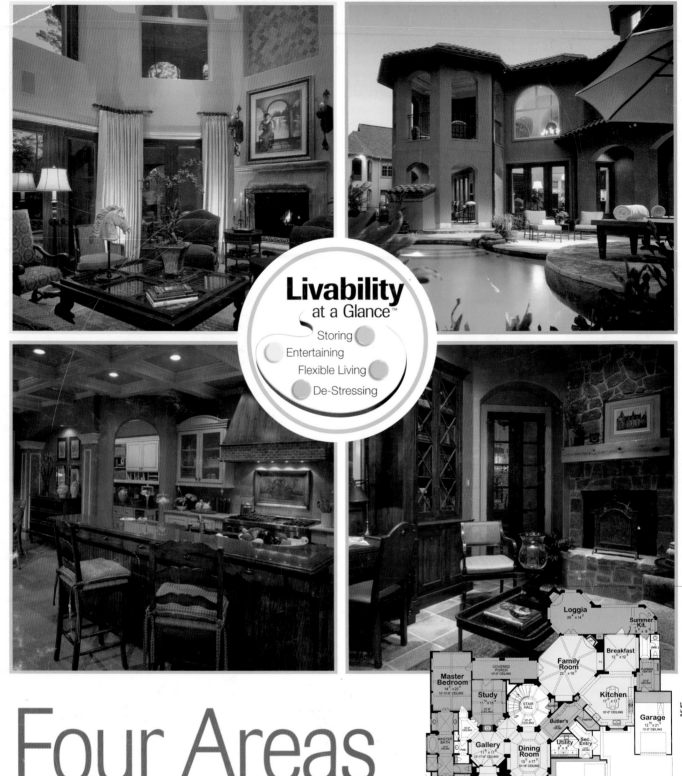

Livability
at a Glance™

Storing
Entertaining
Flexible Living
De-Stressing

Four Areas
Thousands
of Possibilities

HOME PLAN DESIGN SERVICE

800-947-7526
www.designbasics.com